"*Thinking about Evolution* takes the reader on an extraordinary tour through contemporary evolutionary theory. The range of issues covered is astounding, from chemical evolution and abiogenesis to the relationship between the genetic codes of chimpanzees and human beings. The depth of the discussion is also impressive. Each chapter explains the latest studies and applies them to the question at hand. Most important is the strong affirmation of the truth-conducive nature of the scientific enterprise. At the same time, important criticisms are developed and applied to many of the common claims made in the name of evolutionary theory. The thoughtful Christian will be left with a hunger for further study."

—Gregory E. Ganssle
Professor of Philosophy, Talbot School of Theology, Biola University

"*Thinking about Evolution* brings together a helpful overview of modern evolutionary theory alongside an insightful critique of its weaknesses. Combining scientific research, philosophical thinking, and theological inquiry, Anjeanette Roberts and her fellow authors build a strong case for old-earth creationism that should be taken seriously by both Christians and nonbelievers."

—Justin Brierley
Unbelievable? show host

"*Thinking about Evolution* is an immensely helpful book. The authors address some of the most important questions today related to the viability of evolutionary theory. Not only is it thoughtful, but they write with graciousness and fairness toward both Christians and non-Christians who see the issues differently. If you are interested in the state of the origins debate, this book is a must-read."

—Sean McDowell, PhD
Professor at Biola University, popular speaker, and author of
over 18 books including *Evidence That Demands a Verdict*

"Dr. Anjeanette Roberts and her accomplished coauthors have written the must-read book for Christians who have the courage to challenge preconceived ideas about evolution and consider how science, philosophy, and theology intersect. *Thinking about Evolution* is powerful, well-researched, and truly inspiring for people of faith who want to pursue deeper understanding of our world and the God of the Bible."

—Alia Eyres
CEO, Mother's Choice, Hong Kong

"Though I am a scientist who affirms evolutionary science, I still found much with which to agree in *Thinking about Evolution*. Progressive creationists agree the earth is old, but they maintain reservations about macroevolution. Genuinely considering the possibility they might be wrong, the authors explain how evolutionary science could be consistent with Scripture. Dr. Roberts and her colleagues, moreover, have a laudable record of adjusting their views in response to evidence. Their scientific objections to evolution also deserve to be engaged with seriousness and rigor. For all these reasons, even secular scientists should read this book; it is a good faith starting point for meaningful dialogue."

—S. Joshua Swamidass
Washington University in St. Louis
Founder of Peaceful Science, author of *The Genealogical Adam and Eve*

"Evolutionists tell us that the Taung child, the fossilized skull of a young *Australopithecus africanus*, lived as a young child in the terrains of Taung in South Africa. Approximately one hour from my office in South Africa lies the Cradle of Humankind, where I often see the story line in the popular evolutionary literature that our ancestors included *Australopithecus sediba* (a species of *Australopithecus* of the early Pleistocene), Little Foot, as well as Mrs. Ples. Is there a direct lineage between Neanderthals and self-aware human beings? In this meticulously researched and thoroughly referenced book, the authors convincingly argue otherwise. They stand firmly on the grounds that the truth of nature (specifically, our existence) cannot be blindly fused with multitudes of hypotheses, including the so-called symbolic art of the Neanderthals. A must-read for any student, whether young or old, who, like Galileo did, beholds the harmony between the book of nature and the book of Scripture."

—David L. Block, Emeritus Professor
University of the Witwatersrand, Johannesburg, South Africa

THINKING ABOUT
EVOLUTION

25 Questions Christians
Want Answered

Covina, CA

Cover design: 789, Inc.
Interior layout: Christine Talley
Interior figures: Heather Lanz

Names: Roberts, Anjeanette, author. | Rana, Fazale, 1963–, author. | Dykes, Sue, author. | Perez, Mark, author.
Title: Thinking about evolution : 25 questions Christians want answered / Anjeanette Roberts ; Fazale Rana ; Sue Dykes ; and Mark Perez.
Description: Includes bibliographical references and index. | Covina, CA: RTB Press, 2020.
Identifiers: ISBN 978-1-886653-97-9
Subjects: LCSH Evolution (Biology)--Religious aspects--Christianity. | Bible and evolution. | Creationism. | Life--Origin. | Religion and science. | BISAC RELIGION / Christian Theology / Ethics | RELIGION / Religion & Science
Classification: BS651 .R73 2020 | DDC 231.7/65--dc23

Printed in the United States of America

First edition

1 2 3 4 5 6 7 8 9 10 / 24 23 22 21 20

For more information about Reasons to Believe, contact (855) REASONS / (855) 732-7667 or visit reasons.org.

Contents

List of Figures and Tables

Dedication

Life, in all its forms, however it comes to us, is a precious and glorious gift from God. L'Chaim!

To our beloved coauthor, colleague, and friend,
Dr. Sue Dykes

Acknowledgments

The book you hold in your hands is a shared labor that addresses some current fundamental questions about evolution. I would have never taken on this task without the expertise and critical contributions of my colleagues Fazale Rana, Sue Dykes, and Mark Perez. This book was also made possible by countless others, without whom our efforts would have been fruitless.

I am especially grateful for the time and candor of those who offered critical feedback, especially Drs. Gregory Ganssle, Curtis Henderson, Ivana Kuo, Richard Deem, and Jeffrey Zweerink.

To those who offered constant prayer and support throughout—beloved friends Karalee Romaneski, Monica Romig Green, Dr. Julie Davis Good, Dr. Linda Pattillo, Rev. Penelope Swithinbank, Dr. Hannah Palpant and Micah Palpant, and my mother, Dolores Roberts—I am exceedingly grateful. Fazale Rana thanks his wife, Amy Rana, for her love, encouragement, and patience when this book project took "priority" over family matters. Mark Perez thanks his wife, Kathleen Perez, for her support to join this project. We each thank our colleagues at Reasons to Believe for constantly giving of themselves for the sake of others and all the successes that pass through this ministry; may God continue to bless you as you are a blessing to so many others.

We extend our thanks to the editorial team at RTB Press: Sandra Dimas, Maureen Moser, Joe Aguirre, Jocelyn King, and Brett Tarbell, as well as freelance editor Linda Hucks and volunteer Colleen Wingenbach. We also gratefully acknowledge the talented work of cover designers Charley Bell and Richard Silva from 789 Inc., interior layout designer Christine Talley, and figure designer Heather Lanz.

A special thanks to RTB book fund donors Dan and Katy Atwood, Ron and

Bett Behrens, Ken and Tracy Camacho, Jamie and Maria Campbell, Kevin and Karen Donohue, Mark and Valerie Durham, Rodney and Pam Emery, Mike and Marj Harman, Roger and Stefanie Joe, Mathew John, Matt and Janet Jones, David La Pointe, Perry Lanaro, George and Valerie Leiva, Helen Masuda, Troy and Arlen Myers, Gary Parks, David and Diane Rogstad, Steve and Eileen Rogstad, Ron and Judy Sisel, Clark Souers, Brant and Laura Ullman, Harold and Beverly Van Vuren, John Williamson, Colleen Wingenbach, and Josh and Kerri Wolcott. Our work is made possible by your dedicated partnership. It is my prayer that God will use your generosity to impact more lives for his kingdom.

—Anjeanette Roberts

Outing Our Bias

One theory of animal and human origins is a progressive creation model, often called an old-earth creation model.[1] Central to this model is the belief that God created all things in such a way that those created in his image would understand the power and character of their Creator, and in understanding this would seek and find reconciliation with their Creator, with one another, and with creation itself. At Reasons to Believe (RTB), we embrace a progressive creation/old-earth creation model. We believe this model fits the data best.

As we see it, God's primary purpose in all of creation is to be in relationship with us. We believe God makes this apparent through revelation in the created order, in Christian scriptures, and, ultimately, in Jesus Christ. We believe that God's revelation in creation (or nature) and Scripture will *never* conflict when both are rightly understood and interpreted. This is sound reasoning, with precedent in church history, grounded on the basis that God—as both Creator and Author—makes self-disclosure to bring us to true understanding and reconciliation with him.[2] Revelation is always God-initiated whether in creation or in Scripture. It is utterly reliable. Scripture itself teaches us these things; so, we have the confidence of sound reasoning and Scripture in approaching the unity of God's revelation. *(This is a first principle of the RTB creation model.)*

According to RTB's progressive creation model, God created all the material stuff in the universe by fiat, or *ex nihilo*, meaning "out of nothing." This position aligns with biblical creation accounts and big bang cosmology. God also established physical laws, sustaining creation with a regularity and reliability that allow us to thrive, explore, and understand creation and the Creator. As to the details of creation, God employs two principal creation methods while continually sustaining all things providentially. Direct creation (divine fiat) is one method. The other is secondary causal events where God's creation continues to unfold according to physical laws established in the initial creation. Galaxies, stars, and planetary systems are a few examples of the many things that continue to form over time through secondary causal events. Understanding the days of creation as long epochs in which God created some things by fiat (e.g., space, time, matter, and various living creatures in finely tuned ecosystems), while creating other things through secondary causal events is the hallmark *(some might say another first principle)* of RTB's progressive creation model.

Once Earth was primed, through successive periods of God's direct creative activity (including the creation of life itself and many kinds of creatures) and secondary causal effects, God created human beings in his image. The creation of the first couple (Adam and Eve) was something utterly unique. The uniqueness of God's creation of humanity, both male and female, is as miraculous as the creation of the universe from nothing as is reflected in the Hebrew of the Old Testament where these creations are presented. In both instances, the Hebrew word for "made" or "create" is the word *bara*. With one possible exception,[3] the significant use of *bara* indicates the creation of something utterly new, performed by God alone. Although God used some previously created material in forming the first person from the dust and the second from the first, humanity's uniqueness is evident to all. *We believe scientific studies of human uniqueness and common sense experience confirm this interpretation.* We believe the progressive creationist view comports well with all the available data, scientific and scriptural.

It's critical to understand how science and faith together demonstrate the glory of the Creator, who made humans in his image to explore, reason, and discover the purpose of creation and to come to a hope-filled, loving relationship with their Creator.

Thinking about Evolution
by Anjeanette Roberts

I like to ask questions—lots of them and usually not one at a time. When I first came to trust in Jesus as my Lord and Savior at age 12, I remember asking lots of questions. I already loved science and discovery, so asking questions was just part of who I was. Maybe that's primarily why I earned the nickname "Trouble" among the youth leaders at my church. They'd often answer me with something like, "Aw, Trouble, you sure have a lot of questions!" Thankfully, they didn't leave it at that. They pointed me to Scripture, and together we looked for answers and prayed. Sometimes the answers were provisional, but, through the process, I learned to trust God and his Word.

In college, I studied chemistry (and biology and Russian) and plugged into a church that was focused on outreach and missions and grounded in the Bible and the power of the Holy Spirit at work in and through one's life. We had small groups that would meet together, study the Bible, pray for one another, and just share life. The people in this church and my particular small group loved me, although they didn't always really understand me or know what to do with all my questions either. They, along with friends in a campus ministry, provided safe places for me to follow Christ and look for answers while pursuing a degree in science.

Now, despite my experience of many wonderful environments of delightful, loving, faithful Christ followers, I never found anyone who could help me wrestle with questions about the specifics of evolution and the Bible satisfactorily. By the time I reached graduate school, I had grown to view science as a means to gain true understanding about the physical world and the Scriptures as a standard for truth, life, meaning, and purpose. Debates about evolution and creation, I concluded, were fruitless in conversations with others.

Debates about evolution and creation, I concluded, were fruitless in conversations with others.

I was sure God had created everything, but as to how, I had no idea. Perhaps he created everything in six 24-hour days and gave us a world that appeared old. That didn't seem in character for God, who doesn't lie or deceive, but God *could have* done it that way. Perhaps there were gaps of time between the creation days. That seemed most consistent with science and didn't seem inconsistent with the Bible. I camped in that space for a while. Some questions need to be shelved until satisfactory answers could be found. I learned to live with holding some things provisionally.

As I continued my graduate and postdoctoral studies, I remained convinced that God had created all things. Maybe *evolution* was the means through which he did the creating. Maybe. The evidence for macroevolution was not particularly compelling. Good scientific explanations usually require cause-and-effect mechanisms for peer-reviewed publication; yet most evolutionary explanations were inferences lacking specific cause-and-effect mechanisms or pathways.

So, I was a theistic evolutionist who maintained a healthy skepticism about much of macroevolution. When I joined Reasons to Believe, I was just starting to think critically about the *evolutionary paradigm*. I had been a theistic evolutionist by default through all of my graduate, postdoctoral, and research career. For the most part, my research took for granted aspects of well-documented microevolution and microbial evolution (changes in bacteria and viruses). In graduate school and beyond, the kind of research science I was pursuing (the study of viruses and the mechanisms of viral disease) could be done extremely well with great integrity and rigor without one thought of *macroevolution*.

It was at an InterVarsity Christian Fellowship conference, during my postdoctoral days at Yale, that I first heard a scientist tackle the problem of integrating evolution and creation. In a breakout session on science and faith, Dr. Howard J. Van Till, then physics professor at Calvin College, shared insights for reconciling the evolutionary paradigm with a biblical faith. I was encouraged, elated, in fact. But as I left, my elation turned to puzzlement. Two students exiting ahead of me expressed how depressed they were and how they thought it would be tragic if Professor Van Till's perspective were really true. We had attended the same talk, heard the same things, and yet left with opposite impressions! That experience led to my realization that we approach biblical integration (or theology) the same way scientists approach theory formation.

Scientists and scholars learn early on that we build on knowledge gained by our predecessors (standing on the shoulders of giants) *and* we learn best in an environment of diverse peers who also ask lots of questions, pick at models, and offer alternative ways of thinking or viewing the same data. Training in the same institution for undergraduate, graduate, and postdoctoral studies often stifles critical thinking and great science. One can get too bogged down in looking at things from only one vantage point. Life and reality are bigger than a single institution or perspective. The same goes for theology. We need to be in environments that stimulate and challenge thought. If we never question why we believe something is true, then we may never really have good reasons of our own for believing it. Questions and disagreement are fertile soil for good science—and for good theology.

For many, it is difficult to find a safe place to be curious. New ideas can be exciting or disturbing, depending on how well they fit our views of life or how deeply they challenge aspects of our current views. The potential for disturbance is why many people are afraid to ask questions themselves or to allow others to ask.

At Reasons to Believe, we encourage questions about science and Christianity. We believe wrestling with questions together is healthy and good. Digging deep for answers to tough topics builds confidence and allows people to be more comfortable with others' questions.

This book is all about asking questions about evolution and wrestling with the answers together. Because robust perspectives emerge from a diversity of views, and because we realize a collection of voices can help bring clarity, I don't want to be the only voice addressing the following questions. I am joined by my colleagues—biochemist Fazale Rana, paleoanthropologist Sue Dykes, and analytical philosopher Mark Perez.

It is not our intention to summarize the state of evolutionary biology *in toto*, and our answers are not meant to be exhaustive of the theories or disagreements discussed in minutia among its practitioners. Some would assert that the differences among evolutionary theorists are minimal and only on peripheral matters. Our observations are that there are significant discussions regarding major tenets of evolution that provide room for skepticism for those questioning its explanatory power. We have done our best to offer supporting citations to peer-reviewed publications where evolutionary biologists or those in related disciplines raise similar questions. These citations are not meant to portray or convey exhaustive or comprehensive coverage of the field.

Sometimes there is more than one good response to a question. We recognize good questions often raise more questions. Good answers do, too. We hope you find that this resource provides you with good answers but also helps you shape better questions. We don't want anyone to have to say, like I did, that they couldn't find anyone to help them wrestle with the tough questions.

We tackle 25 questions relevant to the specifics of evolutionary mechanisms, the overarching evolutionary paradigm, and challenges to fitting some data to evolutionary models. The first three questions may be among the most important as they address the evolutionary paradigm and how people can have different views of similar data regarding evolution. We address the importance of specific words and how they're used. For example, chapters 6–8 will help you understand the different ways in which the word *evolution* is used. We also dive into questions regarding the scientific support for evolution, specific evolutionary interpretations, and conceptual mechanisms. Our answers point out how the scientific data are often better or equally integrated with a progressive creation model.

> **Curiosity is a hallmark of those who God is longing to reconcile to himself.**

We hope these questions and answers deeply encourage you and stir up greater curiosity. Curiosity is a hallmark of those who God is longing to reconcile to himself. He promises the truth-seeker that they will find answers when they search with enthusiasm. Curiosity also builds bridges, while complacency benefits no one. We hope these questions and answers give you greater confidence to ask more questions and to integrate your understanding of God's self-revelation in the created order and the Christian scriptures. We know integration of God's revelation in the created order and in Scripture is possible. We trust in the faithfulness of God that all truth is God's truth, and God's revelation is meant for our benefit, flourishing, and redemption. We hope you grow to share this confidence, too.

Discussion Questions

1. The author says that by age 12, she was asking questions of church

leaders. Is your experience similar? What is a good way to cultivate and reward curiosity in young people?

2. Are you in an environment that stimulates and challenges thought? Why is it good to question one's beliefs?

Chapter 1

Does Evolution Explain Life on Earth?
by Anjeanette Roberts

Science involves collecting data and building models to explain the mechanisms and processes of the world around us. Various fields of study collect and employ data differently to evaluate causal effects. Regardless of how data is collected and how cause-and-effect relationships are demonstrated or tested, it is beneficial to keep in mind that data alone explains nothing. In fact, science explains nothing.

Scientists explain things. And explanations involve data *plus* interpretations of the data. When we interpret something, we consider things we already know, direct observations, cause-and-effect events, and how things relate to one another. Larger concepts—such as the nature of reality and the plausibility of various speculations—help frame how we think of these things, too.

We also must decide what counts as data and consider inferences dependent upon other conclusions but not encompassed by the data. These aspects of the scientific endeavor—rendering interpretations and offering explanations based on evidence but not constrained to data alone—lead to disagreement over data and to witticisms like Mark Twain's pithy quip, "There is something fascinating about science. One gets such wholesale returns of conjecture out of such a trifling investment of fact."[1]

At the heart of evolution theory is

At the heart of evolution theory is the claim that evolution explains all aspects of life's history and diversity.

the claim that evolution explains all aspects of life's history and diversity. It was a controversial assertion when Charles Darwin's *On the Origin of Species* first hit shelves in 1859. More than 150 years later, evolution is touted as factual—but is it?

A Productive and Powerful Paradigm

Evolution provides a grand unifying theory for research conducted in the biological and life sciences. It is a broad conceptual framework built upon a commitment to mechanistic explanations for the biological diversity and complexity of all life throughout Earth's history.

In science, a paradigm is a comprehensive model that determines the problems, solutions, research methods, and ways of thinking in a scientific community. A paradigm provides researchers with points of reference amid a world of incalculable possibilities. Within this framework scientists can begin to sort through complexities, interrogate individual organisms or systems, make comparisons, and then relate findings back to the whole. Thus, evolution serves as a framework or paradigm for biology and all related fields.

To understand the evolution paradigm and answer this chapter's question, we need to start with Charles Darwin, who remains evolution's most prominent historical figure. (The following chapters will look at revisions to evolution since Darwin's time.)

What Is the Darwinian Paradigm, Really?

In his seminal work, Darwin proposed that all living organisms are related by descent with modification from a (universal) common ancestor. The relatedness of all life through common descent allows that over long periods of time and multiple generations, population changes are driven by gradual, stepwise changes selected by nature based on competitive and reproductive fitness advantages. These long, gradual population changes result in the diversity of organisms observed today whether living or fossilized.

Darwin formed his theory, as any good scientist should do, based on observations and sound reasoning. He noted similarities and differences in closely related organisms, such as pigeons. The variations among these birds were obvious to Darwin and even to casual observers. He noted how breeders could select for certain traits, like color or size, by choosing breeding pairs bearing the desired traits. Thus, breeders could produce a variety of different species by careful selection and patient breeding. Darwin's observations led him to infer that all pigeons were likely descendants of a single ancestral type of rock pigeon that had been bred into distinct species over centuries of animal husbandry.

After observing various species of finches collected in his travels through the Galápagos Islands, Darwin made a similar inference. If selective breeding could produce independent species of pigeons, Darwin inferred that a similar selection of traits occurred in nature under environmental selection to produce a variety of finch species suited for different ecological niches. He reasoned that all the Galápagos finches were likely descended from a common ancestor, but became distinct species due to multiple cycles of natural selection acting upon variations in isolated subpopulations over time.[2]

Darwin inferred that nature had provided a "fitness-filter" that weeded out traits detrimental to survival in specific environments (aka survival of the fittest). Different kinds of finches existed on the islands because the environmental niches provided different selective pressures. Nature must have acted just like human breeders selecting for desired traits and against unwanted ones, resulting in myriad finch species, each well adapted to its habitat.

Great Diversity from Small Variations

Darwin did not have an explanation for the source of the variations between individuals in a population. The mechanisms by which such differences arose were unclear (and often still are). Whatever the source, variation was critical in advancing changes in a population.

Darwin's theory accounted for the data he had collected, namely, diversity among the Galápagos finches. Following a progression of similar inferences, he extended his theory to postulate that *all* organisms arose through eons of descent with modification via natural selection. He imagined that rare variations within populations would allow for even greater distinctions among progeny. Over time and many, many reproductive cycles, small-scale changes would produce distinct types of animals (for example, both pigeons *and* finches, not just varieties of one or the other). Over even longer periods of time, even greater diversity would result (e.g., birds evolving from dinosaurs).

A Paradigm Takes Root

Darwin's theory was not the first to offer an account of life's history, diversity, and complexity, but it was presented well, reasoned well, and persuasive, especially to those who wanted nonreligious explanations. Publication of *On the Origin of Species* began a shift in the prevailing biological paradigm from creation of distinct and relatively static kinds to shared ancestry of all life. The suggested genealogical relatedness of different types of animals was captured

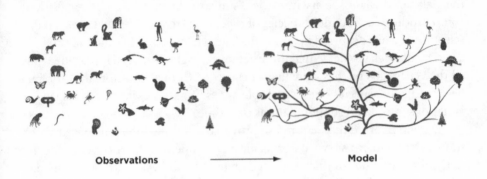

Figure 1: Darwinian Tree of Life – Fitting Observations to a Model

and depicted in what is often referred to as a tree of life. Darwin sketched a rudimentary version of such a tree in his research notebook in 1837, and another depicting hominid evolution in a primate tree of life in 1868.[3]

Evolutionary relationships of real and hypothesized genealogies have been depicted in various tree-like figures ever since. The tips of branches represent actual observations (organisms or fossils). The tree structure, trunk, branches, general shape, and bushiness are the inferences connecting the observations.

Experimental vs. Observational Sciences

Experiments allow scientists to gain reliable understanding of cause-and-effect processes. Being able to reproduce an experiment strengthens our confidence in its results. When studying things that cannot be interrogated or reproduced in a laboratory, we rely more heavily on observations, inferences, and indirect evidence. Darwin relied heavily on these latter concepts in the development of evolution theory.

Processes that can be interrogated via experimentation and verified empirically are generally regarded as factual. However, even if *some* processes within a model become well-evidenced, it does not mean that that verification extends to *all* prior assumptions or inferences. Factual data can accumulate within a theory at the same time other aspects of the theory remain unverified and indemonstrable.

This claim is important in assessing whether evolution is a fact. Some aspects of evolution remain impervious to direct examination. The study of origins is a study of historical events. Events occurring through a progressive series of changes where the next step depends on the previous outcome are referred to as "contingent." Contingent events cannot be reproduced if the conditions under which they occurred are not known or cannot be replicated.

Because of the historically contingent nature of evolution and our inability to know the specific environmental conditions of the past—and because of the complexity, scale, and exceedingly slow processes involved—direct observation, reproduction, and verification of the origins of life and of various species will always be inaccessible and based on inferences. Darwin's theory was not built on demonstrable evolutionary processes or experimental data. At the time, he and others had no way of addressing the basis for trait variations or natural selection experimentally. Nevertheless, there can be good reasons to believe something might be true without it being a verified fact. There may even be good reasons to retain a theory or model despite doubts about whether it is true.

It need not bother us too much that evolution cannot be observed directly at large-scale levels. This is not enough to reject a theory if it plausibly accounts for that which can be observed. Several scientific disciplines are based on observations and large-scale phenomena, yet lack direct experimental data.

Scientific disciplines and subdisciplines (physics, astronomy, chemistry, biology, meteorology, geology, etc.) consider different types of empirical data. In some disciplines data is abundant, easy to generate, and collect, and the supporting theories are easy to interrogate. Some theories are also easier to establish than others because the fundamental mechanisms involved are well-defined and understood. On the other hand, some data is sparse and difficult to generate or collect, and direct interrogation of the system involved may not be possible. Confidence in conclusions varies depending upon the type of empirical data and the means of data generation and collection.

So, Is Evolution a Fact?

At this point, it should be fairly straightforward to see that a paradigm (or conceptual framework) can be consistent with observations and data while still not considered a fact. Inductive inferences support many evolutionary processes, but other evolutionary pathways are based on weak inferences lacking reproducible data, mechanisms, or pathways. At best, evolution is an inference to the best explanation for life on Earth from the perspective that all life-forms share common ancestry. It rests on an interpretation of available data that links all organisms through a mix of demonstrable and speculative processes. Evolution is a paradigm that offers naturalistic explanations for life's history, diversity, and complexity.

Why am I calling evolution a paradigm and not a theory? In science, theories are well-evidenced accounts of reality based on repeated hypothesis testing and ongoing data collection. This is usually what scientists mean when they say evolution is a theory. They *don't* mean it's just a possibility or an idea, as in, "That's just a theory." In reality, evolution is more than that; it is a paradigm.

Over the years, some aspects of Darwin's theory have become well established and more fully understood at molecular and biomolecular levels. For example, scientists have identified microevolutionary mechanisms for generating genetic variation and understanding how these mechanisms contribute to microbial evolution and speciation. These elements are, to varying degrees, considered factual. Other aspects of evolution theory remain dependent primarily on inferences, fitting data to the overarching paradigm in the absence of confirming mechanisms or pathways. Evidence and lack of evidence in support of various forms of evolution are presented more fully in later chapters.

Although evolution fits most data to an explanation consistent with observations, that does not mean it is a fact.

Although evolution fits most data to an explanation consistent with observations, that does not mean it is a fact. A fact is something that is true. Facts may be demonstrably true (that is, confirmed through direct observation) or reasoned to be true through deductive arguments (see "Types of Reasoning"). Still, some things may be true even when we have no way of knowing or proving them to be so.

When people say evolution is a fact, they are not just claiming that it's true—they are claiming it is so well established that no reasonable person should disagree. Concerning its truth, given any particular version, that version is either true or false. The important question, therefore, is whether any version (not just Darwinian versions) of evolution is well evidenced enough to silence disagreement.

Types of Reasoning

We each employ four basic types of reasoning in everyday life. You might be surprised to see which type you rely on to make important conclusions.

Deductive reasoning guarantees the truth of a conclusion only if the premises are true *and* the argument follows the logical rules of inference. If a = b and b = c are both true statements, then the conclusion a = c is necessarily true by deductive reasoning.

Inductive reasoning allows inferences of general conclusions from sets of similar observations. The greater the number of similar observations, the stronger the inductive inference. For example, if I have observed only white swans, I may conclude that all swans are white. I have never been to Australia and never observed a black swan. All swans are not white; some are black. I was fairly confident, but wrong in my conclusion. Thus, inductive conclusions can be reasonable and evidentially based, yet fall short of definitive proof or certainty. One can never exhaust the set of objects studied.

Abductive reasoning is drawing inferences to the best explanations. It incorporates deductive and inductive inferences to render explanations for complex observations. Why is the car in the driveway wet? One possible explanation is that it rained. Is it the best explanation? First, collect or observe additional data. Then ask how much of the data is accounted for in the explanation, how well does the data fit together, what must be imagined to make the data fit together, what is possible, likely, or untenable, and does this explanation affirm, fit, or challenge any other aspect of reality? These questions address the five components of abductive reasoning: (1) explanatory scope, (2) explanatory power, (3) appeal to *ad hoc* elements (data not in evidence), (4) plausibility, and (5) illumination.

We also employ defeasible reasoning—a technical term for belief revision—when new contradictory data leads to amended conclusions, explanations, or beliefs. Premises taken by themselves may justify accepting conclusions, yet when additional information is added, conclusions might no longer be justified.[4] (For example, I was sure I had left the keys on the kitchen counter, but when I found them in the bathroom, I realized I was wrong.) When we obtain new information or hear better arguments, defeasible reasoning can lead us to change our conclusions, our models, or both.

We use these types of reasoning to form a framework of reality and navigate life. Deductive reasoning leads to reliably true conclusions. Inductive reasoning serves us in making less than certain inferences of what is true based on past experiences. Abductively, we form arguments rendering best explanations for what is true as we weigh the merits of competing theories. And defeasible reasoning serves us when we encounter new data and discover we need to revise our understanding of any situation or even our concepts of reality.

New discoveries and better instrumentation allow direct experimentation in ways and areas previously unavailable to investigation. As a result, more data can be generated and collected today than in past generations. More data often leads to revisions in the models or theories being tested. This is definitely true of evolution theory. Will any version of evolution theory rise to the level where the mechanisms and pathways linking all life through common descent are so well established that no reasonable person would contest it? If so, then what? We'll revisit this possibility at the end of the book.

Some will see the distinction I am making between something that is scientifically factual and inferences drawn to bolster the evolution paradigm and think I'm making much ado about nothing. Others will claim, much like Thomas Huxley did,[5] that they are OK with unproven evolutionary inferences because there is no better naturalistic, nonreligious explanation for life's abundant diversity. Still others will claim that the only reason people reject or question the validity of evolution is due to religious beliefs. In the next chapter, we'll see whether this latter claim is true or not, as well as look at two revisions of evolution made due to persistent observations and advances in science.

Discussion Questions

1. How did Charles Darwin form his hypothesis, "descent with modification"? Does this hypothesis seem reasonable?

2. If large-scale evolution cannot be observed directly, is that reason

enough to reject it? Why or why not?

3. What does the author mean by stating that evolution is a paradigm rather than a theory?

4. Explain the four types of reasoning humans employ and how each serves us.

Chapter 2

Is Religious Belief the Only Reason to Question Evolution?

by Anjeanette Roberts

> The most ardent creationists now accept micro-evolution as genuinely Darwinian events. They had better: such are the facts. But the grand evolutionary progressions, such as the transformation of a fish into a man, are examples of *macro-evolution*. They remain out of reach, accessible only at the end of an inferential trail.[1]
>
> —David Berlinski

Darwinian evolution has always had its critics—and not just among theologians and religious believers. Thomas Huxley, a physiologist and anatomist, became known as Darwin's bulldog. He was a contemporary of Darwin's who tenaciously defended the theory of evolution against critics. And yet, Huxley did not always agree with Darwin even on the most fundamental claims of evolution.

Throughout his life, Huxley questioned the two hallmarks of Darwinian evolution: gradualism and natural selection. He felt that both claims lacked evidence, but he remained unwilling to abandon evolution because there wasn't a better naturalistic explanation. The data did not convince Huxley that natural selection could drive species to distinct populations radically different from those from which they arose. He argued that since directed breeding (artificial selection) could not produce a new, fecund, and reproductively independent species, then extrapolating that natural selection could do so was an unfounded claim. Huxley insisted, and I agree, that evidence should drive conclusions, saying, "In matters of the intellect do not pretend that conclusions are certain which are not demonstrated or demonstrable."[2]

It might surprise you that both Huxley and Darwin could embrace and defend evolution, yet disagree on its basic mechanisms. Most scientists today would agree that evolution is a real phenomenon; yet disagreements over underlying mechanisms persist.

Punctuated Equilibria

In 1972, more than 75 years after Huxley's death, Stephen Jay Gould and Niles Eldredge critiqued Darwinian evolution on similar grounds.[3] In contrast to gradual stepwise change, Gould and Eldredge proposed the punctuated equilibria theory, which rendered a naturalistic explanation that better fit the fossil data.

Evolution theory had not predicted long periods of very little change (stasis) of organisms, but rather a gradual evolution and diversification. Yet the fossil record reflects long periods of stasis followed by abrupt appearances of fully formed organisms dissimilar to their predecessors (saltation events). In fact, most animals that roam the earth today strongly resemble the earliest fossils of these same animals—indicating extremely long (geologically speaking) periods of stasis.

Darwin recognized the lack of stepwise changes in the fossil record, but argued that the record was incomplete. He thought transitional forms would turn up as more fossils were discovered. However, despite the fossil record's increasing scope and reliability, Darwin's predicted transitional forms remain absent. Many paleontologists augment Darwin's theory with punctuated equilibria to account for the persistent gaps and abrupt appearances in the fossil record. Thus, evolutionary explanations grew in complexity to accommodate new findings and persistent observations.

> **Data can be, and often is, interpreted in different ways.**

The introduction of punctuated equilibria is an excellent example of inference to the best explanation, the underdetermination of scientific theories, and belief revision.

Inferences to the Best Explanation

There can be debate even among those who embrace evolution as a grand unifying theory. Data can be, and often is, interpreted in different ways, and not always due to theology, ideologies, or religious commitments.

Philosophy, theology, and scientific theory formation share identical means of reasoning in presenting rational arguments (see "Types of Reasoning" on page 29). Abductive reasoning is employed in forensics, detective work, legal arguments and jury deliberations, medical diagnoses, and archaeology, as well as in everyday situations where events cannot be reproduced or proven and when data leads to competing theories or possible explanations where one needs to choose or assign preference to one option over other options.

One example of abductive reasoning is to imagine that you wake one morning, look out your window and notice the car in your driveway is wet. You might conclude that it had rained. Is that the best possible explanation? If it had rained, not just your car but most likely the grass and sidewalk would also be wet. You head outside and discover the lawn and pavement are dry (failed predictions). New data requires belief revision; it likely had *not* just rained. You look and see that the hedge between your yard and the neighbor's is wet, as is his driveway. His car is also shiny and clean. You weigh the evidence observed and abductively reason that your neighbor sprayed your car while washing his. This is the best explanation from all the observed data and does not require the introduction of data not in evidence.

But what if you hadn't noticed the wet hedge or your neighbor's car and driveway? What if there was no more empirical evidence than a wet car and a dry sidewalk and lawn to inform your theory selection? Then you might construct a speculative explanation. An alien spacecraft hovered over your car, soaked it with a giant alien soaker, and collected the run-off for analyses. There is no evidence to support the alien super-soaker theory, yet it is not inconsistent with the data. It's possible, even if highly implausible. The imagined and unevidenced data you introduced yields a (very) tentative explanation. The alien scenario is less believable than the neighbor-car-wash or rain theories, but all three theories fit the data to the same degree. In addition to displaying abductive reasoning, this example also demonstrates the concept of underdetermination.

Underdetermination of Scientific Theories

This phenomenon—first described by John Stuart Mill and further developed by Pierre Duhem, and later by Willard Van Orman Quine—is another reason why there can be so much disagreement over data interpretation.[4] Underdetermination is defined as "the simple idea that the evidence available to us at a given time may be insufficient to determine what beliefs we should hold in response to it."

The underdetermination of theories is true whether the data is sparse or abundant, simple or complex, ambiguous or well-defined. More data may help distinguish the merits of competing theories, but model revision is able to accommodate many unexpected results. Mill sums up the concept best:

> Most thinkers of any degree of sobriety allow, that an hypothesis . . . is not to be received as probably true because it accounts for all the known phenomena, since this is a condition sometimes fulfilled tolerably well by two conflicting hypotheses; while there are probably many others which are equally possible, but which, for want of anything analogous in our experience, our minds are unfitted to conceive.[5]

In other words, there may be several hypotheses that account for any given set of data and, therefore, might be true. Indeed, the number of hypotheses is limited only by one's inability to imagine a scenario that fits the data into a cohesive whole.

I remember a writing exercise in fourth grade where the teacher gave me a picture of three objects: a wrangler on horseback, a fluffy white housecat lying on a kitchen table, and a butterfly in flight. She directed me to write a story that fit the disparate objects into a single narrative. I never finished that assignment. I was bad at that type of creative thinking in fourth grade (I may still be).

I had never encountered a scenario involving a wrangler, a house cat (we were dog people), and a butterfly. Given that data, I had no theory to hold it all together. Possible stories for the threesome were limitless. The limits existed only by the poverty of my fourth-grade imagination.

Let's consider another example that requires creativity and abductive reasoning. Given a string of numbers 2, 4, 8 (the data), predict the next number in the series. If you think the numbers represent a simple doubling of the preceding number, then 16 would be your answer. Another person, thinking the numbers are generated by multiplying the two preceding numbers, could predict 32. Yet another possible answer is 64 (multiplying all preceding numbers to generate the next). But what if someone thought of something a little more convoluted? Perhaps this is a series of even numbers not divisible by 6, which makes 10 the next number.

This simple numerical challenge provides an excellent example of the fact that the data always (always!) underdetermines the theory. Given *any* set of data, a variety of theories can explain how the data relate to one another and generate many different models (or explanations) accounting for the observed data.

The concept of underdetermination is critical to scientific theory formation and, as my examples demonstrate, it's true of all theories, not just scientific ones. People can even determine two (or more) competing theories to be equally good based on the data at hand. These are referred to as empirical equivalents. More data might tip the scales one way or the other—then again, it might maintain the equivalence. Quine argued that at any given point in time, whether in scientific contexts or any area of human reasoning, there will always be incompatible interpretations that are empirically equivalent.[6]

Belief Revision

John Pollock, an American philosopher known for work in artificial intelligence and theories of knowledge, said that we are all making decisions from positions of prevailing ignorance.[7] His point is this: of all that is true in reality, we know only an extraordinarily small fraction and can prove even less. Even if we consider the sum of human knowledge, we are only scratching the surface of all that exists or all that can be known. This is a delightful place to be for someone who loves discovery—but for anyone desiring immutable certainties, it can be frustrating.

Defeasible reasoning—the action of withdrawing conclusions based on new contradictory information—becomes especially important when new data falsifies previous predictions. As the decades roll by, scientific inquiry uncovers more mysteries and complexities than imagined by our greatest fiction writers. When we discover or encounter new things, we employ belief revision—a hallmark and virtue of scientific inquiry. New data need not be empirical evidence, but may be new inferences, ideas, or arguments.

Persuasive Rhetoric

Belief revision may occur in the presence or absence of new evidence. Sometimes belief revision hinges on a new argument or inference to the best explanation. Punctuated equilibria is a great example of introducing a novel idea to better account for the same set of data that Darwin had observed. One could even make the case, as some have, that it was rhetoric more than data that led to the establishment of Darwinian evolution as the new paradigm.

At the heart of belief revision and revision of scientific theories is the persuasiveness of the argument that fits the observed data. In *Mapping the Origins Debate*, Gerald Rau makes this observation, "In court, neither the evidences nor the inferences stand on their own—they must be combined into a coherent argument. Often it is the rhetorical skill of the presenter [attorney], rather than the weight of the evidence itself, that convinces a jury to view the evidence a certain way."[8] Although science is mostly driven by evidence, constructing logical explanations and persuading others of a given interpretation or theory is often about the quality of the story we tell.

New Discoveries
As might be imagined, new observations and discoveries have led to ongoing revisions of evolutionary theory. With new data and discoveries, explanations fitting the data often change, too. Let's look at two major revisions to Darwinian evolution.

Modern Synthesis
Darwin, of course, had little understanding of the mechanisms of inheritance. It seems he remained uninformed of the work of Gregor Mendel (1866), which proved foundational in the advent of population genetics (in the early twentieth century). Population genetics remains a major component of current evolutionary theory. Darwin also knew nothing about DNA. The discovery of DNA as the cellular component of heredity would not come about for another century in the work of Avery, MacLeod, and McCarty in 1944, with confirmation and general acceptance following the work of Hershey and Chase in 1952.

The structure and informational nature of DNA followed quickly, based primarily on the x-ray crystallographic work of Rosalind Franklin (1953) and the work of Nirenberg, Khorana, Matthaei, and Leder in breaking the DNA code (1961–1966). These discoveries led to the first major revisions of Darwinian evolution.

The modern synthesis, or neo-Darwinism, modified Darwin's theory through the incorporation of population genetics and the gene theory of inheritance. Mendel's work with pea plants established that inherited traits were not blended intermediates of parental traits, but discrete traits passed from both parents to offspring. Inheritance of traits could be mathematically modeled and resulted in the field of population genetics.

The discovery of DNA as the biomolecule encoding discrete traits resulted in the gene theory of inheritance, where genes (segments of DNA encoding proteins) were identified as the basis for Mendel's heritable traits. DNA as the basis of inheritance overturned a long-held belief among scientists that proteins were most likely the basis for heredity due to their greater molecular diversity

(20 amino acids in proteins compared to four nucleotide bases in DNA).

These discoveries laid the basis for trait variations between different organisms, which result from changes in gene sequences, gene regulation, or both. Mendelian genetics and traits encoded in the DNA (genes) were foundational components leading to the modern synthesis of evolution theory.

The modern synthesis described how evolution occurs within populations and how it can be measured by changes in the frequency of genetic markers (alleles) within populations. Within the modern synthesis, microevolution is defined as changes in populations (allele frequencies) at or below the species level and macroevolution as changes in higher level taxonomical classifications (taxa) above the level of species. Macroevolution is considered an extension of gradual, successive iterations of microevolution that eventually led to distinct taxa. It remains a string of inferences built on observations of microevolutionary changes. (For more on speciation, see online bonus material at reasons.org/evolutionbonus.)

The modern synthesis maintained fundamental Darwinian tenets of descent with modification, gradualism, and nonteleological natural selection acting on (random) variations in populations. This was basically as Darwin had postulated, but now there was a better understanding of how changes occurred at molecular levels and how those changes could be modeled within populations. Important mechanisms underlying allele frequency changes in populations include gene drift in isolated populations and sexual reproduction as a major means of variability through gene flow and recombination.

An Extended Evolutionary Synthesis (Not Your Great-Grandfather's Evolution)
In more recent decades, the challenge of incorporating several unanticipated discoveries and observations has evolutionary biologists debating whether continued revision of the modern synthesis is possible or if it needs to be scrapped and replaced with an extended evolutionary synthesis (EES).

Many discoveries considered in an EES will be discussed in greater detail in the following chapters. The mechanisms in an EES include genome duplication, horizontal gene transfer (HGT), transposition, symbiogenesis, and epigenetics, as well as work arising in evolutionary developmental biology (evo-devo) studies that entail developmental systems, timing, and patterning. The modern synthesis incorporates some of these mechanisms (e.g., transposition) rather easily, but others (e.g., symbiogenesis, HGT, and epigenetics) seem incongruent with its fundamental tenets.

Comparative genomics has also led to the introduction of many new concepts in population genetics that present difficulties for maintaining the modern synthesis (e.g., convergence, homoplasy, exaptation, gene loss, neutral theory, etc.). As evolutionary biologist Eugene Koonin puts it, "The biological universe seen through the lens of genomics is a far cry from the orderly, rather simple picture envisioned by Darwin and the creators of the Modern Synthesis."[9] He elaborates elsewhere:

> Comparative genomics and systems biology offer unprecedented opportunities for testing central tenets of evolutionary biology formulated by Darwin . . . and expanded in the Modern Synthesis. . . . Evolutionary-genomic studies show that natural selection is only one of the forces that shape genome evolution and is not quantitatively dominant, whereas non-adaptive processes are much more prominent than previously suspected. Major contributions of horizontal gene transfer and diverse selfish genetic elements to genome evolution undermine the Tree of Life concept. An adequate depiction of evolution requires the more complex concept of a network or "forest" of life. There is no consistent tendency of evolution towards increased genomic complexity, and when complexity increases, this appears to be a non-adaptive consequence of evolution under weak purifying selection rather than an adaptation.[10]

Neutral Theory

Critics of neo-Darwinism point out that natural selection is not always, or even often, selecting fitness advantages within populations. In other words, nature allows for purifying selection more than positive selection. Only failures perish, while the less fit persist and even reproduce adequately. This allows for much more variation as genomes carry many neutral mutations (neither beneficial nor deleterious). Neutral theory, proposed and mathematically modeled by Motoo Kimura in 1968,[11] was developed in response to genetic sequence analyses and computational modeling that challenged the adequacy of modern synthesis's mechanisms.

In challenges to the modern synthesis it is primarily neutral mutations, especially large-scale neutral mutations occurring via macromutational mechanisms, accruing within populations over time that drive complexity and evolutionary progression. In a paper titled "The Origin at 150: Is a New

Evolutionary Synthesis in Sight?," Koonin observes that neutral theory is the culmination of the molecular revolution.[12] He goes on:

> In a world dominated by HGT, gene duplication, gene loss, and such momentous events as endosymbiosis, the idea of evolution being driven primarily by infinitesimal heritable changes in the Darwinian tradition has become untenable.[13]

In other words, to the critics of the modern synthesis, fitness advantages and natural selection are no longer the most important elements of macroevolution; neutral theory and mechanisms that introduce large-scale changes are. The implication is that evolution is not a gradual process but one that depends on large, nondisruptive, genome-level changes in populations that eventually result in new organisms and macroevolutionary type changes consistent with punctuated equilibria.

Persistent Paradigm

Despite revisions and challenges, evolution itself is not abandoned; it remains *the* paradigm, even if not a fact *per se*. Some elements have been confirmed or experimentally verified (e.g., Mendelian genetics and DNA-trait inheritance). Others, however, are still inferences built on ideologies of a modern synthesis, neutral theory, or EES model.

What endures in the paradigm is a commitment to naturalistic processes accounting for life's complexity and diversity. So, although evolutionists may disagree over the components and mechanisms, descent with modification and natural selection (with or without adaptive, fitness advantages) remain the unifying factors. There are also disagreements as to whether variations are random or directed through environmental signals (or in the case of evolutionary creationists, through undetectable supernatural tweaking), over the gradual nature of these changes, the significance of various mechanisms, and the significance of neutral theory.

Belief revision is part of being alive, seeking truth, and growing in understanding.

Human Experience Requires Belief Revision

Revisions to evolutionary theories are not unique. Theory revision and belief revision are part of human experience and growing in understanding. My understanding of God and what it means to follow Jesus has changed significantly over the years.

Debate about underlying mechanisms for the origin and diversity of life predates Darwin's publications. Although Darwin is credited with evolutionary theory, he was not the first to propose a naturalistic account for life. Philosophers, scientists, and theologians have debated for millennia whether reality can be reduced to physical explanations or if metaphysical explanations should include nonmaterial, spiritual, or supernatural entities as well. What Darwin, Huxley, Gould, and modern evolutionary scientists have in common is not the mechanisms of evolution but the commitment to a naturalistic explanation of life's origins and history.

Many scientists today would agree that the modern synthesis needs revision or replacement. These scientists would enthusiastically deny that they are in any way driven by faith, theology, or religious beliefs. Their rejection of Darwinian evolution and critiques of the modern synthesis are based on scientific data alone. My colleagues and I at Reasons to Believe reject these theories for the exact reasons as these scientists do. Darwinian evolution and the modern synthesis inadequately account for the scientific data garnered in numerous fields of study over the past 150 and 80 years, respectively.

So, it is not just theology that raises questions about evolution. Scientists themselves challenge outdated theories—but seemingly never the underlying paradigm. Is such bulldogged tenacity in clinging to evolution due to the science or to something else? Is it due to a paradigm that transcends the data and is it more philosophical than scientific? Perhaps. Let's consider this in our next question.

Discussion Questions

1. The author cites Thomas Huxley's assertion that evidence should drive conclusions. Is this what you observe today when it comes to claims about evolution or creation?

2. What is the concept of underdetermination and how does it affect theory formation?

3. What role does rhetoric play in establishing truth?

4. Describe the two revisions to Darwinian evolution and how they came about.

5. The author ends this chapter with, "Is such bulldogged tenacity in clinging to evolution due to the science or to something else?" How would you answer that question?

Chapter 3

What's Philosophy Got to Do with Evolution?

by Anjeanette Roberts

The unexamined life is not worth living.
—Socrates

Examining and exploring the world around us and the world of our own actions and relationships is the warp and woof of human experience. Science is arguably one of the greatest human pursuits of all. As we examine nature and discover fundamental properties, laws, and mechanisms that govern the universe, we realize how research has led to amazing advancements in human technology and civilization. Maybe this examination and exploration of the world around us is what Socrates was encouraging. After all, the Socratic method is much like a scientific hypothesis and the ensuing scientific testing—putting up questions and trying their answers. But could this great Athenian philosopher have meant we need to examine our *philosophies*, not just our surroundings and behaviors? Some say he meant precisely this: "A life without philosophy is not worth living."[1]

But if science is all about examining nature's fundamental properties, laws, and mechanisms, how does philosophy fit in? I can think of several good answers, not the least of which is that science raises questions that science itself cannot answer. Science has boundaries and whenever one of those boundaries is encountered, we have philosophical decisions to make.

Another answer is best presented as a question. What if competing theories view the nature of reality differently? Differing views of reality would affect what is considered possible, likely, plausible, or impossible when assessing the theories. A third reason to care about philosophy gets more at the self-examination Socrates encouraged. Philosophical presuppositions are the foundation for each person's view of reality. Unexamined philosophical commitments inhibit meaningful communication about our own beliefs or with others whose philosophical starting points differ from ours. Even if we don't reach an extreme, nihilistic conclusion, we will live impoverished lives without such examination and understanding of our underlying philosophies.

Finally, the success of science depends on a set of assumptions that require philosophical justification. For example, we assume that our sensory perceptions are generally reliable and that lawlike regularities governing nature can be discovered. These philosophical assumptions ground scientific inquiry.

What Is the Fundamental Nature of Reality?

As mentioned earlier, interpreting and fitting data to conceptual frameworks requires reasoning and making inferences. Our frameworks take into account direct observations, cause-and-effect events, and how things relate to one another, but they also include much larger concepts, such as the nature of reality and the plausibility of various speculations. One can't really assess the plausibility of an explanation if one hasn't first formed assumptions about the nature of reality. Both mental activities involve philosophy.

There are two basic options for the nature of reality. First, reality is strictly materialistic. Space, time, energy, and mechanistic processes are all that exist. Second, reality consists of more than the material stuff of the universe. In other words, there is a nonmaterial, supernatural aspect of reality. In philosophy, these perspectives are known as metaphysical views. The second perspective leads to numerous explanations for how supernatural and natural realms might interact with one another. These two contrasting views usually lead to atheism (or materialism) and theism, respectively.

Agnosticism is an epistemological position. An agnostic claims that there is not enough data to know whether the nonmaterial exists. Agnosticism can entail a strong skepticism where one could never determine if a nonmaterial reality exists, even if it does. Alternatively, it could entail a more open skepticism where one could hold that the existence of the supernatural is highly plausible, based upon the idea that what could be true of reality remains yet unknown. I think agnosticism and theism are the only two intellectually honest positions. Still, regardless of one's metaphysical views, one can learn a lot about the physical world through a systematic study of nature.

Science Works Great Until It Doesn't

We have great confidence in certain things because of scientific discoveries and applications, such as air travel, antibiotics, internet technologies, and SPF products. Sometimes certain scientific facts might be the only things we can all agree upon. Nevertheless, this does not mean that only scientifically proven facts are *all* that is true. Eventually, each of us reaches conclusions about reality that entail things that can't be measured scientifically.

Remember that science has boundaries. The only way to reason to explanations beyond those boundaries is to employ our (collective or individual) wisdom. When we do this, we are doing philosophy, not science. We are adding inferences from human reasoning, worldviews, and philosophy to inferences grounded in scientific observations. *This is a very important point.* When we reason to best explanations, we draw from our metaphysical beliefs as well as scientifically determined evidence. It is worth the effort to determine which of our inferences are drawn from philosophical commitments and which are drawn from science or other empirical (objective) evidence.

> **Regardless of one's metaphysical views, one can learn a lot about the physical world through a systematic study of nature.**

What kinds of questions are beyond the boundary of science?
One may think that science primarily answers *what* and *how* questions, and sometimes *when* questions (e.g., *When* will we next see Venus near the Moon in the northern hemisphere's night sky?). And one may think that *why* questions are not addressed by science at all, except in cases where one asks "why" and really means "how," according to a series within a causal chain, e.g., *Why* do satellite orbits decay over time? The answer is a mechanistic description of cause-and-effect chains involving gravity, friction, and kinetic energy. In other words, the answer is telling you *how* satellite orbits decay.

Answers to the *why* questions that entail purpose or goals, which are central to the kinds of questions we ask in life, are not addressed by science. *Why* questions often arise at the boundaries of scientific inquiry. That some of our deepest questions about life arise at the boundaries of scientific studies seems odd. In a sense, it hints that the nature of reality may entail something more.

Theism and Teleology in a Materialistic Universe

In regard to the orderliness at the heart of nature and scientific inquiry, Albert Einstein is often misquoted as having said, "The most incomprehensible thing about the universe is that it is comprehensible." What he actually said was, "The very fact that the totality of our sense experiences is such that by means of thinking . . . it can be put in order, this fact is one which leaves us in awe, but which we shall never understand. One may say 'the eternal mystery of the world is its comprehensibility.'"[2] Either of these quotes is as much a comment on the rational mind observing order as it is on the order itself. Yet, it is strange that in a materialistic universe one would ever expect to see any component demonstrating any self-awareness, consciousness, abstract thinking, or capacity for reasoning at all. It is equally strange that a sense of the nonmaterial (spiritual) would develop or that *why* questions would emerge from material-only causal chains. In other words, how could (or why would) any such creatures or minds ever happen in a material-only reality?

Nature also presents us with an intractable problem of teleology, not just with the problems of its comprehensibility and our abilities to wonder and reason. Everything in the natural world seems to have purpose and any process that leads to purposeful outcomes is teleological or goal-oriented. This also seems odd if we inhabit a strictly material universe. Furthermore, much of nature seems fitted to work in concert, in interdependent networks and systems (see chapter 11). This gives rise to puzzling questions. Why is there something rather than nothing? Why is there order in the universe? Why isn't reality more chaotic? Why does nature follow fundamental laws that allow intelligent beings to thrive, reliably test nature, and build complex societies? Others who wrestle with these kinds of questions add the observation that nature cannot explain its own existence. Science shows us that nature exhibits rational and contingent order. Yet, the laws and initial conditions of the universe were not necessarily so. Nature itself needs an explanation.

All such questions, and those involving origins, purpose, meaning, destiny, and morals, add depth to the human experience and pursuit of knowledge, and all the answers to these lay outside the bounds of science. Yet, they are the marrow of philosophy and theology.

Can Science Be Used to Favor One Metaphysical View?

Science can't be used to prove any metaphysical version of reality because it is limited to exploring physical aspects of reality. Adherents to materialism and theism can both employ science to study the fundamental principles and properties governing the universe.

Nevertheless, the contrasting metaphysical views each have unique claims to science. Materialists infer that in a material-only universe science will eventually be able to explain almost everything because everything would have a materialistic explanation. This perspective often leads to a reductionist understanding of extremely complex systems, including ones that seem incongruent with a materialist universe (like human consciousness and abstract reasoning). Theists, on the other hand, infer that since science gives reliable, rational knowledge of the material world, it is logically reasonable to believe the universe is ordered, comprehensible, and likely structured to be so by a rational, creative being.

The universe seems to make sense, as do questions raised at and beyond the boundaries of science. This fits with a materialistic view of reality *if* one concedes that conscious self-awareness can arise from unguided material processes, but seems far more congruent with a theistic metaphysical view. Christian theism provides an additional level of confidence since it asserts that God created everything so we can thrive and come to know him through his self-revelation in nature, Scripture, and the person of Jesus. The universe and the things within it have order and point to purpose for perceptive beings.

Much of what we do in research science employs some very basic principles (often taken for granted) detached from any philosophical interpretative position. This is one of the beauties of science. When one follows basic principles, one generates empirical data. If I follow certain experimental processes, I generate certain outcomes. Another individual in another time and place, speaking a different language and worshiping or not worshiping the same deity as I do, can repeat the process and reproduce the same outcome. The processes and properties remain constant regardless of who runs the experiment. Reproducibility is at the heart of establishing scientific facts. But recall, historical sciences dealing with origins cannot be verified this way. Even if we had the time, we do not have the knowledge of original conditions or components to reproduce life from nonlife or to reproduce origination of various organisms or humans. So, evolutionary biology, drawing on an unobservable past, always involves layers of inferences, which always presume conceptual frameworks or philosophical commitments.

Competing Worldviews

If science cannot prove a "nature only" or a "nature plus" interpretation of reality, how do we choose one metaphysical view over another? At a very fundamental level, one's metaphysical perspective is the basis for one's view of the world. And one's worldview determines what types of conclusions or explanations one will accept and give regarding one's experiences.

Most of us want to believe true things about reality, ourselves, and others. So what do we do when we encounter different explanations that seem coherent and seem to correspond to reality? How does one choose between competing ideas, theories, paradigms, or worldviews, considering the underdetermination problem? How do we determine which worldview to embrace when science seems a neutral ally because we find we're now asking questions way outside science's limitations?

Although evolution is a scientific paradigm, it is often employed as a comprehensive worldview in conjunction with materialism. Choosing—and continuing to choose—a particular worldview comes down to which one best answers our deepest questions and helps explain our place in the world. As with competing theories, when worldviews collide we watch for new evidence to help clarify which perspective fits the data better and how well different explanations accommodate new (and especially surprising) data.

Although science is a modernist activity driven by cause-and-effect processes and hard data, science theory formation and data-fitting can be rather postmodern, addressing an overarching story or metanarrative. Explanations drawn from scientific study are, to a certain extent, about the stories we tell— or the theories we build to account for the data. We need to be careful as we incorporate more and more unevidenced concepts. In the words of astronomer Sir Fred Hoyle, "Be suspicious of a theory if more and more hypotheses are needed to support it as new facts become available, or as new considerations are brought to bear."[3]

Is an Evolutionary Paradigm Truly Better?

My research as a molecular biologist focused on viruses, associated disease processes, and ways of preventing disease. My work entailed experimental verification of cause-and-effect relationships. I conducted successful research projects with little to no consideration of the evolutionary paradigm or macroevolution. Microevolutionary changes, of course, were well established and accepted. Yet, if Theodosius Dobzhansky's often repeated claim is true that biology makes sense only in the light of evolution, why were macroevolutionary concepts superfluous to my research?

A bright and accomplished student, I'm going to call him "Einstein," was in the class ahead of mine at UPenn. Einstein worked on a project in a prestigious

HHMI[4] lab, finished in under five years, published multiple peer-reviewed articles on his research, and went on to a productive tenured faculty position at a top-tier research institution. Every time I heard him give a talk in grad school—whether it was a chalk-talk on a research technique or a departmental seminar or journal club—it was clear that Einstein knew his stuff. He articulated his hypotheses and research findings with finesse. His insights into his own research and that of others were remarkable. He excelled in answering every question in classes, at seminars, in meetings—until he faced the last question posed to him at his public thesis defense. The question went something like this, "Einstein, this is great work you've done, but what do your findings tell us about the evolutionary benefit or significance in the development of these phenomena?"

For the first time in four years, Einstein didn't answer right away. He was silent and looked pensive for several seconds. When he began to speak, his signature, highly articulate response was strikingly absent. He answered very tentatively. He "umm-ed" and stalled as he uttered a few disjointed observations and speculations, and concluded by wondering aloud, "Maybe something like that, but I don't really know. I haven't really thought about it." I was stunned and feared for his inability to answer this faculty member's question. I was equally, if not more, stunned by her reply, "Well, good; at least now you're thinking about it."

This memory has stuck with me for two reasons. One, it reflects the reality that brilliant people can conduct excellent research without one thought to an evolutionary paradigm's significance. Two, it has become obvious to me that a culture of fitting research findings into an evolutionary narrative through speculations and possibilities has been honed and propagated for decades in institutions of higher learning.

Before starting this book, I looked up my friend Einstein's publications. He has several publications from his postdoctoral and faculty work, in addition to the trove from his graduate research. I pored over each peer-reviewed article in search of any reference to evolution. I found none. Not one reference to

Brilliant people can conduct excellent research without one thought to an evolutionary paradigm's significance.

evolution appeared throughout this man's highly successful career in academics and research. His work is science at its best and yet is silent regarding an evolutionary narrative. My own experience has been similar. The evolutionary narrative either had no impact *or had a negative impact* on my actual research and meaningful interpretations of the data.

Underdetermination and Plausibility

Once we realize the role of philosophy and the limitations of science, we see how different individuals can look at the same data and form very different conclusions to explain it when direct observations of cause-and-effect mechanisms are not possible. They can form different conclusions because they can make different inferences. If one gives a materialistic explanation in the absence of direct cause-and-effect mechanisms or reproducibility, one is still making an inference.

Claims of macroevolutionary processes yielding proposed outcomes are examples of inferences without confirmation. If these processes occured, they occured over very long periods of time. Radical transformations of organisms from one higher level taxonomical group to another have never been observed. Any supposed macroevolutionary leap in life's history would have been contingent on unknown conditions and sequences of events or outcomes. Therefore, such leaps remain irreproducible and indemonstrable. Nevertheless, evolutionists fit observed data to the paradigm while turning a blind eye to real challenges posed by radical transformations occurring in relatively little time.

Overcoming Worldview Bias in This Book

As we address questions in the following chapters, we seek to make it clear when conclusions are driven by data and by identified, observable, and reproducible mechanisms and when conclusions are based on inferences lacking specific mechanisms and cause-and-effect explanations. We will offer alternative, possible interpretations to mainstream evolutionary interpretations and confirm when our interpretations match evolutionary interpretations. Ultimately, you must decide which are inferences to the best explanations.

We also want to challenge you to consider explanations that are new to you. Understanding is not static. We continue to accumulate data, and new data invites revision. Someone who is curious and seeking truth with integrity should always be open to belief revision. Our limited perspectives and general human finitude mean reality presents us with an inexhaustible potential for discovery. Whenever we encounter new information, data, or ideas that challenge our conceptual frameworks, we can react in at least four different ways. We can reject the data, somehow disqualifying its relevance. We can adjust our models to accommodate the new data. We can look for or create better models. Finally, we can remain skeptical and continue to collect more data until we select one of the previous courses of action. In this last process, I often think of new ideas or data as items to hang on my central framework. Sometimes new data fits nicely, but when it doesn't, I often find myself hanging those items on a side rack, so to speak. (I rarely throw items out.)

Remember the story of Professor Van Till's lecture and the two grad students whose reactions to the talk differed radically from mine? (See introduction.) Going into the session we almost certainly held a common belief in God, trust in the Christian scriptures, a background in science, a fundamental trust in the regularity of nature, etc. We almost certainly shared access to the same types of reasoning, value for rational explanations, and a commitment to grow in and share our Christian faith. Otherwise we wouldn't have been at this particular conference (Following Christ: Shaping Our World, Chicago, 1999). Yet when we heard Van Till's ideas for integrating science and the Christian faith, we reacted differently. How is that possible?

It was apparent each of us had heard something new. We had received new data, if you will, for consideration. What I heard allowed me to clear many items off my side racks and hang them on my central conceptual framework. I suspect it was more disruptive to the other guys' conceptual models than to mine, though I don't know the details of the presumed disruption. Perhaps I should have taken time to ask them.

In all this talk of philosophy and worldviews, I hope we take time to hear how others fit the data together and what philosophical commitments we bring to the scientific data. I hope we learn to distinguish mechanistic (cause-and-effect) conclusions from inference-driven conclusions. And I hope we have the curiosity and intellectual humility to consider ideas we haven't heard before and learn from one another as we seek clearer understanding of the world around us.

Discussion Questions

1. Regarding the nature of reality, on what basis does the author posit agnosticism and theism as the "only two intellectually honest positions"?

2. Does science have boundaries? Explain.

3. In a materialist universe, science could eventually be able to explain everything. Do you see any challenges to this view?

4. Is the evolutionary paradigm necessary for scientific research? Why or why not?

Chapter 4

How Can We Keep Our Thinking Free from Fallacy?
by Mark Perez

Fallacies are errors in reasoning that often do not look like errors in reasoning. They are important to avoid because they can distract us from important facts or conceal weaknesses in claims that need to be answered. As an instructor in critical thinking, I have worked with people from widely varied backgrounds, from undergraduates to mature professionals with PhDs. One of the things we all have in common is that we can miss seeing fallacies in our own arguments and those of others if we are not careful. Everyone is vulnerable.

Evolution-creation debates include many important claims. So in this chapter we will look at a few fallacies that arise in them, particularly in publications designed for popular audiences.

One or the Other?
The evolution-creation debate is an interesting paradox. It is reasonable to present the two positions as an either-or choice. For example, we could say either all life diversified entirely from natural processes from a singular ancestor or it diversified entirely from God's direct action. This makes for good drama—but not good reasoning. There may, for example, be a way to harmonize at least some features of both positions to create alternatives we cannot now see. When an argument is presented as only an "either-or" proposition when other alternatives may exist, we see an example of the fallacy of "false dilemma." The false dilemma fallacy is particularly important to avoid in science because it can inhibit research into alternatives the false dilemma ignores.

Argument from Ignorance
Claiming that something is false because it is not known to be true is an

argument from ignorance. The explanation for vestigial organs is an example of this fallacy. For decades, evolution adherents have explained various anatomical parts or biochemical processes as evolutionary "leftovers" or vestiges. The claim is that these structures and processes appear to have no function today, therefore they must have lost their functions as the species evolved.[1] However, merely not knowing that there is a function does not prove none exists.

Examples of purported vestigial structures in humans abound. For over a century, the appendix was considered nonfunctional, in part because there were no apparent side effects in its removal. Research in the past 20 years has shown otherwise. The appendix helps produce hormones in fetuses starting at eleven weeks and then assists in immune functions starting shortly after birth.[2]

A more recent example is so-called junk DNA. Many researchers originally believed over 90 percent of the human genome was "junk" (a term coined by the late geneticist Susumu Ohno in 1972) because it does not code for proteins. For over 20 years, scientists avoided research into junk DNA because it was considered "genomic garbage."[3] However in 2003, the Encyclopedia of DNA Elements (ENCODE) Project began to determine the purpose of the remaining 99 percent of the genome. This worldwide project included over 30 research groups and 400 scientists resulting in discoveries concluding that at least 80 percent of junk DNA is biochemically active and presumably functions to regulate gene expression.[4]

Bald Assertion

Research requires that scientists present evidence—direct or indirect—to support their claims. Unevidenced scientific claims are one of two things: *conjectures* or *bald assertions*. Conjecture is valuable in science as a conditional starting point for research, a guess to begin a new line of experiments. A scientific conjecture, properly made, clearly declares its status as conjecture. A bald assertion, on the other hand, is a claim without evidence to support it presented as if it were true or otherwise well-founded.

Examples of bald assertions appear in the field of evolutionary psychology. This research field applies evolution theory to explain the origins and functions of human thinking and behavior. Its practitioners make several assumptions: (1) the brain controls thoughts and behaviors, (2) the brain evolved from more primitive ancestral forms, and (3) the brain adapted to environmental conditions in ways favoring survival and fitness to conditions. For example, consider the human fear of the unknown. An evolutionary psychologist's explanation of this phenomenon might go something like, "Fear of the unknown is an adaptation of our prehistoric ancestors to dangerous situations." One need only spend a few minutes perusing web articles or popular magazines to find many such claims of evolutionary explanations for human behaviors from common fears to dating preferences to belief in the supernatural.[5]

Such explanations are bald assertions because they lack evidence to support them. One cannot explain current human behavior based on changes and conditions of prehistoric ancestors when one has never seen the ancestor's environment, behaviors, and adaptations concurrently and in detail through time. Some of the most important data we would need includes observations of interpersonal or group interactions, something inaccessible to paleontology. Without observational data of the prehistoric ancestors, especially observations of their responses (and failures to respond) to the full array of physical and mental stimuli under varying conditions, there is no basis to evolutionary psychologists' claims that evolution-based theoretical explanations for particular modern human behaviors are true.

Slippery Slope

The essential feature of a *slippery slope* argument is that it assumes *without good causal evidence* that a particular position taken is the first in a series of events necessarily leading to a problematic end. Here is an example. Coffee is a stimulant with mild addictive properties. Drinking coffee will lead to addictions to stronger and stronger stimulants, ultimately leading to addiction to methamphetamines and other dangerous drugs. Therefore, we should not drink coffee. The claim shows no causal evidence to link coffee drinking to methamphetamine addiction. It thus suffers the slippery slope fallacy.

An example of the slippery slope at work among evolution theorists is the claim that progressive creation theory fills in knowledge gaps with God. For instance, the fossil records of the Cambrian and Precambrian eras exhibit many fossils with no overlapping features evincing evolutionary change. In some cases, the fossils appear to be radically new phyla, leading to at least two conclusions: either the fossil in question has no evolutionary ancestor or the closest evolutionary ancestor fossils have been destroyed or made otherwise unavailable. Likewise, at least two

If evolution is true, then the intermediary creatures left no fossils or none we can find.

inferences are available. If evolution is true, then the intermediary creatures left no fossils or none we can find. If progressive creation theory is true, then God created creatures *de novo*—the fossils evince no ancestral intermediaries because there were none.

Although the data fits both theories equally well, evolution theorists reject the theistic explanation not because it is proved wrong, but because, as the "god-of-the-gaps" argument goes, if you explain these intractable gaps with God, you will explain *all* difficult gaps with God. Science can't progress by defaulting to divine intervention every time gaps of knowledge seem intractable.

This slippery slope fallacy fails where it assumes that if the progressive creation theorist's appeal to divine intervention is accepted as plausible at any time, it will be used in other cases where research alone could fill the knowledge gap. Evolution theorists offer no causal chain supporting that assumption. For the god-of-the-gaps argument to move from fallacy to description, its proponents would have to at least show that the interests of progressive creation theorists are advanced by asserting divine intervention where research on a given problem has revealed a strong, noncircular[6] likelihood of solving that problem with a physical explanation. But progressive creation theory entails that its proponents have the same interests in preserving natural explanations as do evolution theorists wherever possible. Progressive creation theory seeks, in part, to understand the nature and mechanisms of what God has made in nature to learn more about his character. Using a routine god-of-the-gaps procedure is *contrary* to the creation theorist's interests. Thus, the claim that progressive creation theory will lead to god-of-the-gaps science is fallacious.

There is a side-effect to the god-of-the-gaps slippery slope fallacy. If the fallacious claim is accepted, it permits evolution theorists to preserve evolution as uncontested, even where progressive creation might explain the same data with equal, or better, power. If science remains a quest for true explanations of natural phenomena, then rejecting competitor theories by arguing fallacies endangers the reliability and progress of science. Such is the case when evolution theorists invoke the god-of-the-gaps slippery slope to summarily dismiss the progressive creation model.

The *a priori* Fallacy of Evolution

The choice to exclude God as a possible cause for some physical phenomena is not a scientific decision. It is a philosophical one assuming a metaphysical position. There is no experiment that can "prove" a metaphysical preference. Thus, when evolution theorists reject the possibility that God could even be considered in an explanation, they have invoked metaphysics, not science, to deny the theory's explanatory power.

The *a priori fallacy* takes the form of a position presumed true before its claims can be empirically tested. In this case, the position that God did not create and directly intervene in nature is presumed true without allowing the claim to be empirically tested.

Scientific theory selection is a contest between theories competing based on their explanatory or predictive success. When theories are excluded *a priori*, the prevailing theory's competitors can disappear solely by metaphysical preemption, not explanatory or predictive success. Evolution proponents who reject progressive creation explanations on metaphysical grounds employ the *a priori* fallacy.

> **The choice to exclude God as a possible cause for some physical phenomena is not a scientific decision.**

Progressive Creation Isn't Science

The argument that progressive creation theory is nonscientific suffers from the *fallacy of question-begging*, a form of circular reasoning where the conclusion is assumed in one of the premises. Here's a simple example:

Person 1: "Only fools watch TV."
Person 2: "How do you know that?"
Person 1: "Because no one with any brains would watch TV."

When evolution theorists (ETs) reject the consideration of God as a possible cause for some physical phenomena, the exchange with a progressive creation theorist (PCT) might go like this:

ET: "Physical phenomena can only be explained by physical causes."
PCT: "How do you know physical phenomena can only be explained by physical causes?"
ET: "Because only physical explanations explain physical phenomena."

This simplistic exchange does not, of course, represent all arguments posed to exclude God as a causal explanation, but it does represent an important and frequent one. It takes the form of restating its objection to God-as-causal-explanation in ways that merely seem persuasive, but on close inspection are logically trivial.

A Straw Man Fallacy: The Earth Is Young

A *straw man fallacy* occurs when a debater avoids the opponent's real claim in favor of defeating a similar, but weaker position. It can also take the form of setting up a misrepresentation of the opposing argument and then debating the misrepresentation. In popular media, evolution is often presented as scientifically superior to "creationism" by attacking young-earth creation theory, which holds that the earth and universe are only 6,000–10,000 years old.[7] The attack *appears* to be legitimate, as is typical of fallacies. However, it ignores progressive creation theory, which agrees with evolution theorists on the age of the earth.

Because young-earth creation theory is so easy to defeat for its scientifically incommensurable age of the earth, it is the "straw man" of the fallacy. The fallacy occurs so frequently as to be nearly ubiquitous and is a particularly misleading presentation of progressive creation theory.

Equivocal Evolution

An *equivocation fallacy* involves using a single term that can refer to two or more subjects without distinguishing which subject is being referred to. In popular evolution discussions this fallacy occurs when microevolution and macroevolution are both referred to as *evolution* without any explanation that the two are different.

Microevolution is uncontested as a process of change in gene frequency within a population, such as occurs when bacteria mutate and acquire antibiotic resistance. Both evolution theorists and progressive creation theorists agree that microevolution occurs because biochemical cause-and-effect relationships have been observed, precisely and unequivocally characterized, and verified through replicated studies.

Macroevolution is the much longer process of change at the largest scales, including changes from one higher-ordered taxon to one or more new ones. The evolution of fish to land mammals would be an example of macroevolution. However, macroevolution lacks the epistemological warrant of microevolution. No transition from one higher-ordered taxon to another has been observed; and no biochemical cause-and-effect process bridging them has ever been characterized. Evolution theorists would argue that there are other forms of evidence showing macroevolution—such as the fossil record and genetic studies—that act as indirect evidence. However, these forms of evidence do not yield uncontested conclusions from the data and none have the precision and certitude of the biochemical (mechanistic) causal chains of microevolution.

Thus, when popular commentators and others speak about *evolution* with well-founded certainty *without* clearly restricting the discourse to microevolution (or microbial evolution or speciation), then the speaker hides the uncertainties of "evolution" through the fallacy of equivocation.

Rhetoric and the Fallacy of Irrelevant Conclusion

The popular science magazine *Scientific American* aggressively embraces evolution and opposes all forms of creation theory. It is a good representation of how evolutionary proponents critique creation theory. Former editor in chief John Rennie wrote an article critiquing 15 putative claims of "creationists" to show, among other things, that creationism adds "nothing of intellectual value" to solving "the riddle of how the living world took shape."[8]

Rennie's article commits multiple fallacies, including straw man arguments and equivocation. For example, he equivocates when he uses the term *creationist* without distinguishing among the various creation-theoretical positions. He ignores, or is ignorant of, the fact that progressive creation does not make some of the claims he critiques. Full analysis of Rennie's article is beyond the scope of this chapter; so, we will look at one excerpt where Rennie writes:

> Complexity of a different kind—"specified complexity"—is the cornerstone of the intelligent-design arguments of author William A. Dembski in his books *The Design Inference* and *No Free Lunch*. Essentially his argument is that living things are complex in a way that undirected, random processes could never produce. The only logical conclusion, Dembski asserts, in an echo of Paley 200 years ago, is that some superhuman intelligence created and shaped life.

> Dembski's argument contains several holes. It is wrong to insinuate that the field of explanations consists only of random processes or designing intelligences. Researchers into nonlinear systems and cellular automata at the Santa Fe Institute and elsewhere have demonstrated that simple, undirected

processes can yield extraordinarily complex patterns. Some of the complexity seen in organisms may therefore emerge through natural phenomena that we *as yet barely understand*. But that is far different from saying that the complexity could not have arisen naturally. (emphasis added)

The rhetorical sleight-of-hand—or more accurately, the fallacy of irrelevant conclusion— arises from Rennie sidestepping Dembski's point.[9] The existence of "extraordinarily complex patterns" in the computer and mathematical models of the Santa Fe Institute led Rennie to the conclusion that some of the complexity seen in organisms *may* emerge through "phenomena that we *as yet barely understand*" (emphasis added). It is important to see that this is Rennie speculating, not offering counterevidence. His speculation does not show that "Dembski's argument contains several holes." Further, his speculation masquerading as evidence is a distraction from his failure to answer Dembski's claim that the complexity of *life*—not the products of computer simulations— does not emerge on its own.

Rennie's final sentence makes it seem as if it is answering the question, but it isn't. The question is not whether his speculation says something different from Dembski's claim. The question is whether Dembski's claim is false or "contains several holes," as Rennie alleged up front. Rennie's speculative conclusion is irrelevant, as is his nonresponsive final sentence.

Why Bother?

This short list of evolution fallacy examples is not exhaustive. Others occur but take much more elaboration than we have space for here.[10] The fallacies and discussions presented in this chapter can help readers evaluate popular presentations of evolution. Even so, there is one crucial caveat: the presence of a fallacy in an argument does not necessarily falsify the argument. As an error in reasoning, a fallacy invites the critic of the fallacy to identify it and rectify the argument so the facts can be seen and properly tested, and the conclusion evaluated for its soundness or strength. When dealing with the question of evolution and its popular presentations, testing for fallacies is particularly important because fallacies can be profoundly misleading, often allowing polemics and rhetoric to suppress facts and their serious implications.

Discussion Questions

1. Explain the argument from ignorance and discuss an example from the chapter. What effect does this fallacy have on scientific advance?

2. When accounting for the fossil record during the Cambrian era, does progressive creation theory lead to god-of-the-gaps science? Why or why not?

3. If proponents of evolution reject progressive creation theory on metaphysical grounds, are they committing a fallacy? Explain.

4. Why is it important to test ideas for fallacies? How are people subject to fallacious thinking?

Chapter 5

Is Evolution Really a Problem for the Christian Faith?

by Fazale Rana

When I began my college career, I was an agnostic. I wasn't sure if God existed. Frankly, I couldn't have cared less.

Through my coursework in chemistry and biology, I became convinced that evolutionary mechanisms were more than adequate to account for the origin, design, and history of life. It wasn't the evidence for biological evolution that convinced me. I accepted evolution largely based on the authority of my professors, women and men whom I respect and admire to this day. After all, it was the prevailing scientific view of origins and I wanted to be intellectually credible.

Today, I meet a lot of people who accept evolution for the same reasons I did as an undergraduate student. Scientific authorities tell them it is the prevailing explanation for biological origins.

In retrospect, I realize how much embracing the evolutionary paradigm fueled my agnostic views. If evolutionary mechanisms can explain everything in biology, what role would there have been for a Creator to play? I also meet a lot of people who share this sentiment. Richard Dawkins has put it most plainly: "although atheism may have been *logically* tenable before Darwin, Darwin made it possible to be an intellectually fulfilled atheist."[1]

If evolutionary mechanisms can explain everything in biology, what role would there have been for a Creator to play?

Graduate school changed my perspective. As a biochemistry student, I examined the various chemical evolutionary scenarios for abiogenesis (the evolutionary process that generates the first cell, beginning with simple chemicals that self-organize) and I came to the conviction that chemical and physical processes could not explain the origin of life. (See chapter 6.) I also came to see the elegant, sophisticated designs of biochemical systems as the fingerprints of a Creator (see chapter 21). In other words, I became convinced that evolutionary processes cannot account for the origin and fundamental design of life. To me that opened the possibility of a Creator playing some role in life's origin and history. At that point, I believed that the origin of life required divine intervention, but that, once created, life evolved to produce the biodiversity that we see today (and throughout Earth's history).

Soon afterward, I converted to Christianity. I remember reading Genesis 1 with my newfound convictions about life's origin and history. I was amazed how the sequence of events described in Genesis 1 corresponds to Earth's history and life's history (with *day* understood as a long period of time). I didn't think that Genesis 1 contradicted an evolutionary view of life's history. In fact, I saw statements in Genesis 1 (such as, "let the land produce vegetation," "let the water teem with living creatures," and "let the land produce living creatures") as *compatible* with an evolutionary history. When it came to human origins, I reasoned that God breathed the breath of life into a hominin and by doing so created human beings in his image. Unwittingly, I had stumbled upon a view called theistic evolution (TE) or, as some adherents now say, evolutionary creation (EC).

Lately, a growing number of evangelical and conservative Christians embrace theistic evolution/evolutionary creation (TE/EC). That is, they hold the position that God used biological evolution as the means to create life. They think, as I did, that this view is fully compatible with the Christian faith.

The idea of God using evolution to create is nothing new. In fact, this idea made its first appearance shortly after Darwin published *On the Origin of Species*. One of the first people to espouse theistic evolution was Harvard botanist Asa Gray (1810–1888). Gray was among the first American scientists to adopt Darwin's theory of evolution. Gray was also a devout Christian.

In his book *Darwiniana* (1876), Gray presents essays defending Darwin's theory.[2] He also expresses his deepest convictions that nature is filled with the signatures of design. He attributed that design to a type of God-ordained, God-guided process. Gray argues that God is the ultimate causal factor and the source of all evolutionary change.

Gray's ideas ignited a maelstrom of controversy. Some were opposed to his theological musings for scientific reasons. Others were opposed to his ideas for philosophical and theological reasons. In many respects, the same controversy surrounding theistic evolution exists today—both inside and outside the church.

I entered this fray a few decades ago when I began to question whether evolutionary processes could adequately account for the major transitions in life's history and create biological novelty (see chapter 10)—two scientific problems I think confront the evolutionary paradigm. As my knowledge of Scripture and Christian theology deepened, I also started questioning the compatibility of the evolutionary paradigm and Christianity. Today, I see some serious biblical and theological problems with TE/EC. I have also come to appreciate some of the more serious philosophical problems with this view.

Philosophical Challenges for Theistic Evolution

One of the more serious philosophical challenges confronting theistic evolution is illustrated by a letter exchange between Gray and Darwin. Gray asked Darwin if he thought it possible that God used evolution to create. Darwin didn't think that possible because of the brutality he saw in nature. Darwin writes:

> I cannot persuade myself that a beneficent and omnipotent God would have designedly created the Ichneumonidae [parasitic wasps] with the express intention of their feeding within the living bodies of caterpillars, or that a cat should play with mice. Not believing this, I see no necessity in the belief that the eye was expressly designed. On the other hand I cannot anyhow be contented to view this wonderful universe and especially the nature of man, & to conclude that everything is the result of brute force. I am inclined to look at everything as resulting from designed laws, with the details, whether good or bad, left to the working out of what we may call chance. Not that this notion *at all* satisfies me. I feel most deeply that the whole subject is too profound for the human intellect. A dog might as well speculate on the mind of Newton. Let each man hope & believe what he can.[3]

Darwin expressed a similar sentiment in a letter he wrote to his friend

Joseph Hooker: "What a book a Devil's chaplain might write on the clumsy, wasteful, blundering low and horridly cruel works of nature!"[4]

Recognizing the complexity of the question and human limitations, Darwin saw a significant problem with an all-powerful, all-knowing, and all-good God employing unguided (sometimes brutal) evolutionary processes as the mode of creation. For Darwin, evolutionary processes spawned a biological realm characterized by cruelty and flawed designs—not the first things that come to mind when one imagines what God's handiwork would look like.

Compounding this problem is the dependence of the evolutionary process on natural selection to drive innovations, resulting in survival of the fittest. In an evolutionary framework, reproductive success (with associated suffering and death) serves as the engine of creation. The problem of animal death, pain, and suffering plagues a progressive creation view as well, but it isn't as poignant a problem. In a progressive creation framework, God isn't employing death to drive the creation of new life-forms, but rather to serve good purposes (for example, maintaining stable ecosystems). Death is also a consequence of the laws of nature that God put in place.

Another problem confronting theistic evolution relates to the nature of the evolutionary process and its impact on humanity's place in the cosmos. If we turn to evolution to account for human origins, it becomes difficult to maintain that humans have any special status in the cosmos. We are merely one of countless species that have existed throughout Earth's history. Nothing distinguishes our origins from other organisms'. We occupy an insignificant place on the evolutionary tree of life. In his book *The Accidental Species*, paleontologist Henry Gee puts it this way:

> It is clear that evolution has no plan. It has neither memory nor foresight. No vestige of cosmic strivings from some remote beginning; no prospect of revelatory culmination in some transcendent end. Rather than being at the pinnacle of creation, human beings are just one species on the tangled bank of Darwin's imagination.[5]

Gee's point becomes more poignant and troubling when we consider the nature of the evolutionary process. Many people think of biological evolution as unguided and historically contingent, without any direction or goal. If human evolution is true, then there can be no real meaning to our existence.

This is the way the late evolutionary biologist Stephen Jay Gould described the implications of his understanding of the evolutionary process in his book *Wonderful Life*:

> This means—and we must face the implications squarely—that the origin of *Homo sapiens*, as a tiny twig on an improbable branch of a contingent limb on a fortunate tree, lies well below the boundary. In Darwin's scheme, we are a detail, not a purpose or embodiment of the whole—with the details, whether good or bad, left to the working out of what we may call chance.[6]

In my opinion, this view of humanity—which reasonably flows from the evolutionary paradigm—is devastating for the biblical view of human origins and human nature. Because of science's influence, the evolutionary paradigm pervades cultures around the world. I would argue (though some may accuse me of being dramatic in doing so) that the evolutionary view of humanity creates an intellectual milieu that encourages many of the injustices and social ills we see in our world today. If human beings are merely animals, then we have no inherent value, we lack dignity, and any act of cruelty can be justified.

Compatibility Question

Clearly, these philosophical challenges are serious. Yet, are these concerns valid for TE/EC proponents? My friend Darrel Falk, former president of the BioLogos Foundation (an advocacy group for TE/EC), argues that these types of philosophical criticisms are unwarranted. He believes that these critiques are "overextending the reach of science" and, therefore, have no merit:

> It [science] simply doesn't address matters of purpose, human or otherwise. . . . It simply does not have the tools to do so, and to take the position it does is misleading and perhaps even in some cases disingenuous. The science of biology addresses questions such as what, when, and how life forms came into being. However, it says nothing of the possibility of the existence of a who through whom all things exist, or the why of their existence.[7]

I am sympathetic to Falk's point. To some extent, I agree with it. The concerns raised by Darwin, Dawkins, Gee, and Gould *are* philosophical points, not scientific ones. And to be fair, many evolutionary creationists see God guiding the evolutionary process (though his work is not detectable scientifically).

While it is critical to recognize the distinction between scientific and philosophical conclusions, we mustn't sidestep the very real philosophical implications of scientific ideas. From my perspective, I contend that the points these evolutionary scientists make are *metaphysical* implications that logically follow given how some people perceive the nature of the evolutionary process. These metaphysical conclusions are not outlandish by any means, but are quite reasonable, particularly for someone who holds to a materialistic worldview. I would go so far as to argue that for many people the metaphysical position these evolutionary biologists adopt is much more reasonable than the one adopted by Christians who argue that God used evolution as the means to create. When it comes to the nature of human beings, science, philosophy and theology all make truth claims. It is important to ask if these various claims are compatible or not.

So, what evidence is there to suggest that the evolutionary process bears God's imprint? How does theistic evolution differ from an atheistic version? If I were an atheist, what would compel me to see purpose and directionality in the evolutionary process?

I have yet to find satisfactory answers to these questions. I struggle to see God's fingerprints in evolution, a process that appears to me unguided, contingent, and driven by survival of the fittest. Yet I know several Christians who don't share my concerns and who wouldn't agree with me.

Creation of Humanity

If God used evolution (whether directed or undirected) to create life, including human beings, then it also raises questions about the historicity of Adam and Eve, the uniqueness of humanity, and other important theological concepts. In my view, Scripture clearly teaches that Adam and Eve were the first human beings and the sole progenitors of all humanity. Clinging to the unique creation of Adam and Eve is not merely a question of biblical inerrancy.

The historicity of Adam and Eve as humanity's sole progenitors has wide-ranging implications for key theological doctrines.[8] In the view of many Christians (including me), it becomes too great a cost to put these important doctrines at risk to align our views with the evolutionary paradigm—even if it is the mainstream scientific model for the origin and history of life. I don't think there is any reason (scientifically or theologically) to pay this cost because—as we discuss throughout the remainder of this book—evolution has demonstrable shortcomings and it is possible to accommodate homologies and the fossil record in a creation model.

The Allure of Mainstream Science and Methodological Naturalism

Over the years, I have engaged numerous TE/EC proponents. Through these interactions, I have learned that one of the reasons Christians find theistic evolution so attractive is that it provides a way for them to embrace mainstream scientific ideas in biology. I am sympathetic to this desire. It is no fun being labeled a "pseudoscientist" simply for questioning the validity of a scientific idea.

My concern with this desire to remain intellectually credible by choosing theistic evolution is that Christians have unwittingly become beholden to methodological naturalism. Methodological naturalism (sometimes called provisional atheism or benchtop atheism) asserts that when engaging in the scientific enterprise it is necessary to operate as if God doesn't play any discernable role in effecting the origin and history of life. The only explanations allowed for the universe and phenomena within it are natural processes. One cannot appeal to the supernatural. But that doesn't mean the supernatural doesn't exist. Simply put, the supernatural is not given a place in the scientific enterprise.

This restriction makes methodological naturalism functionally equivalent to philosophical naturalism, rendering science an inherently atheistic enterprise, though, again, its practitioners may well believe God exists. Problems arise primarily by a failure to distinguish the difference between the necessary methodological limitations of scientific inquiry and limitations in rendering ultimate explanations constrained by metaphysical (or philosophical) naturalism. Accordingly, misappropriating methodological naturalism restricts the available explanations for the universe and phenomena within the universe, such as the origin of humanity. Explanations that evoke any role for a supernatural agent are off the table *a priori*. Consequently, a creation model can have no part in naturalistic explanations. Any explanation that states an intelligent agent is responsible for, say, life's origin or history is prohibited. A model of this type is considered nonscientific; it is considered "not even false." As a result, the evolutionary paradigm is the only available alternative for someone who's trying to account scientifically for biological origins. Thus, biological evolution is true by default, regardless of the evidence at hand. No matter how much evidence exists challenging the evolutionary paradigm, it cannot be supplanted because there is no other alternative explanation that is allowed. Although a progressive creation model may account for the data as well or better, it will not be given a scientific hearing. It will be dismissed due to philosophical commitments.

Most scientists would likely defend these restrictions by arguing that science can't "put God in a test tube." Yet it is a straightforward argument to show that science does have the tool kit to detect the work of intelligent agents within nature and to characterize their capabilities. The Search for Extraterrestrial Intelligence (SETI) is an intelligent design research program that drives home the point I am making. By extension, science should have no problem detecting a Creator's handiwork—and even determining a Creator's attributes.

> **Science should have no problem detecting a Creator's handiwork—and even determining a Creator's attributes.**

As we consider these things, it is important to recognize that scientific inferences form a subset of human reasoning. They can be used in support of naturalistic *or* theistic narratives. In other words, when we reason to the best explanations we should not limit ourselves to scientifically (naturalistically) derived inferences.[9] When scientists relax restrictive explanatory requirements driven by naturalistic philosophical commitments, it becomes evident that the evolutionary paradigm is not unique in its capacity to account for the origin, design, and history of life. A creation model approach offers the same explanatory power, as we will show throughout the remainder of this book.

A creation model approach is *not* anti-scientific. In fact, there is a historical precedent for viewing biology in teleological terms. Prior to Charles Darwin, distinguished biologist Sir Richard Owen interpreted shared biological structures as manifestations of an archetype that originated in the mind of the "First Cause," as he put it. Owen's model played a key role in shaping biology in the early to mid-1800s.[10] Darwin later replaced Owen's archetype with a common ancestor. Absent the discovery of an actual common ancestor for a particular evolutionary lineage, the common ancestor concept is as abstract as Owen's archetype. Yet today, Owen's model would not even be offered a place at the table.

So, does evolution stand as a threat to Christianity?

It depends on your beliefs. Since Darwin's time, some Christians have entertained the idea of God deploying evolutionary processes as the means to create. On the other hand, many skeptics and believers have identified several biblical, theological, and philosophical challenges for integrating evolution and Christianity. For some people, these challenges don't fundamentally threaten Christianity, nor do they make God irrelevant. And, adherents have good reasons to hold that perspective. (See chapter 25.) For others, these challenges are significant and can't be brushed aside. I am in the latter camp. There is good news for people in my camp. The evolutionary paradigm comes up short in fully being able to account for the origin, design, and history of life. At the same time, a creation model framework can account for the features of biology as readily as the evolutionary paradigm. Toward that end, it is worth noting that the two approaches are empirically equivalent.

Discussion Questions

1. What philosophical challenge to God-guided evolution did Darwin identify? Do you find it compelling?

2. Complete this sentence: "If human beings are merely animals, then ..."

3. According to the author, what is the "cost" of adopting an evolutionary origin of humanity? Is it worth it?

4. Evaluate the following assertion: Science can't put God in a test tube.

Chapter 6

What Is Chemical Evolution?

by Fazale Rana

Did life on Earth emerge out of a prebiotic or primordial soup? If you are like many students I meet, you probably learned about this idea in a high school science class. Or maybe, if you were like me, your first exposure to this theory came in an introductory biology class in college.

Many people in the scientific community believe that chemical and physical processes—collectively referred to as chemical evolution—transformed simple chemical compounds on early Earth (such as methane, ammonia, hydrogen, carbon dioxide, carbon monoxide, hydrogen sulfide, etc.) into the first life-forms (most likely single-celled organisms that resemble modern-day bacteria and archaea). Some scientists think this happened in a primodial soup. Others think it may have occurred at deep sea hydrothermal vents on the ocean floor.

Also called abiogenesis or the origin of life, chemical evolution is believed to have occurred in a stepwise manner, with each step progressively yielding greater-and-greater complexity (that involved self-assembly, self-replication, formation of autocatalytic cycles, and encapsulation by membranes) until the first life-form appeared. Presumably, chemical evolution began when small gaseous molecules began to react with each other to form simple organic materials. In turn, origin-of-life researchers think that these compounds reacted to form the building block materials for life (such as amino acids, sugars, lipids, nucleobases, etc.). Under this scenario, once these compounds formed, these building blocks combined to form more complex molecular entities, such as RNA, and organized into reaction cycles. Eventually, physicochemical mechanisms assembled these chemical entities into protocellular super-systems that assumed some of the properties of life.

Origin-of-life investigators believe that once these protocellular systems could replicate, a form of "Darwinian" evolution took over, transforming these protocells into the very first true cells. Eventually, these first cells coalesced to form the last universal common ancestor (LUCA), which many life scientists believe rooted the evolutionary tree of life on Earth.

Admittedly, what I have just presented is a simplified overview. What you may not know is that origin-of-life researchers actively debate how each of these steps took place and in what order they occurred. These investigators have proposed a variety of models for chemical evolution that differ in the source of prebiotic materials and the location of their synthesis. They also disagree on which originated first: information-rich molecules (such as RNA), metabolic systems, or membranes. (For a more detailed discussion of some of the most prominent origin-of-life models, see my books *Origins of Life* and *Creating Life in the Lab*.)

It is safe to say that no one knows how life originated on Earth.

Every one of the many scenarios proposed by origin-of-life researchers has strengths, but they all face seemingly intractable problems. It is safe to say that no one knows how life originated on Earth. As a case in point, in a 2013 journal article, astrobiologists Paul Davies and Sara Imari Walker state, "It would not be an exaggeration to say that the origin of life is one of the greatest unanswered questions in science."[1] So, if the origin of life is one of the greatest unanswered questions in science, why do origin-of-life researchers feel so confident that chemical evolution produced the first life-forms, kick-starting an evolutionary history of life?

Prebiotic Simulation Studies

Though origin-of-life researchers don't know how life emerged through chemical evolution, they are confident that it did. Part of this confidence reflects a precommitment to mechanistic, materialistic explanations. In his book *The Fifth Miracle*, Paul Davies makes this exact point:

> Although biogenesis strikes many as virtually miraculous, the starting point of any scientific investigation must be the assumption that life emerged naturally, via a sequence of normal physical processes.[2]

In other words, the widespread view that many scientists hold about chemical evolution is driven, in large measure, by their prior commitment to a specific category of explanations.

To be fair, the results of laboratory experiments also undergird researchers' belief that chemical evolution explains abiogenesis. Experiments in prebiotic chemistry attempt to simulate the conditions of early Earth in a laboratory setting, with the hopes of identifying the specific physicochemical processes that contributed to the origin of life. Through these types of experiments, researchers have:

- Made most building block molecules
- Produced several classes of biopolymers
- Evolved functional RNA molecules
- Generated self-replicating systems
- Manufactured protocells

Origin-of-life scientists view these achievements as important clues as to how life emerged through mechanistic processes, with these types of studies boosting their confidence in evolutionary explanations.

The Miller-Urey Experiment

Chemists Stanley Miller and Harold Urey set the standard for prebiotic simulation experiments in 1953. Their work is described in virtually every high school biology textbook and heralded as the experiment that launched the origin of life as a formal field of scientific investigation.

To simulate the appropriate conditions, Miller, a graduate student of Nobel Laureate Urey, filled the headspace of a glass apparatus with methane, ammonia, and hydrogen. He diligently excluded oxygen from the system. At that time, scientists thought the gases Miller used had existed in early Earth's atmosphere. A flask of boiling water connected to the glassware introduced water vapor into the headspace and simulated early Earth's oceans. Miller passed a continuous electric discharge through the gas mix. He showed that the primitive atmosphere could, in principle, generate amino acids. Miller later determined that the reaction mechanism responsible for amino acids was closely related to the Strecker reaction, a chemical process discovered in 1850 by German chemist Adolph Strecker.

Beyond its scientific impact, Miller's work has had profound philosophical and even theological consequences. For many people, the generation of amino acids from simple chemical compounds thought to be present in early Earth's atmosphere meant that life could originate all on its own without the need for a Creator. This was the view I held as an undergraduate student uncertain about God's existence. I've met many people who have struggled with their faith as Christians after learning about this experiment in high school or college. And I've known many nontheists who use this experiment as part of the rationale to reject belief in a personal God.

Although Miller's experiment was a landmark origin-of-life study and remains a textbook mainstay, it has not withstood the test of time. In the intervening decades between 1953 and Miller's death in 2007, studies of Earth's early planetary conditions rendered the experiment irrelevant to the origin-of-life question and invalidated its support for chemical evolution.

Current understanding of early Earth's atmosphere differs significantly from the gas mix Miller used. Most planetary scientists now think that Earth's primeval atmosphere consisted of carbon dioxide, nitrogen, and water vapor. Miller-Urey-type experiments indicate that this gas mixture is incapable of yielding any organic materials. In his book *Biogenesis*, origin-of-life researcher Noam Lahav passes similar judgment:

> The prebiotic conditions assumed by Miller and Urey were essentially those of a reducing atmosphere. Under slightly reducing conditions, the Miller-Urey reaction does not produce amino acids, nor does it produce the chemicals that may serve as the predecessors of other important biopolymer building blocks. Thus, by challenging the assumption of a reducing atmosphere, we challenge the very existence of the "prebiotic soup," with its richness of biologically important organic compounds.[3]

The Problem of Geochemical Relevance

The changed perspective on the Miller-Urey experiment highlights a universal problem facing prebiotic chemistry and abiogenesis: geochemical relevance.

For more than 60 years, origin-of-life investigators have done a masterful job at identifying chemical routes that—in principle—could have contributed to life's origin. *However*, they have consistently failed to demonstrate the geochemical relevance of these processes. That is, they have failed to demonstrate how the processes they study in the laboratory could have ever transpired on early Earth.

When investigators go into the lab and perform prebiotic chemistry studies, they are working under highly controlled conditions. They assemble the glass apparatus and fill it with the appropriate solvents. They add the just-right chemicals, at the just-right time, at the just-right concentrations. They control the temperature of the reaction. They control the pH of the reaction and the energy source. For some experiments, researchers must dry and then rehydrate the contents of the reaction vessel at the just-right point in the process. They intervene at key moments to remove waste by-products from the reaction that would otherwise steer the chemical pathway into the wrong direction or confound it completely. They stop the reaction at the just-right time. In other words, the chemists are making significant and indispensable contributions to the success of the prebiotic chemistry studies. It is highly questionable if these exacting conditions would have existed on early Earth.

Herein lies the problem. Prebiotic simulations are successful only because the researchers involve themselves in the experimental design. To put it another way, the researchers (who are intelligent agents) manipulate the experimental conditions in nonnatural ways to ensure the success of prebiotic reactions in the lab. Ironically, the very experiments performed to demonstrate chemical evolution's viability instead illustrate that intelligent agency is required for life to originate whether in the laboratory or on early Earth.

This is one reason why I am skeptical about chemical evolution. The following two case studies emphasize my point. The first example relates to replicator-first models for the origin of life and the second to metabolism-first models.

The Creation of Self-Replicating RNA Molecules

The RNA world hypothesis is the leading replicator-first model for the origin of life. Many researchers think that RNA predated both DNA and proteins as the premier replicator and information-harboring molecule. In this scenario, RNA operated as a self-replicator that catalyzed its own synthesis and, over time, numerous RNA molecules representing a wide range of catalytic activity emerged. Biochemistry centered exclusively on RNA. With time, proteins (and eventually DNA) joined RNA in the cell's arsenal. During the transition to the contemporary DNA-protein world, RNA's original function became partitioned between proteins and DNA, and RNA assumed its current intermediary role.

For the RNA world scenario to be viable, researchers need to discover self-replicating RNA molecules. Only limited progress has been made toward discovering this type of biomolecule. Nevertheless, researchers are hopeful because they have produced a variety of RNAs that (1) assist in the synthesis of ribonucleotides; (2) join two RNA chains together (in a process called ligation); and (3) add ribonucleotide subunits to the end of an RNA molecule, extending the chain. These activities are necessary for RNA replication, but biochemists have yet to make RNA with genuine self-replicating capability.

In 2017, scientists from The Scripps Research Institute (TSRI) moved closer to the goal.[4] They extended the work of earlier studies using *in vitro* evolution (evolution occurring in the lab) to modify the class I RNA polymerase ribozyme. This molecule can join together some RNA molecules (once they bind to a template). TSRI scientists modified the original version of the polymerase so that it could use a template to form RNA chains over 100 nucleotides in length. Unfortunately, the modified version of the class I RNA polymerase ribozyme is quite finicky. It can only transcribe RNA with certain nucleotide sequences and cannot transcribe RNA with complex three-dimensional structures.

TSRI scientists randomly mutated the RNA sequence of the modified polymerase to generate a population of 100 trillion molecules. From this population, they selected those ribozymes that could transcribe two different RNA molecules with a complex three-dimensional structure. Once they identified the ribozymes with the desired properties, they repeated the process, mutating the newly identified ribozymes to produce a new population of molecules. After 24 rounds, they had successfully evolved a ribozyme (they called it the 24-3 ribozyme) that can copy RNA with complex three-dimensional structures and, in turn, duplicate RNA molecules it had already copied. That is, the 24-3 polymerase can amplify specific RNA molecules 10,000-fold.

Origin-of-life researchers and evolutionary biologists count these types of studies as support for the RNA world hypothesis. They also count these studies as evidence that evolutionary processes can generate information-rich molecules from random sequences and transform existing biomolecules into ones with new or improved function (see chapter 12). While this is an important advance for the RNA world hypothesis, the 24-3 polymerase can't copy itself, a necessary requirement for self-replication.

As someone who is skeptical about chemical evolution's capacity to generate the first life-forms, I acknowledge that these scientists have a point. In principle, RNA self-replicators may be possible and evolutionary mechanisms can generate bio-information. I submit that studies of *in vitro* evolution have failed to provide any evidence that evolutionary processes can generate these types of molecular systems under the conditions of early Earth. That is, researchers have failed to show the geochemical relevance of their laboratory work.

Evolution in a lab setting relies on a meticulous experimental design and researcher intervention. The protocol begins with a large pool of RNA molecules with random nucleotide sequences and, hence, random structures. From this pool, researchers select RNA molecules based on predetermined requirements. These selected RNA molecules are recovered and their number amplified in a process that utilizes two different protein enzymes. The researchers then randomly alter the new RNA sequence to generate a new pool of RNA molecules using yet another enzyme. This process is repeated until RNA molecules with the desired chemical properties emerge. Production of the RNA self-replicators requires not only the use of three different protein enzymes. Researchers must also use rational design principles to modify the structure of ribozymes generated by *in vitro* evolution and, thus, improve upon the ribozymes' function.

The "evolution" of RNA molecules in the laboratory is a carefully orchestrated process devised and managed by intelligent agents. Its success hinges on thoughtful experimental design. Researchers are manipulating the evolutionary process, guiding it to the desired outcome. It must also be noted that the enzymes essential to the success of *in vitro* evolution studies would never have existed in an RNA world. It stretches the bounds of credulity to think that this process, or one like it, could have occurred naturally on early Earth.

Mineral-Catalyzed Reaction Cycles

Alternative to replicator-first scenarios are metabolism-first models. Some origin-of-life researchers postulate that once prebiotic materials formed, these relatively small molecules self-organized to form chemical cycles and networks of chemical reactions that gave rise to metabolic systems. Once encapsulated within a membrane, these complex, reticulated systems became the first protocells.

Metabolism-first adherents believe that these protometabolic pathways were catalyzed in one of two ways: either by individual chemical species within the cycles (a type of autocatalysis) or by mineral surfaces.

The late Leslie Orgel, a prominent origin-of-life researcher, was critical of metabolism-first ideas. He argued that chemical plausibility must be assessed *within* the context of the conditions of early Earth by focusing on the efficiencies and specificities of the protometabolic cycles.

Orgel illustrated the importance of these criteria for assessing the likelihood of metabolism-first scenarios by applying them to the reverse citric acid cycle.[5]

Some bacteria utilize this cycle to fix carbon by converting carbon dioxide and water into organic compounds. Because of this property, some origin-of-life researchers think that the reverse citric acid cycle was one of the first metabolic pathways to emerge. Orgel found this implausible.

The reverse citric acid cycle consists of eleven steps. If these eleven chemical reactions took place on early Earth (without the benefit of enzyme catalysts), then each one would have required a specific mineral catalyst. The cycle also depends on six fundamentally distinct chemical transformations. Inside cells, this metabolic process employs a series of complex enzyme catalysts possessing high specificities and capacities for molecular-level discrimination among the components of the cycle.

Orgel rightly argued that this scenario suffers a specificity problem. Enzymes that mediate metabolic pathways and cycles in the cell bind reactants with a high degree of specificity, discriminating reactant molecules from other molecules with a high degree of accuracy. As Orgel pointed out, minerals lack this type of specificity. It's unlikely that the necessary minerals would have coexisted on early Earth in such a way to support the reverse citric acid cycle. Evolving the cycle toward greater complexity—a requirement for life to originate—exacerbates the specificity problem. Presumably, complexity increases when additional reaction sequences are appended onto the core reactions of the cycle. According to Orgel, "Given the difficulty of finding an ensemble of catalysts that are sufficiently specific to enable the original cycle, it is hard to see how one could hope to find an ensemble capable of enabling two or more."[6]

Discrimination, or more appropriately, the lack of discrimination, is also a problem. Many of the compounds in the reverse citric acid cycle share structural similarities. Enzymes inside of cells can readily distinguish between these similar compounds, but mineral catalysts can't. This means, in a protometabolic scenario, that key components of the cycle would have been siphoned into unwanted, disruptive side reactions that compromise the efficiency of the cycle to the point that it becomes quenched. These problems apply to every conceivable protometabolic cycle on early Earth.

In both case studies, it is evident that geochemical relevance is a big problem for studies in prebiotic chemistry. Researcher intervention is the only reason that key steps for the origin of life proceed successfully in the laboratory.

Is Chemical Evolution Part of the Theory of Evolution?

Many biologists regard chemical evolution as distinct from other categories of evolution—which I agree with—but also as an entirely separate category of processes that have no bearing on questions surrounding biological evolution—with which I disagree.

I would insist that chemical evolution *is* an integral part of the grand claim that the origin, design, history, and diversity of life can be explained exclusively through naturalistic evolutionary mechanisms. This assertion stands, in part, because introductory biology textbooks include discussions on chemical evolution in the section on biological evolution.

More significantly, I make this claim because the endpoint of chemical evolution is LUCA, and LUCA is the base of the evolutionary tree of life. Despite biologists' protests, there must be a continuum between the first chemical species on Earth and life's history—according to the evolutionary paradigm. Chemical evolution shapes LUCA and, hence, the entirety of life. For example, many evolutionary biologists point to the "universal" nature of biochemistry as evidence for universal common descent. In the evolutionary framework, the universal nature of biochemistry is the outworking of abiogenesis.

As we have pointed out, origin-of-life researchers have no idea how life originated. They claim that prebiotic chemistry provides them with clues, but, as we have shown, these studies provide better proof for intelligent agency than they do for abiogenesis. It can't be underestimated how much a commitment to naturalism shapes the confidence many biologists have in chemical evolution.

Discussion Questions

1. How do evolutionary proponents explain the development of the last universal common ancestor?

2. What did the Miller-Urey experiment seek to explain, and how has it fared since 1953?

3. Is the RNA world hypothesis a viable model for the origin of life? Why or why not?

4. What role does geochemical relevance play in prebiotic chemistry?

Chapter 7

Is Microevolution a Fact?

by Anjeanette Roberts

Maybe you've heard of 23 and Me. It's a company that analyzes human genome sequences. "Genome" refers to all of the DNA in a given organism. We humans have 23 pairs of chromosomes—one chromosome in each pair coming from our biological mother and the other from our biological father. Therefore, "the human genome" refers collectively to the DNA sequences in all 23 chromosomal pairs.

DNA lies at the heart of heredity. It provides all organisms with a blueprint passed on from parents to offspring via chromosomes. For most bacteria the blueprint is a single bacterial chromosome (although plasmids, circular pieces of DNA, provide additional genetic material). For you or me, it's 23.

DNA: The Heart of Heredity

Establishing DNA as the substance of heredity was challenging since chromosomes are not merely DNA, but complex structures of DNA, RNAs, and proteins. It took scientists 20 years (1944–1964) to identify DNA as the substance of heredity and demonstrate the links between DNA, RNA, and protein synthesis.

Importantly, changes to DNA get passed on to RNAs during transcription and changes in RNAs get passed on to proteins in translation. This chain of changes leads to variations at the organism level that are subject to fitness (natural) selection by environmental conditions. DNA alterations may affect production, production levels, structures, and functions of RNAs and proteins. Thus, even small changes in DNA can result in large changes at the cellular or organismic level. Such changes can be deleterious, rendering offspring unfit. The corresponding mutations are often lost within the population (purifying

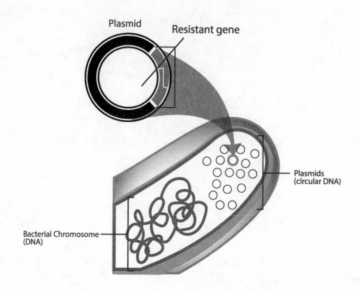

Figure 7.1: Bacterial Chromosome and Plasmids

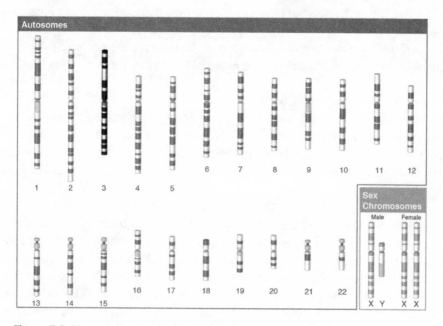

Figure 7.2: Human Chromosomes, 23 Pairs

Highlights of Scientific Discoveries Involving DNA	
1928	Transforming principle (the hypothesis that a substance in nonliving cells could transform other living cells) postulated
1944	DNA identified as the transforming substance
1952	DNA identified as the substance of heredity
1953	DNA structure determined
1961–1964	DNA/RNA code for amino acids determined

selection). Less frequently, mutations may prove beneficial and will increase within the population over time (positive selection). Many more (neutral) changes will not affect the fitness of the organism one way or another.

Genetic drift and gene flow add more variability. When one small group becomes isolated from the larger population, it carries only its own subset of variability with it (genetic drift). Any further mutations will be unique to this group. If the subgroup later rejoins the larger population, it will create additional variability within the larger population (gene flow).

Of course, Darwin didn't know that DNA was the substance of heredity since these discoveries took place in the century after him. But evolutionary biologists have incorporated knowledge of DNA into Darwin's theory of descent with modification. This modified version is known as the modern synthesis or neo-Darwinism and has been around since the 1950s. (See chapter 2 for more details.) Computational biology, the lifeblood of the modern synthesis, models estimated molecular rates of change in estimated

What are these molecular mechanisms that introduce change to DNA and how do they fit into evolutionary claims?

populations. But what are these molecular mechanisms that introduce change to DNA and how do they fit into evolutionary claims?

Mutations and Microevolution

Evolution simply means change over time. The introduction of the prefixes *micro-* and *macro-* add a comparative dimension of scale. Microevolution encompasses single cell, single organism, and species-level population changes. Macroevolution encompasses large-scale changes occurring over geologic time that result in formation of new groups at higher taxonomic levels (e.g., phyla, order, etc.). But it's not just a comparative difference of scale—these two types of evolution appeal to different mechanisms of change.

Microevolutionary changes result from many different events:
- Single base mutations or substitutions
- Deletions (loss of one or more bases in a sequence)
- Insertions (gain of one or more bases in a sequence)
- Duplication (resulting in repetition of one or more bases)
- Relocating sequence segments—with or without inversions or duplications—from one genetic string to another within a single organism (via transposition or recombination) or between two different organisms (via horizontal gene transfer in single-celled organisms)

The last of these actually creates larger (macro) changes, but all of these are well-established genome-altering phenomena. They are implemented and observed daily in laboratories across the globe. But they don't just happen in a laboratory. Our DNA is being peppered with small changes in countless cells even as we sit reading, writing, or playing a video game. Even more microchanges are occurring if we're sunbathing on the beach or fighting off an infection.

Triggers of Microevolution

Researchers have identified a myriad of triggers for small changes in cellular DNA, from environmental stresses to "hiccups" in normal cellular processes (such as replication and transcription).

Ultraviolet light (from the sun), other forms of ionizing radiation, and certain types of chemicals (like those in smoke from cigarettes or forest fires) can damage a cell's DNA. These triggers cause nicks and changes in the molecular forms of nucleotides in DNA chains that can lead to mismatches in DNA base pairing. Upon replication, daughter cells incorporate DNA sequence changes because of previously damaged and mismatched bases. Yes, ionizing radiation and mutagenic chemicals can damage sequences and contribute to cancer onset, but don't panic. Living organisms contain repair mechanisms (hundreds of different DNA repair proteins with thousands of copies per cell) for just such cellular emergencies.[1]

Although crucial for survival, repair of damaged DNA is not always perfect. In fact, repair itself can introduce genomic alterations, since it involves repair enzymes breaking one or two strands of DNA. Point mutations, known as substitutions, can easily result. Some types of repair involve breaking at least one strand to replace damaged (chemically altered) nucleotides. When breaks are repaired and ends of broken DNA rejoined, different bases may be inserted or, more likely, some bases may be lost. This type of activity leads to insertions and deletions (collectively known as indels). Since the gene code is read in 3-letter "words" (codons), indels that result in the loss or gain of one or two nucleotides ("letters") in the DNA sequence can have dramatic effects, altering not just one, but all codons downstream of the change!

It's not just environmental stress; even unwinding DNA for synthesis or transcription can involve breaks, repairs, and changes. Normal DNA replication also introduces mutations due to polymerase infidelity. So changes to our DNA can occur pretty much anywhere and anytime.

These microevolutionary changes introduce unguided (sometimes random) mutations in genetic sequences. Such changes are a source of variation upon which (purifying and positive) natural selection acts. The modern synthesis (neo-Darwinism) emphasizes that it is these variations that form the foundation for large-scale evolution through gradual, stepwise changes that offer adaptive reproductive fitness benefits selected under environmental conditions. But we have known for some time that these limited forms of microevolutionary changes are insufficient to account for the observations of complexity and diversity encountered in various fields of biological inquiry. Microevolutionary changes like those described here are at the heart of the modern synthesis but are not the whole story.

Larger Changes in DNA Sequences

Additional molecular mechanisms provide larger changes to DNA sequences where longer segments of DNA may be shuffled within an organism or exchanged between organisms. These mechanisms include transposition, recombination, inversion, duplication, gene transfer, and introgression (gene flow).

All contribute significantly larger changes and diversity to DNA than do microevolutionary changes. Some of these mechanisms will be covered in greater detail as we view them in specific contexts (e.g., microbial evolution), but let's look at some of them now.

Recombination and Inversion

Recombination is a major way of moving genetic material from one chromosome to another or to different locations on the same chromosome. Recombination is fairly ubiquitous; it occurs in animal, plant, bacterial, and even in some viral genomes. It can even happen during horizontal gene transfer if DNA is exchanged between plasmids and bacterial chromosomes. (See chapter 8, "Horizontal Gene Transfer" and figure 7.1).

There are two basic kinds of recombination: homologous and nonhomologous. Homologous recombination allows exchange of DNA between nearly identical chromosomes or DNA chains. It is responsible for generating new allelic combinations in eukaryotes during meiosis and in repairing damaged DNA. Nonhomologous recombination is the exchange of DNA between dissimilar chains and results in the loss of original DNA sequence at sites of recombination. Translocation, a type of nonhomologous recombination, involves the transfer of genomic sequence from one chromosome to a nonhomologous chromosome. Such relocations can lead to loss of genes or previous gene linkage and are often associated with disease. Recombination is a major player in generating genetic diversity.

Inversions of DNA sequences within a given chromosome may occur during recombination and possibly during DNA replication. In such instances segments of DNA are flipped in the context of the original sequence. If breakpoints occur in functional elements, inversions may present phenotypically.

Transposition

First observed by Barbara McClintock in 1948, transpositions involve replication or relocation of mobile DNA elements known as transposons or jumping genes. Some transposons will copy themselves before jumping; the copy will insert into a new chromosomal location and leave the original sequence intact. Others will be excised from the genome and relocated to a new site with no replication involved. The nonreplicative form of transposition creates two changes in the genome, one at the site of excision and another at the site of integration. Replicative transposition creates one change in the genome at the site of integration of the copied transposon.

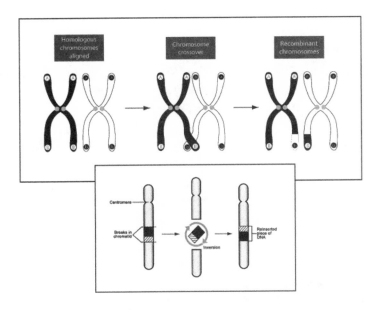

Figure 7.3: Rearranging Genomes – Recombination and Inversion

Transposons exist in both prokaryotes and eukaryotes and are highly variable. Biologists divide these mobile elements into two classes: retrotransposons (Class I; e.g., short and long interspersed nuclear elements, or SINEs and LINEs) and transposons (Class II; discovered by McClintock). At a bare minimum, Class II transposons contain a gene (transposase) responsible for transposition (including excision and integration). Some transposons carry additional genes such as antibiotic resistance genes.

Genome Duplication and Hybridization

As its name implies, genome duplication refers to a doubling of DNA segments, chromosomes, or entire genomes. Segment duplication results from errors in DNA repair or replication and results in tandem repeats of DNA sequences at the site of duplication. Imprecise homologous recombination leads to repeated sequences at the site of repair. During replication, polymerase protein complexes may slip backward along the DNA strand, copying the same sequence each time it slips, thus introducing repetitive sequences into the genome.

Some organisms, such as plants, tolerate entire chromosome duplication quite well. Hybridization, crossing two different types of organisms, is fairly common in plants, resulting in increased copies of chromosomes (polyploidy).

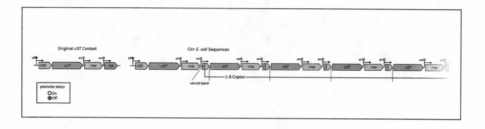

Figure 7.4: LTEE Tandem Repeats

All Cit+ bacteria harbor a ~3 kb tandem repeat of a portion of the endogenous *citT* operon (gene and regulatory elements), resulting in the introduction of additional *citT* genes in the *E. coli* genome. The critical (but not sole) changes hinge on the duplication of an endogenous promoter (*rnk*) that is active under aerobic conditions, the duplication of the *citT* gene, the encoding of a citrate transporter, and the juxtaposition of these elements in tandem repeats. The tandem copies of the *citT* gene are no longer under the regulatory control of the endogenous *citG/citT* promoter but are under the regulation of copies of an endogenous, downstream *rnk* promoter. The *rnk-citT* element allows the production of a citrate transporter under aerobic conditions. These changes allow Cit+ *E. coli* to utilize the citrate in the growth media via mechanisms and metabolic pathways already present. (See reasons.org/explore/blogs/theorems-theology/read/theorems-theology/2016/12/02/what-exactly-is-novelty-in-evolution for more details.)

In successful animal hybridizations, parental genomes undergo recombination (or shuffling) while offspring remain diploid (with two sets of chromosomes; or haploid, one set, in gametes). Animal hybrids, in contrast to plant hybrids, are almost always infertile. When genome duplications (triploidy, polyploidy and aneuploidy) occur in animals, they are almost always fatal or associated with disease.[2] Ploidy refers to the number of chromosome copies per cell. (See "Interspecies Hybridization and Plants" on page 96.)

Gene Transfer

Genes can be transferred from one organism to another through a variety of means including bacterial conjugation, sexual reproduction, and vector-mediated transfers. Mechanisms involved in horizontal gene transfer are covered in greater detail in chapter 8.

As you can see there are a variety of mechanisms that generate genetic diversity and changes within all kinds of cells. Certain mechanisms like DNA repair and genome replication may produce point mutations and indels or trigger recombination events. These seem to be products of normal, universal biological processes. Other mechanisms like conjugation seem to have specific, although not necessarily identifiable, environmental triggers. Others like whole chromosome duplication and polymerase slippage seem to result from errors in normal biological processes. Many of these processes work in combination, provide an impressive array of mechanisms contributing to genetic changes foundational for molecular adaptations, and function as proposed mechanisms for macroevolutionary leaps as well.

Epigenetics

It may sound a little non-Darwinian to say that parent organisms may pass *acquired* traits on to offspring. This was a major tenet of Lamarckism, an early-nineteenth-century theory of evolution[3] that Darwin's theory and the discovery of DNA as the substance of heredity supplanted long ago. Yet that's what more recent evidence may point to. Environmentally triggered chemical modifications of nucleic acids (e.g., DNA, mRNA, ncRNAs) and proteins (e.g., histones—chromosomal proteins that affect genome structure) affect protein expression and gene regulation and can have substantial phenotypic outcomes at cellular and organismic levels. By definition, epigenetic modifications (e.g., acetylation, methylation, phosphorylation, and sumoylation) do not result from genomic sequence changes. Nevertheless, they can be heritable. Some extended evolutionary synthesis (EES) proponents even claim that epigenetic changes can eventually be fixed genetically, a process termed genetic accommodation where genotype follows phenotype.

Epigenetic inheritance and horizontal gene transfer challenge views of simple descent with modification based on DNA inheritance alone in multicellular organisms. This evidence is leading some well-established scientists to call for an extended evolutionary synthesis, raising significant challenges and calling for serious revision or replacement of the modern synthesis. (See chapter 2, "An Extended Evolutionary Synthesis.")

Changing an Organism by Changing Its Chromosomes

Effects of mutations in haploid organisms

For single-cell organisms, mutations of any kind can have a radical effect on the cell and all its progeny. Haploid, single-cell organisms reproduce rapidly compared to multicellular, sexual organisms. A mutation that provides a fitness advantage will be transmitted to single-cell progeny and become prevalent throughout the population within a very short period of time. In this context, rapid selection of mutations, providing fitness advantages, occurs quickly and even large genetic changes (e.g., HGT) are considered examples of microevolution. This type of evolution is sometimes referred to as microbial evolution. It is noncontroversial.

Multicellular, Diploid Challenges

In multicellular, sexually reproductive, diploid (two sets of chromosomes) organisms, most mutations occur in somatic (nonreproductive) cells and in sites (alleles) on only one chromosome. These mutations can have an immediate effect on the single cell's function or progeny cells if it undergoes division. Significantly, however, somatic mutations are not passed on to offspring. For a mutation to be inherited, it must occur in a gamete—the haploid cell of a sperm or egg—or its precursors.[4] If a mutation occurs within a sperm or egg, upon fusion with the corresponding unmutated gamete (egg or sperm, respectively) the resulting diploid progeny becomes heterozygous for the mutation, meaning the mutation occurs in one chromosome but not the other, resulting in two different alleles.

If a mutation is heterozygous but not dominant in its phenotype, the mutation must occur independently and concurrently in individual gametes of both members of the reproductive pair (or their predecessors) in order to have a phenotypic effect in offspring and for subsequent positive selection to occur within a population. Mutations would almost certainly need to have spontaneously occurred in multiple germ-line cells of both individuals, or their predecessors, to result in a likely fertilization of a mutated sperm with a mutated egg. Therefore, in multicellular organisms, for a *single* change to be passed to progeny, such fitness mutations must be heterozygous dominant, or occur independently and concurrently in multiple cells in each member of a reproductive pair (or their predecessors). And they must occur within germ-line cells, not just somatic cells.

The previous description of inheritance is basic biology and Mendelian genetics but is often overlooked in discussions of the modern synthesis (and

EES), which defines evolution based on changes in allele frequencies in populations. The intricate, complex nature of this nontrivial type of molecular change and germ-line heredity—unknown to evolutionary champion Charles Darwin and his followers—is not often given adequate attention in explanations of how unique alleles (or beneficial mutations) *enter* the gene pool (gametes) of multicellular, sexually reproducing populations. Instead most of the attention centers on how unique alleles become *fixed* in populations.

Transfer of genes between individuals, or populations, may have mechanistic explanations of varying plausibility (e.g., gene flow vs. HGT). But these, too, have conceptual gaps in explanations of how newly acquired genes reach germ-line cells in order to begin spreading through populations.

Furthermore, selection of advantageous mutations in large-organism populations is extensively prolonged in two ways compared to simple, single-cell organisms or asexual reproductive populations. First, progeny, or recipients of the germ-line mutations, must reach reproductive age and successfully reproduce. Second, the spread of the trait is prolonged by the previously unmutated allele's predominance in the existing population, which would not necessarily result in an immediate inability or inhibited ability to compete for resources or mates.

Advantage: Design over Darwinism

Nevertheless, the existence of mutations (or variations) within alleles that provide obvious environmental advantages for specific populations is uncontested. (See "The Peppered Moth" on page 97.) Molecular adaptation is often heralded as a hallmark of naturalistic evolution. In evolutionary dogma, however, these nontrivial molecular changes are employed to explain not only the observation of complex organisms' adaptive abilities but also the emergence of entirely new species.

Macroevolutionary changes, on the other hand, pose significant problems for naturalistic evolution. The advancements necessary for observed differences in biologically advanced organisms are far more complex. To employ microevolutionary (undisputed) explanations in an attempt to address macroevolutionary (highly disputed) advancement seems wholly inadequate. It is like citing the discovery and repeated verification of the use of stone tools as an explanation for the computer laptops and tablets humans use today.

From my perspective as a scientist, there is no rational reason why molecular adaptation should be co-opted and relegated only to naturalistic evolutionary explanations of the origin of species. Mechanisms and advantages

There is no rational reason why molecular adaptation should be co-opted and relegated only to naturalistic evolutionary explanations of the origin of species.

of molecular adaptation fit equally well or better in a biblically compatible design narrative than in an evolutionary one. In a design narrative, one starts with complex organisms that have allelic variability and a capacity for molecular adaptation. Such molecular adaptation provides mechanisms of survival, persistence, and thriving. An insightful designer would anticipate various external challenges and environmental changes between different geographical climes and creatively engineer organisms with the capacity to accommodate such changes. Any species subject to environmental stresses would be short-lived if not for innate abilities to adapt. This design narrative also suggests that there would be limitations to the range of adaptability and, in catastrophic environmental stresses, possible species extinctions.

Microevolution and Naturalistic Explanations of Life's History, Diversity, and Complexity

Microevolution is evident and ubiquitous. But just because something is evident and ubiquitous does not mean that it provides a continuum that leads to macroevolution. Microevolutionary mechanisms discussed here provide an understanding of the types of change that occur at an intracellular, molecular level. Specific examples of microevolutionary changes will be discussed in more detail in subsequent chapters. Their role and contribution to proposed macroevolutionary changes must be weighed in light of scientific evidence, not according to a naturalistic philosophical or supernatural theological explanation. For interpretations and explanations we must suspend judgment until we read ahead and consider the data.

Interspecies Hybridization and Plants: Amazing but Weird

Hybridization is a powerful tool for change. It can produce leaps in genomic complexity. Hybridization generates grand phenotypic variation in the plant

---

The Peppered Moth

An iconic textbook example of evolution—the peppered moth—demonstrates how underlying variations within a species or population leads to environmental flourishing and predominance of a particular phenotype.[5]

In polluted, industrialized areas the melanic (black-winged) variant of peppered moths predominated (>90 percent of moths). In post-industrialized areas with lower pollutants, moths bearing the "typical" phenotype (white wings peppered with black) made a return and melanics dropped to below 10 percent.

Predominance of one phenotypic variant over another is contingent upon the respective moths' abilities for successful camouflage on darker or lighter tree trunks, thus avoiding predation by hungry birds. The variation of color depends on underlying allele frequencies: alleles for melanic coloration being the dominant phenotype and peppered "typical" patterning being the recessive phenotype.

---

world. But plants are weird, just weird, that way. Many plants can accommodate polyploidy (multiple copies of identical or similar chromosome sets) as easily as they bend to the wind. Yet in animal models, polyploidy and aneuploidy (any deviation from the normal number of chromosomes) are disruptive and almost always associated with programmed cell death, cancer, disease, and other dysfunctions. Although hybridizations in lower-complexity taxa are sometimes productive, successful hybridization in birds, mammals, and higher complexity taxa are extremely rare, often resulting in sterile offspring, e.g., mules or hinnies. Although we can learn much by studying hybridization in plants, appealing to the power of interspecies hybridizations to drive evolutionary progressions in mammalian or other organismal systems seems like a complete misunderstanding of mechanisms and limitations.

Discussion Questions

1. If microevolutionary changes introduce unguided mutations in genetic sequences, is it reasonable to hold that these changes lead to large-

scale evolution? Why or why not?

2. Discuss the biological scenario required for multicellular organisms to pass a single change to progeny. Does the process seem feasible?

3. Do the mechanisms and advantages of molecular adaptation fit better in an evolutionary or a design narrative? Why?

Chapter 8

Does Microbial Evolution Prove Evolution Is True?

by Anjeanette Roberts

Microbes are everywhere. They surround and outnumber us in staggering numbers. They are masters of survival, adaptation, and reproduction. Each of us carries at least as many "bugs" in our bodies as we do human cells!

Do microbes evolve? If they do, what do we mean by microbial evolution? In addition to microevolutionary changes (see chapter 7), many other molecular mechanisms contribute to genetic alterations and relatively rapid adaptations of microbes. Environmental stresses act as triggers, increasing activity of these genome-altering mechanisms. Advantageous alterations in just a few lucky microbes provide the necessary characteristics for population survival under new environmental conditions. This is the hallmark of microbial evolution.

Microbial evolution is observed readily in nature and recapitulated daily by scientists harnessing its mechanisms in laboratories. It is best understood as microevolutionary and adaptive mechanisms at work in single cells that contribute to diversification and relatively rapid changes in microbial populations. Changes occur via horizontal gene transfers (i.e., transduction, transformation, and conjugation), "errors" in replication (e.g., indels, polymerase slippage, segment duplication), translocations, and recombinations. These mechanisms are a constant, if inaudible, background hum coming from the dynamic reality of the microbial world in which we live.

Like the subsonic hum, many other changes in microbial populations go unnoticed, for only advantageous changes that allow organisms to persist or thrive in competition with other organisms emerge for observation. The continued reproduction of only the successful gives an appearance that microorganisms are adapting in order to survive. This is an illusion of sorts.

Microbial evolution is observed readily in nature and recapitulated daily by scientists harnessing its mechanisms in laboratories.

According to the prevailing evolutionary paradigm, mechanisms leading to change in microbial phenotype act within nonteleological parameters. This means many rearrangements, duplications, and perhaps even gene transfers are *not* conducive to survival. *Such failures prohibit observation of all actual genetic changes.* Microbes that change in deleterious ways either succumb to death or are out-competed for resources. So, although we observe microbial evolution, much of what is transpiring in the population at an individual organism level is unobserved because of a failure to survive. Microbial evolution demonstrates the power of natural selection at work.

So, what mechanisms and types of changes contribute to the evolution and molecular adaptation of the successful? We'll look at those mentioned and zoom in on a couple as case studies for microbial evolution.

Horizontal Gene Transfer

Horizontal gene transfer (HGT) refers to the transfer of genetic material from one organism to another. Newly transferred genetic material may become part of the new host's genome or carried as extrachromosomal plasmids. (See figure 7.1 on page 86.) When recipient bacteria or other single-cell organisms reproduce, any newly acquired genetic material will be copied and passed on to all progeny or offspring just like the host DNA.

There are three types of HGT: transduction, transformation, and conjugation. All involve the transfer of genetic information from one organism to another, but by different routes or mechanisms. All three take place in bacteria. Transduction and transfection also take place or can be utilized in eukaryotic cells.

Transduction

In 1952, American biologists Norton Zinder and Joshua Lederberg discovered that viruses infecting bacteria (bacteriophage) were able to transfer genetic material from one bacterium to another. Such vector-mediated transfer of genetic information—transduction—does not require cell-to-cell contact since viruses act as genetic transporters.

When viruses infect cells, their genetic material provides the blueprint for production of many new virus particles. New copies of viral genetic material are packaged into new virus particles, but the packaging process is imprecise. Sometimes new viruses pick up pieces of the host's genetic material, which can contain fragments of chromosomal DNA or plasmid DNA. The new viruses then deliver whatever genetic payload they carry to the next cell they infect. In this way, viral infections can transfer cellular, not just viral, genetic material to new hosts.

Once transferred to a new bacterium, newly introduced genetic material may be sustained as a plasmid. Or if chromosomal DNA is transferred, it too can be sustained in the new bacterium by integrating into the host chromosome through DNA recombination or insertion. Or if viral DNA is integrated into the bacterial chromosome, it may carry the foreign chromosomal DNA with it. These mechanisms allow foreign bacterial DNA, not just viral DNA, to be transferred to new hosts.

Transduction is how some bacteria become resistant to antibiotics (more on this later). Scientists take advantage of this natural process and use transduction to deliver viral payloads to specific cells. Transduction refers to all vector-mediated transfer of genetic information whether to bacteria or other organisms. It is usually an efficient means of HGT, but its staying power varies based on the recipient cells.

If transduction occurs between unicellular organisms, entire organisms and subsequent populations can be genetically and phenotypically changed by a single event. If the recipient cells are localized to a particular tissue of a multicellular organism, viral payloads can be targeted for delivery in a tissue-specific fashion. Germ-line cells, altered by transduction, can lead to genetic and phenotypic changes in offspring. The use of transgenic animals in research is dependent upon these techniques. However, altering the genetic content of somatic cells using transducing particles will have temporal and spatial limitations and will not affect subsequent generations. This is true for all forms of HGT, not just transduction.

Transformation

Transformation is an indirect transfer of genetic material from the environment into bacterial cells. When bacterial cells burst open due to viral lysis or when bacteria die and lose membrane integrity, bacterial DNA (and RNA) is released into the surrounding environment. Under certain conditions, nearby "competent" bacteria may take up the DNA debris and incorporate it into their own genetic makeup as plasmid DNA or chromosomal DNA.

In the laboratory, competent bacteria can take up environmental DNA under controlled experimental conditions. The term *transfection* is used for similar experiments that introduce plasmid DNA into eukaryotic cells. Transformation in eukaryotic cells refers to something quite different. It refers to changes in the cell's regulatory mechanisms that lead to dysregulation or possibly unregulated cell growth and reproduction.

Transformation and transfection are nonspecific transfers of DNA. Any competent cell can take up the DNA, but not all will. Transfer efficiencies of genetic material are highly variable by transformation and transfection and likely occur in nature at extremely low efficiencies.

Conjugation

Conjugation is the transfer of genetic information from one bacteria to another by direct contact. It involves bacterial tube-like structures known as pili, which come in a variety of lengths, diameters, and rigidities. DNA is transferred from the donor cell to the recipient through the pili. Pili also provide the critical structures for tethering two conjugating cells together. Both plasmids and chromosomal elements may be transferred by conjugation.

Almost all kinds of bacteria have conjugating plasmids and chromosomal elements—known as integrating conjugative elements (ICEs)—associated with them. Conjugating plasmids and ICEs are self-transmissible. They contain many genes that provide the proteins necessary for DNA transfer from cell to cell. Other plasmids and chromosomal elements can be mobilized and transferred along with self-transmissible plasmids and ICEs if they contain the proper DNA elements for mobilization. ICEs are like (and used to be classified as) transposons (discussed on page 90), but have a different way of integrating into bacterial chromosomes. Under some conditions the efficiency of DNA transfer by bacterial conjugation is nearly 100 percent!

Self-transmissible plasmids are not always restricted to DNA transfer from bacterium to bacterium. At least one instance of plasmid transfer from bacteria to eukaryotic plant cells has been identified.[1]

Zooming in on Antibiotic Resistance

One of the greatest threats to human health is the ongoing expansion of antibiotic-resistant microbes. Antibiotics derive their name from their bacterial killing effects. Once thought to be the final solution to combat microbial infections, it is now clear that they can no longer be considered as such. Many pathogenic bacteria show an increased rate of antibiotic resistance.

Antibiotics are naturally occurring compounds isolated from various microbes (fungi or bacteria) or synthetic molecules of similar structure, developed to mimic the activities of the naturally occurring compounds. Antibiotics work through various mechanisms. For example, they can chemically alter amino acids or nucleotides to inhibit DNA, RNA, and protein synthesis. They can also inhibit the cellular machinery (ribosomes and enzymes) critical for bacterial survival.

Antibiotic resistance involves disrupting the mechanisms of antibiotic activities. Bacteria become resistant either by transfer of antibiotic-resistant genes via transduction, conjugation, or transformation, or through adaptive, molecular changes to the bacterial targets of antibiotic activity.

Resistance to Tetracycline

To understand mechanisms of antibiotic resistance it is helpful to know how antibiotics work in the first place. For tetracycline antibiotics, the mechanism of activity is protein synthesis inhibition. Tetracyclines bind to a subunit of the protein translation machinery (ribosomes) and block protein formation. If bacteria are no longer able to synthesize proteins, they fail to reproduce and die.

Tetracycline resistance (Tet-res) is widespread among Gram-positive and Gram-negative bacteria (over 130 genera as of July 2016) and is associated with over 60 different genes. Bacteria usually acquire tetracycline resistance via HGT of plasmids and transposons that encode Tet-res genes. Resistance occurs via one of three basic mechanisms or a combination of the three: (1) efflux of the antibiotic, (2) ribosomal protection, and (3) enzyme modification of the antibiotic. Most identified Tet-res genes (~60 percent) encode energy-dependent efflux proteins. These membrane-associated proteins actuate resistance by transporting the tetracycline antibiotics out of the bacterial cells.[2]

The most widespread mechanism of resistance is ribosomal protection. Researchers have identified a dozen Tet-res genes associated with ribosomal protection. These Tet-res proteins bind ribosomal complexes and alter their shapes in such a way that tetracyclines are disassociated from the 30S subunits. Unable to bind ribosomal subunits, tetracyclines fail to inhibit protein translation. The "bugs" become resistant to the effects of tetracycline through acquisition of Tet-res genes. Another dozen or so Tet-res genes actuate resistance via enzyme modification, and at least one mechanism of tetracycline resistance remains unidentified.[3]

Most acquired tetracycline resistance occurs via conjugation and involves HGT of mobile elements between different species and genera of bacteria. Due to this promiscuous gene swapping, antibiotic resistance is spreading among many different genera of bacteria and involves swapping an array of antibiotic resistance genes, not just Tet-res genes.

One of the greatest health risks facing us today is the rise of multidrug resistant bacteria like MRSA and NDM-1. These "superbugs" acquired resistance through enzyme modification. MRSA stands for methicillin-resistant *Staphylococcus aureus* and designates bacteria that are resistant to beta-lactam antibiotics such as penicillins and cephalosporins. Doctors can treat MRSA with other antibiotics, nevertheless it is highly contagious and can result in life-threatening disease if it reaches the lungs or blood. NDM-1 superbugs are resistant to beta-lactam antibiotics of the carbapenem family, the class of antibiotics most often used to treat antibiotic-resistant bacteria! Carbapenems inhibit cell wall formation. NDM-1 resistance is dependent on a gene that encodes an enzyme that breaks down carbapenems through a chemical reaction with water.

Antibiotic resistance does not occur at the level of the host organism (e.g., an infected person). It occurs at the microbial level through promiscuous gene swapping or mutations that alter cellular targets or enzyme activities.

Mechanisms of HGT are powerful tools for change. But microbial adaptation is not solely dependent upon the introduction of new genes from other organisms or viruses.

Zooming Out

Whether vector-mediated, environmentally mediated, or directly orchestrated, plasmids and chromosomal DNA can be transferred from cell to cell in nature and in the laboratory. These mechanisms of HGT are powerful tools for change. But microbial adaptation is not solely dependent upon the introduction of new genes from other organisms or viruses. Rearrangement and duplication of genetic material contribute to the evolution of microbes, too. Let's take a look at one case where these led to the evolution of a new strain of E. *coli* bacteria in a very long (and ongoing) lab experiment.

The Adaptable Bac

You may have heard of the long-term evolution experiment (LTEE) in E. *coli*. This experiment by a research group at Michigan State University (MSU) in the laboratory of Richard Lenski began in 1988 when a single (clonal) bacterial culture was split into 12 cultures.[4] The evolution of one of these subpopulations is fascinating. It shows how microevolutionary mechanisms can result in microbial evolution. (It also raises questions about whether these mechanisms can be employed to account for increasing jumps in complexity and the evolution of something novel, which we'll discuss in chapter 10.)

Since the onset in 1988, the bacterial growth conditions have been carefully controlled. Researchers collect culture samples every 500 generations (every 75 days) to follow the evolutionary course of E. *coli* over time. For the past 30 years, each culture has been raised in growth medium in the presence of citrate, but limited glucose, and propagated via daily serial passage.

One culture of interest in this LTEE evolved a novel trait: the ability to utilize citrate as a primary food source under aerobic conditions. E. *coli* have been classically characterized by an inability to use environmental citrate under aerobic conditions. Using the collected samples, MSU researchers retraced the history of this culture (Cit$^+$). They discovered that, prior to generation 31,000, the Cit$^+$ bacteria accrued potentiating mutations, so that, by generation 31,500, the Cit$^+$ phenotype was actualized via duplication of a gene segment and its regulatory elements that control citrate transport under anaerobic conditions. Additional mutations, including amplification of the duplicated segment, occurred in the Cit$^+$ bacteria by generation 33,000, refining or fine-tuning its growth on citrate. All these changes contributed to a new Cit$^+$ lineage of E. *coli*. They occurred, not as rare simultaneous events of multiple or single mutations, but in a stepwise and contingent fashion—demonstrating a hallmark of evolution.[5]

The Cit$^+$ bacteria are able to utilize citrate from the environment due to the novel expression of a citrate/succinate transporter (CitT). This acquisition of a new trait allows Cit$^+$ E. *coli* to expand into a citrate-containing ecological niche that was previously not utilized. And, as a result, subsequent cultures (after 34,000 generations) in this lineage of the LTEE demonstrate greater biodiversity than the ancestral cultures because they now contain two notable types of

E. coli: (1) those that utilize citrate as their primary energy source (Cit⁺) and (2) a smaller subpopulation of *E. coli* that utilizes glucose at a much faster rate than the Cit⁺ bacteria. The researchers rightly conclude that the LTEE allowed evolution of a novel trait in *E. coli* and led to an increase in biodiversity. These, too, are hallmarks of evolution. Thus, the emergence of Cit⁺ *E. coli* is an excellent example of microbial evolution.

So, Does Microbial Evolution Occur?

You bet it does! The amazing thing is the variety of ways that genetic change is introduced into single-cell organisms. We've looked at three examples in this chapter: mutations, HGT in acquiring antibiotic resistance, and genome segment duplication in the LTEE. Although we don't know the number of genetic changes that result in fatalities, the sheer number and reproductive capacities of the survivors allow single-cell populations to display extreme adaptability and genetic diversity. This is exactly what is seen in the LTEE.

But does microbial evolution involve production of totally novel protein products, cellular structures, cellular functions, metabolic pathways, or stepping stones to major transitions between kinds of organisms? In other words, even at a microbial level, are these mechanisms powerful enough to account for the transition of *E. coli* into another bacterial species? Are these mechanisms sufficient to account for the transition from prokaryote to eukaryote? That's highly debatable. This debate is at the heart of the questions about evolution's potential novelty problem and convergence. These questions are addressed in chapters 10 and 19, respectively.

Discussion Questions

1. How does microbial evolution demonstrate the power of natural selection at work?

2. The author notes that the expansion of antibiotic-resistant microbes presents a great threat to human health. What thoughts come to mind as you consider this possibility?

3. The long-term evolution experiment (LTEE) evolved a novel trait involving citrate as a primary food source. Does this type of novelty point to the possible transition to another bacterial species?

Chapter 9

Is Natural Selection the Blind Force Driving Evolution?
by Anjeanette Roberts

Descent with modification by natural selection explains the
adaptations of organisms and the unity and diversity of life.[1]
—*Campbell's Biology* (textbook)

All forms of evolution harness the workhorse of natural selection. Acting
on variation, natural selection is the single most *definitive* mechanism
accounting for life's complexity, diversity, and history—according to evolutionary theories in all their forms. Natural selection is the composite selective
(in contrast to generative) process that environmental elements impose upon
reproductive populations. It is the directional mechanism in evolution's shifting populations. Though not the *source* of variations per se, it encompasses all
nonteleological, environmentally dependent mechanisms that inhibit growth
and reproduction of unfit organisms (purifying selection) and that promote
the spread of alleles rendering fitness and reproductive advantages (positive
selection) to their bearers within a population. Natural selection—the bedrock
of Darwinian evolution—remains the most important factor in the modern
synthesis and a contributing factor in variations of non-Darwinian evolution
such as the extended evolutionary synthesis (EES). It remains in even the sim-
plest invocations of evolution, defined as common descent with neutral theory
(genetic drift and gene flow) and natural selection.

But what exactly is natural selection?

Campbell's Biology, a leading college textbook in biological sciences, introduces natural selection as the driver of evolution:

Evolution occurs as the unequal reproductive success of individuals ultimately leads to adaptation to their environment,
as long as the environment remains the same. Darwin called
this mechanism of evolutionary adaptation natural selection
because the natural environment "selects" for the propagation
of certain traits among naturally occurring variant traits in
the population.[2]

Prominent geneticist and architect of the modern synthesis Theodosius
Dobzhansky, in an article titled "Nothing in Biology Makes Sense Except in
the Light of Evolution," asks what makes the colossal diversity of living beings
intelligible to reason?[3] He answers himself, "The best way to envisage the situation is as follows: the environment presents challenges to living species, to
which the latter may respond by adaptive genetic changes." He unpacks this
further:

An unoccupied ecological niche, an unexploited opportunity
for living, is a challenge. So is an environmental change such
as the Ice Age climate giving place to a warmer climate. Natural selection may cause a living species to respond to the challenge by adaptive genetic changes. These changes may enable
the species to occupy the formally empty ecological niche as a
new opportunity for living. . . . But the response may or may
not be successful. This depends on many factors, the chief of
which is the genetic composition of the responding species at
the time the response is called for. Lack of successful response
may cause the species to become extinct. The evidence of fossils shows clearly that the eventual end of most evolutionary
lines is extinction. Organisms now living are successful descendants of only a minority of the species that lived in the
past and of smaller and smaller minorities the farther back
you look.

This doesn't exactly clarify what natural selection is or how it works, but it
alludes to the results of its action and what it accomplishes. Dobzhansky posits
that natural selection "may cause" genetic adaptation, but this is an ambiguous definition. Natural selection does not *cause* the change at an individual
level; rather it leads to accrual of traits to predominance within a population

in response to the fitness and reproductive advantages they provide.

Unlike many who discuss evolution today, Dobzhansky, to his credit, tries to clarify that natural selection cannot have intent or strategy. He concedes, "Only a human being could make such conscious decisions." However, he adds, "Natural selection is at one and the same time a blind and creative process. Only the creative and blind process could produce, on the one hand, the tremendous biologic success that is the human species and, on the other, forms of adaptedness as narrow and as constraining as those of the overspecialized fungus, beetle, and flies mentioned [earlier in his article]." Thus, Dobzhansky reintroduces a measure of ambiguity to the process of natural selection by endowing it with creativity.

Natural selection does not *cause* the change at an individual level.

Campbell's Biology attempts to correct such misconceptions of natural selection's creative process in the context of the modern synthesis:

> Natural selection is a process of editing, not a creative mechanism. A drug does not create resistant pathogens; it selects for resistant individuals that are already present in the population. Second, natural selection depends on time and place. It favors those characteristics in a genetically variable population that provide advantage in the current, local environment. What is beneficial in one situation may be useless or even harmful in another.[4]

The textbook goes on to invite students to ponder the processes of evolution and how editing is a good metaphor for natural selection.[5] This definition of what natural selection does and doesn't do seems much clearer and more precise. Yet, it is not much better than Dobzhansky's claim of blind creativity. *Campbell's Biology* denies natural selection creativity and, presumably as Dobzhansky did, consciousness, intent, or foresight, but still attributes editing capabilities to the selection process. Good luck getting this book's editorial team to accept this concept! Editors know they are intentional in how they choose to correct or adjust text to provide clearer communication (or clearer function).

Natural selection is less like editing and more like a filtering process; one where no (or no noticeable) errors between a template and a functional product clear selection. It is wholly unlike editing except that it has a function-based filter that weeds out egregious errors. Moreover, natural selection's "editing" takes place at a functional (phenotypic) level, not a genetic level, thus allowing for continued diversity at the genetic level within a surviving population. This latter process is referred to as genetic drift, and natural selection's weeding-out effect is imperfect.

Campbell's Biology presents natural selection clearly at times: "Darwin recognized that a population evolves through the differential reproductive success of its variant members. On average, those individuals best suited to the local environment leave the most offspring, thereby transmitting their genes. Thus, natural selection results in the accumulation of genetic variations favored by the environment."[6] At other times throughout the text, ambiguity is introduced as to the role of natural selection in the evolutionary process (e.g., stating how evolutionary adaptations arise by natural selection): "This theory proposes that natural selection is the evolutionary mechanism that accounts for an enormous variety of adaptations, of which coat color in mice is but one example."[7] Or here, "A second type of evidence for evolution comes from analyzing similarities among different organisms. As we've discussed, evolution is a process of descent with modification: characteristics present in an ancestral organism are altered (by natural selection) in its descendants over time as they face different environmental conditions."[8] These statements attribute enormous variety of adaptations and alterations of ancestral organisms to natural selection. But natural selection is not accomplishing the alterations or producing the variations; it is merely a selective, sorting, or filtering process that accounts for the accumulation of certain fit and viable variants in certain populations or subpopulations.

Blind but Not Creative

Dobzhansky and others credit natural selection with both an ability to create the variations upon which it acts and to weed out ill-adapted organisms, thus increasing diversity and complexity in surviving populations. Yet Dobzhansky simultaneously fails to explain any actual mechanism capable of producing increased complexity or diversity and fails to identify any creative mechanism of natural selection. A mechanism that sorts is not the same as a mechanism that creates. And, as far as evolving something into something more complex is concerned, selection devoid of creative or corrective power and of teleological intent is not much of anything.

However, a blind process that sorts out failures can allow increased diversity in the outcomes available for further mutations. For example, given an original sequence of aag, blind sorting might allow aaag, aagg, aag, agg, ag, and aa to all make it through, whereas more pronounced (such as cag or atg) differences might be rejected. Under little selective pressure, diversity would increase while also being constrained. Under *specific* selective pressures, specific traits would emerge from those *preexisting* in the population. This is the extent and role of natural selection. As far as *creativity* goes, it is fairly anemic, limited to sorting through variations within a population.

What Can Natural Selection Accomplish?

In evolution, natural selection is the selecting mechanism—not the generative mechanism—at a molecular level. It accounts for the frequencies of specific traits in a population. The *prevalence* of beak thickness in subsets of the Galápagos finches, favored coloration in peppered moths, Cit⁺ *E. coli* growing on citrate under aerobic conditions, and variations in human skin pigmentation are all adaptive responses to new and changing environments where natural selection leads the way.[9] In each of these cases the natural selection mechanism favored reproduction of organisms bearing specific traits in specific environments. This resulted in shifting traits and allele frequencies within the population. In many, if not all, cases the less favored traits (or the genetic variants allowing those traits) remain at lower frequencies. Their persistence provides the capacity for oscillations in observed traits within populations if environmental or ecological conditions shift again. In all cases, natural selection did not provide variations underlying the means of change. These were generated by a variety of evolutionary mechanisms including gene flow, drift, and mutations. The reproductively unfit and unsuccessful were merely sorted out in natural selection. In other words, it provides for the survival of the fittest, not the arrival of the fittest.[10]

Harsh Criticism

It has been evident from Darwin's time (to some) that natural selection shares limitations similar to those of artificial selection. Like artificial selection, natural selection can only act on variation already present in the parental genomes and thus lacks the necessary power to account for the vast diversity and complexity of living organisms. For large-scale evolution to occur, offspring in evolving populations must somehow be able to gain changes in leaps in comparison to the genetic information of their ancestors. In rare instances garbling genetic information generates new information, but the system must be able to recognize, select, and maintain such chance gains. This is a necessary component for increasing complexity in a nonteleological system, but it is also the greatest obstacle to credibility. Any gain in function must be selected and, therefore, be specific for *current* environmental conditions—not for any unforeseen condition. In their theory of punctuated equilibria, Niles Eldredge and Stephen Jay Gould proposed a process to explain sudden jumps in complexity in the absence of gradualist transitions. But working out actual mechanisms coincidental to such leaps has remained, for the most part, unsolved and unarticulated. The only exceptions are recent attempts to offer conceptual, but unverifiable, processes via a constructive neutral evolution theory (CNE).[11] (See, also, chapter 10.)

Michael Egnor of the Discovery Institute levies harsh criticism against natural selection's usefulness in science:

> Survival of survivors is tautological. The genuine study of evolutionary change (e.g., in populations of bacteria exposed to antibiotics) entails genetics, biochemistry, molecular biology, pharmacology, etc. "Natural selection" adds nothing to our understanding of bacterial resistance, and in fact is a prime impediment to biology and medicine over the past century and a half. . . . Darwinism is a mere "narrative gloss" . . . and a crippling impediment to science.[12]

He has a valid point. Natural selection is often misunderstood as something more creative and prescient. It can drive adaptation within populations, but it lacks the power to create even iteratively, if it cannot preserve genetic foundations for future needs and success. It cannot account for this selection and preservation apart from immediate fitness advantages (panadaptationism).

Even before we knew the molecular foundations for inheritance, many questioned the sufficiency of natural selection, including Darwin's bulldog Thomas Huxley. When the modern synthesis incorporated genetics into our understanding of inheritance, many, like Dobzhansky, were certain of its ability to provide the necessary driving force. Although most agree that natural selection is the only evolutionary mechanism that consistently leads to adaptive evolution,[13] the stepwise changes and gradual accrual of these to account for leaps in complexity have been challenged deeply in the scientific community as understanding has increased. EES proponents are at the center of some of these challenges, as are proponents of intelligent design and creation.

Natural Selection in Developing Evolutionary Theories

Natural selection is not generative and it is blind beyond its immediate context. Due to these two characteristics, adaptations leading to fitness and reproductive advantages are necessary components of the modern synthesis and Darwinian forms of evolution. It is these components (specifically blind and nongenerative forces necessitating adaptive fitness advantages) that critics scrutinize. Proponents of extended evolutionary synthesis (EES) and constructive neutral evolution theory (CNE) downplay natural selection primarily because functional adaptations tend toward a necessary gradual, stepwise process called panadaptationism, where each step must gain a functional advantage to spread through and be fixed in a population. EES and CNE proponents argue this type of evolution is insufficient and indemonstrable at levels needed for leaps in complexity and macroevolutionary progression (climbing the tree, not just filling in bushier branches). The fossil record and extant populations do not support a continuum of complexity across Earth's life. They show discontinuities. Comparative genomics across higher taxa demonstrate that rather large genetic changes must occur to get from one type of organism to another.

Evolutionary biologist and EES proponent Gerd B. Müller, in a presentation to the Royal Society of London in 2016, stated that the modern synthesis can explain gradual variations, adaptations of phenotypic characteristics, and some genetic variations in speciation. But, he argued, it is inadequate in explaining higher levels of evolution, including the origin of body plans, complex behaviors, complex physiologies, and developmental differences.[14] CNE supporters argue similarly, "We offered (in fact reoffered) the CNE paradigm as a counterpoint to purely adaptationist/selectionist schemes that are often favored by biologists, and molecular biologists in particular, to explain the evolution of structural and biochemical complexity."[15]

In place of necessary adaptive selections, evolutionists appeal to neutral theory, along with mechanisms that introduce macromutations in genetic information and changes in developmental systems to drive evolution. Neutral theory allows for silent changes (small and large) with no loss of competitive function. These changes drift through a population, accruing more and more neutral changes. Eventually they produce some advantageous trait and are selected (nonprovidentially) and fixed within the population. This is a long process, occurring within an environment where a blind natural selection weeds out only abject failures. In this scenario, however, it would seem any successes introducing constructive novelties would occur with even rarer statistical probabilities than beneficial mutations under immediate selective (fitness) conditions.

Natural selection can only preserve currently functioning components, not neutrally drifting ones. Comments by astronomer and mathematician Sir Fred Hoyle confirm this challenge:

> There is a very small, not strictly zero, probability that the garbling of a message will turn out to improve it. So if one has a means for noticing and grabbing hold of the improved copy in the rare case in which it happens, the information content of the message can actually be improved. This is the logic of the Darwinian theory of evolution. The logic turns on the ability to recognize the rare improved copy.[16]

In nature, this recognition takes place *only* through adaptive fitness or reproductive advantages. No selection of anything useful takes place in the absence of a selectable benefit. So, at some point positive selection, not just negative selection, of adaptive changes must still contribute to evolution's progress. For this reason, EES proponents do not abandon natural selection entirely. Evolutionary biologist Eugene Koonin explains Darwinism's place in present-day evolutionary theory:

> It is, however, counter-productive, and ultimately, a disservice to Darwin's legacy, to define modern evolutionary biology as neo-Darwinism. The current picture of evolution, informed, in particular, by results of comparative genomics and systems biology, is by far more complex than that presented in the *Origin of Species*, so that Darwinian principles, including natural selection, are incorporated into the evolving new synthesis as important but certainly not all-embracing tenets.[17]

Even if successful, an additional problem is that any new leap in function must fit within the existing cell structures and pathways to be properly regulated and beneficial to the organism. Imagining how neutral theory and natural mechanisms can account for this—apart from an adaptive, stepwise natural selection—is at the heart of the EES and CNE theories (see chapter 10).

For these non-Darwinian versions of evolution to succeed and progress, with or without neutral theory, something must act as the director or preserver of phenotypic function toward specific goals. If this directing mechanism is not within the system itself, it must somehow be imposed upon or built into the containing system.

Cells as Agents of Change

If mutation and selection are insufficient to explain evolution, what drives it? To address this problem, EES proponents offer some creative solutions. Many EES proponents move away from strictly mechanistic explanations and toward explanations of agency. For many, an EES doesn't simply add new mechanisms to natural selection; it reverses cause-and-effect. Organisms under stress exchange genes, reprogram epigenetic networks, and steal code from viruses. In the modern synthesis, natural selection is the only directional force; in EES, cells are agents of their own change.

In *Evolution 2.0*, author and engineer Perry Marshall likens the EES process to duplicating and rearranging words from a previous sentence (an analogy to genome duplication to account for evolutionary advances).[18] In this example, duplicated words continue to mutate, not merely randomly, but according to linguistic-type rules (as yet unidentified) to form new words and new sentences.

One feature of this model is that it generates information *via the agency of the cell* through words that may require few (or many) changes to have new meanings (functions) emerge. The integrity of these unused, redundant words is safeguarded throughout the nonrandom duplicating, restructuring, and rearranging processes.

In other words, while mutations occur around them, the soon-to-be new words are not subject to random mutations themselves, but remain under control of the cell itself. Future viability of unused structures is not maintained by the pressure of natural selection but by the system's internal bias toward preserving elements that may be useful in the future. In other words, the organism is claimed to have agency and anticipates future threats. There is no selective pressure maintaining their future viability, yet somehow the system maintains the needed function of what will be necessary for future success.

Critics of cellular agency point out that no element or process in nature can provide such maintenance. They say that such an EES scenario faces a greater challenge than the modern synthesis's more immediate selection of fitness advantages. Marshall and advocates of EES don't claim to fully understand how it works, but they respond by pointing to massive restructuring of genomes by cancer cells and in symbiotic mergers in real time. EES advocates cite live evolutionary experiments that suggest cells possess powerful evolutionary machinery with some ability to predict future outcomes.

Ray and Denis Noble exemplify the agency of the cell in their paper, "Was the Watchmaker Blind? Or Was She One-Eyed?" In this paper, the authors say that "organisms have demonstrably evolved guided random mutation mechanisms that can respond rapidly and correctly to environmental challenges."[19]

While it may be impossible to characterize the philosophical views of EES proponents, it would be fair to say most reject strict reductionist and conventionally materialistic interpretations of biology. In an Oxford 2018 meeting, Third Way of Evolution members agreed the central question in evolution is *agency*. For 200 years, materialists and reductionists tried to ban teleology from science, but EES advocates say that not only is teleology essential to evolution, but ancient questions about mind vs. body and free will vs. determinism don't merely apply to humans. They reach all the way down to the cell.

Clinging to Natural Selection

Proponents of both the modern synthesis and EES will continue to work out what's doing what in evolutionary progressions and adaptations. As they do, they need to be clearer and more precise in their communication, especially regarding the role of natural selection, cellular agency, and mechanisms that preserve future potential functionality in the absence of immediate selective advantages.

Natural selection explains only one thing: observed adaptations that were selected from preexisting options within a group or combinations present in an ancestral population. The spread of those traits can be successfully modeled through population genetics and can give historical insight into evolutionary changes within related groups. When advocates overstate the capacity of natural selection, their statements should be recognized and acknowledged as unevidenced claims made only to support or fit the preferred evolutionary paradigm.

If successful climbing of an evolutionary tree occurs, then it requires mechanisms for increasing complexity and creating novelties (more in chapter 10). Natural selection fails to accomplish this, but jettisoning it as the primary driver of change creates a worse problem for future progression. If natural selection does not preserve potentially advantageous changes, then the chances of beneficial changes arising decrease unless cells are somehow prescient themselves.

The absence of a mechanical explanation for the preservation of neutral changes presents evolutionists with a teleological problem. Yet all naturalistic philosophies of the origin and diversity of life utterly reject guided or directed evolution. This is the teleology problem in a nutshell (see chapter 11). One way for nontheistic evolutionists to avoid this issue is to endow DNA or cells with volition, but even Dobzhansky got that right in his critiques of what nature is *not* doing.

Despite all natural selection's shortcomings, many continue to uncritically accept its ability to drive evolutionary systems forward. One has little choice but to do so in a strictly materialistic universe.

Discussion Questions

1. Explain what proponents of natural selection mean when they say this mechanism is the driver of evolution.

2. Is natural selection creative? Why or why not?

3. Critics of Darwinian evolution say "panadaptationism" is not sufficient to support the theory. On what basis do they say so?

4. Evaluate the idea that natural selection provides for the "survival of the fittest, not the arrival of the fittest."

5. Does natural selection explain increasing complexity in organisms? Why or why not?

Chapter 10

Is There a Novelty Problem for Evolution?

by Anjeanette Roberts

Popular-level depictions of evolution tend to simplify the transition from organism to organism. Quips like "from microbe to man" or "from mouse to man" come to mind. Going from simple to complex organisms requires additional genetic material, new regulatory elements and systems, origination of new genes, and new developmental pathways as the basis for changes in body type and diversity. With advances in genome sequencing, comparative genomics opens the door for discovering critical novelties and what drives their origins. Surprisingly, the sources and causes of novelty often still elude us and novelty remains one of the greatest challenges to any evolutionary scenario.

The term *novelty* refers to something new or unique. However, evolutionary biologists apply the concept differently when studying biological phenomena and aspects of evolution. This ambiguity complicates things, especially when evaluating how large or small a problem accounting for novelty may be when seeking evolutionary justifications of the common ancestry for all life. In evolution, there are several ways to understand innovation or novelty as Gerd B. Müller and Stuart Newman acknowledge in "The Innovation Triad: An EvoDevo Agenda":

> If we assume that origination, innovation, and novelty represent a distinct complex of interrelated problems of phenotypic evolution, a number of theoretical issues arise in attempting to account for them. In particular, as with all biological phenomena, it will be necessary to distinguish what earlier had been called ultimate and proximate causation. . . . Constraint, integration, and fixation represent further important issues

that arise from regarding the innovation triad as distinct, and, finally, there is the problem of the transitional functionality of novelties.[1]

Once we've considered what we label as new or novel, it becomes critical to ascertain whether it is the type of novelty needed to drive large-scale evolutionary progressions. Even then, "the problem of the transitional functionality of novelties"—explaining how existing intracellular biological systems incorporate novelties—persists.

Almost everyone agrees that novel traits emerge phenotypically in response to environmental selective pressures as selection acts on preexisting variations. Although all sources of variation cannot be ascertained, many identifiable mechanisms contribute to phenotypic differences.

This Is Not the Novelty You're Looking For
Recall from chapter 8 that *E. coli* bacteria are classically characterized by an inability to use environmental citrate under aerobic conditions. Yet one subculture developed in Michigan State University's long-term evolution experiment (LTEE) overcame this handicap.

The researchers' 2012 report in *Nature* opens with this statement: "Evolutionary novelties are qualitatively new traits that open up ecological opportunities and thereby promote diversification."[2] Elsewhere, they comment on the same phenomena stating that *E. coli* underwent a "long-delayed and unique evolution" encompassing a "key innovation" involving multiple steps that resulted in a "new Cit$^+$ function."[3] (Cit$^+$ is the label assigned to this *E. coli* subculture.) The research indeed shows that multiple, stepwise mutations were needed to potentiate, acquire, and refine the bacteria for citrate metabolism under aerobic conditions. It also shows that this one lineage of *E. coli* acquired a novel function in a contingent fashion.

Evolution of this new function "transcends the phenotypic boundaries of a diverse and well-studied species [*E. coli*]."[4] This claim is substantiated by the fact that lack of growth on citrate under aerobic conditions has long been a defining characteristic of *E. coli*. Utilization of citrate by the evolving population resulted in "an ecological transition from a single population to a two-member community," since Cit$^-$ (non-citrate utilizing) *E. coli* remain and outcompete the Cit$^+$ bugs for low levels of glucose in the media. *Voila!* We have a new trait, a new function, a new species of *E. coli* (Cit$^+$). It's evolution 101!

It seems Cit$^+$ *E. coli* meet the criteria for evolutionary novelty—but have

they really? Is innovation demonstrated at a genetic level? Have genetic mutations produced a new gene? Has *E. coli* evolved a new metabolic pathway? No.
E. coli has developed a new trait, but true innovation has arguably not occurred.

It isn't utterly new for *E. coli* to utilize citrate as a primary food source. *E.
coli* utilize citrate via a citrate fermentation cycle under anaerobic conditions
just fine. Under anaerobic conditions, *E. coli* produce a protein that transports
citrate from the environment into the bacteria.

In nature *E. coli* occasionally acquire an ability to utilize citrate under aerobic conditions. In such instances, the bacteria attain the function through horizontal gene transfer (HGT) of plasmids (small circular pieces of DNA). Recipients of the "new" plasmid grow aerobically on citrate because the plasmid encodes a citrate transporter that functions in the presence of oxygen. The trait is novel to the recipient microbes, but the transporter gene and promoter complex are preexisting.[5]

The trait is novel to the recipient microbes, but the transporter gene and promoter complex are preexisting.

But that's not what happened in the LTEE. A citrate transporter was not co-opted or transferred from another organism. In the LTEE, critical changes hinged on duplication of an endogenous promoter (*rnk*—active under aerobic conditions), duplication of the gene encoding a citrate transporter (CitT), and juxtaposition of these elements in tandem repeats. No longer under the control of the oxygen-inhibited promoter, the tandem copies of CitT were now regulated by copies of the uninhibited *rnk* promoter. The Cit+ mutation produces the citrate transporter in the presence of oxygen and, through the transporter, citrate is taken up from the media and utilized via mechanisms already present in the *E. coli* bacteria.

It is important to note that the Cit[+] bacteria still utilized citrate through the *preexisting* metabolic citric acid cycle. A *preexisting* gene produces the citrate transporter under aerobic conditions simply by switching the promoter that controls its expression. It is a novel trait, but the underlying mechanisms are not *originations* or *innovations of new genes or promoters*. The Cit[+] bacteria did *not* evolve a new transporter, a new promoter, or a new metabolic pathway. They may have co-opted an existing internal promoter, but a case for claiming true innovation falls flat.

Affirming Adaptations Does Not Help Us Climb the Tree

Microbial evolution has taken place. Stepwise changes have accrued in a contingent fashion. Some *E. coli* have gained the ability to import citrate in the presence of oxygen. An untapped ecological niche is now accessible. In the lab, the new phenotype resulted from partial genome duplication. In nature, the new phenotype may be acquired through HGT.

But we can also affirm that nothing analogous to innovation or macroevolution has truly happened here. Biodiversity has increased, but *E. coli* with or without aerobic expression of a citrate transporter are still *E. coli*. They've adapted, but there is no sign of tree-climbing.

These gradual, adaptive changes observed in microbes (and similar alterations observed in speciation) are where evolutionary mechanisms and corresponding explanations thrive. Nevertheless, countless examples such as these get us no closer to the major biological transitions needed to connect all life through common descent. Nor do they lead to the increased complexity observed at higher branches in evolution's tree. Such examples fail to get us any closer to true innovation of new genes, pathways, systems, or types, especially in complex, sexually reproducing populations.

Evolutionary biologist Gerd B. Müller shares similar assessments of the adequacy and inadequacy of the modern synthesis's evolutionary framework, which centers on arguments focused on variations in populations and their genetic underpinnings. In "The Extended Evolutionary Synthesis," Müller's criticisms included the insufficiency of natural selection to drive macroevolutionary progress.[6] Natural selection can explain gradual variations and adaptations of phenotypic characteristics and some genetic variations in speciation, but it is inadequate in explaining complex levels of evolution, including the origin of body plans, complex behaviors, complex physiologies, and developmental differences. Overcoming these inadequacies requires mechanisms or processes capable of innovation (i.e., generating new or novel genes, systems, organs, and body plans).

Like Müller, many critics of the modern synthesis and neo-Darwinism argue that gradualism and natural selection are grossly insufficient[7] (see chapter 9). They suggest the macro-mechanisms of EES—and especially evo-devo-dependent processes—are needed to supplement the insufficient mechanics of the modern synthesis in order to account for transitions and increasing systems-level complexities.[8]

Getting a Leg Up the Tree

Evolutionary developmental biology (evo-devo) is the field of study shedding the greatest light on generating large morphological novelties in evolution. The work is fascinating and opens many avenues of fruitful exploration.

Evo-devo concepts rest on the foundation that genes do not build bodies, but cells, tissues, and organisms do. Furthermore, gene expression and function are linked and hierarchically organized in gene regulatory networks (GRNs). Factors affecting differential development on cellular, tissue, and organismal levels are primarily nongenetic factors. Such development is not based on simplistic relationships between genes and phenotype but encompasses system-level relationships that are mediated and interpreted by development itself.[9]

In evo-devo, developmental systems' mechanics define developmental trajectories. Each level of tissue—and organismal—development has dynamic factors added to the simple genetic changes foundational to modern synthesis explanations. And each of these factors is influenced by the intra-organismal as well as the external environment. Developmental systems can be directly influenced by their environments in immediate and nongenetically determined ways.

Evo-devo introduces other concepts besides GRNs:

- Patterning effects characterized by intracellular locales and gradients
- Thresholds that act as switches in multistability or bistability systems, in which GRNs get locked into different stable expression states depending on the levels of other biological components[10]
- Additional developmental effects that influence changes in progression, timing, and duration of gene expression (heterochrony) within systems and developmental processes

Some of these effects are likely mediated through epigenetic modifications that affect not just patterning or timing, but also concentrations of gene products and molecular regulatory factors. Furthermore, the concept of niche construction, where a cell or organism is influencing its environment, can lead to recursive feedback in ongoing development shifts in populations.[11]

A review by Müller and Günter P. Wagner is informative in the scope and application of evo-devo explanations, including empirically demonstrated cases where changes in early embryogenesis have profound morphological restructuring effects.[12] Generative modes, including changes in hierarchical organization, interactivity, and dissociability of genes in regulatory networks, equilibria, and thresholds, may all play into the development of a single novelty or set of morphological novelties.[13] Though each of these has the potential to trigger rapid morphological transitions, many scientists consider these types of transitions extensively disruptive (or lethal), rather than progressive, for organisms.

Evo-Devo's Challenges

Although development of several morphological novelties and specific epigenetic factors contributing to their generation have been identified, in some of these cases no significant amount of heritable variation has been demonstrated. Yet there must be either genetic changes, heritable epigenetic changes, or consistent environmental triggers that account for common morphological novelties or for reproducible induction of these novelties in subsequent generations.

It is possible to conceptualize that heritability depends on changes, whether genetic or epigenetic, that have gone undetected by researchers. However, as structuralist and biochemist Michael Denton points out (as do Müller and Wagner), some researchers gloss over significant underlying details and extrapolate empirical observations to cross structural and functional hurdles that seem to prevent the generation of new body plans and organismal types.

These glosses occur in response to two persistent challenges. The first is that although biologists understand the developmental progressions of morphological changes, the ability of these changes to integrate into hierarchical, preexisting processes and structures of intracellular and organismal developmental systems remains unexplained. Denton covers the challenges and their significance in greater detail in the chapter "EvoDevo" in *Evolution, Still a Theory in Crisis.*[14]

Secondly, once new *and successful* variants (morphologically distinct transformations) have occurred, their fixation in the population must also be explained. Researchers can model changes in allele frequencies once a distinct population is established, but modeling doesn't account for the process of establishing morphologically or developmentally distinct ancestral populations. This highlights a problem at the interface of empiricists and theorists. Empiricists want mechanistic pathways for the introduction and establishment of descriptive, plausible transitions, not just models of how they spread within populations. Theorists gloss over the need for these pathways. Rather, they appeal to successful theory-dependent, computational algorithms to describe the dynamics of the spread of new phenotypes through populations.

Although evo-devo studies, findings, and explanations are beginning to close some difficult conceptual gaps, they still fall short in addressing the two previous points as well as the generation of orphan genes or true innovations. Thus, despite rich gains of developmental knowledge made available to us through studies in evo-devo, persistent challenges remain in describing evolutionary progressions.

Can an Extended Evolutionary Synthesis (EES) Get Us Closer to True Novelty?

In addition to morphological evo-devo effects (and any abstract relationship to changes in populations), Müller points out that EES mechanisms provide necessary large-scale genetic changes and, coupled with neutral theory, contribute to explanations of discontinuous development in an all-or-nothing fashion and provisionally account for leaps in complexity.[15]

In *Evolution 2.0*, Perry Marshall presents five mechanistic tools at the disposal of EES: (1) transposition, (2) horizontal gene transfer, (3) epigenetics, (4) genome duplication (including hybridization), and (5) symbiogenesis. All but epigenetics involve relatively large-scale changes at the DNA level. All, *including* epigenetics, may impact gene regulation and/or development in significant ways. Marshall shares the sentiment of many professional scientists with this summary statement: "With these five . . . we can in principle get from any one spot on the tree of life to any other. . . . Finally we're beginning to form a reasonable sketch of how life proliferated on Earth—how life has managed to fill every niche with amazing diversity."[16]

Increasing genetic complexity (at DNA/genome and regulatory/systems levels) is necessary to get from simple eukaryotes to humans along an evolutionary path. Many acknowledge the need for large-scale genetic changes and appeal to the most radical molecular altering mechanisms observed in nature (symbiogenesis, hybridization, and genome duplication) to provide large excesses of genetic material, fuel genuine innovations, and provide leaps in complexity.[17] Large excesses of genetic material allow additional changes to accrue over time, which is important to all forms of evolution, especially those appealing to neutral theory.

Bacterial geneticist James Shapiro is known for his theory of natural genetic engineering.[18] According to this theory, cells and organisms employ genome duplication, as well as HGT and transposition, as biomolecular tools to disrupt their own genomes through major rearrangements and expansive acquisitions of new material (something Shapiro refers to as genetic shock). Thus, cells and organisms facilitate their own evolution when they encounter environmental

Species	Genes	Transcripts	Genes with orthologs		Orphan genes
H. sapiens	20,907	46,259	18,485	88%	2,422
M. musculus	22,848	40,052	19,067	83%	3,781
C. familiaris	19,292	25,546	17,436	90%	1,856
M. domestica	19,458	32,544	17,025	87%	2,433
O. anatinus	17,936	26,821	14,879	83%	3,057
G. gallus	16,723	22,181	14,465	86%	2,258
T. guttata	17,475	18,191	15,820	91%	1,655
T. nigroviridis	19,581	23,097	15,371	78%	4,210

H. sapiens = human; M. musculus = house mouse; C. familiaris = dog; M. domestica = opossum; O. anatinus = duck-billed platypus; G. gallus = (red jungle fowl) chicken; T. guttata = zebra finch; T. nigroviridis = spotted green pufferfish

Table 10: Orphan Genes[19]

stress, disruptions, or triggers.[20] Natural genetic engineering may work well in bacterial populations, archaea, simple eukaryotic organisms, and some plants, but it does not pass muster for driving major biological transitions in birds, mammals, and other higher organisms where it faces genuine, widespread species reproductive barriers. (See "Interspecies Hybridization and Plants" in chapter 7.) Shapiro's scientific peers also raise objections to using natural genetic engineering to explain major changes at higher organismal levels.[21]

The question remains as to whether these mechanisms are sufficient to account for novelty. The same critique raised earlier in the context of evo-devo certainly applies here, at least at the level of complex organisms in regard to interspecies hybridizations accounting for major biological transitions, "empirical evidence is needed to evaluate enthusiastic speculation."[22]

Can EES Mechanisms Account for Novel Genes?
The ability to sequence and compare entire genomes from microbial species— and nearly entire genomes of other organisms—has lent support to elements of natural genetic engineering, namely observations consistent with genome modularity, reshuffling, transposition, recombination, duplication events,

---

Homologues, Orthologues, and Paralogues

Homologues are genes that occur in different organisms that share a common lineage or descend from a common ancestor. Paralogues are genes that arise from duplication of preexisting similar sequences. Orthologues are genes that exist in different lineages.[23] To be true orphans, genes must be without traceable ancestry and should lack paralogues and orthologues. Taxonomically restricted genes (TRGs) may have homologues. The level at which homologues exist defines the level of taxonomic restriction. The terminology can become rather confusing, but it is important in identifying potential genetic sources (or contributors) for originating TRGs or orphan genes.

---

increased genome complexity (size), and gene transfer.[24] Yet, it has also led to one of the most surprising findings for evolutionary biology.

New genome analysis reports often identify genes that appear to be limited to one species or lineage. These species-specific genes are identified by sequence analyses that demonstrate uninterrupted open reading frames (ORFs) and can contribute 10–45 percent of the newly annotated genes.[25] ORFs are stretches of DNA that correspond to putative protein-coding sequences; different studies employ different cut-off lengths for identifying ORFs. Compared to previously reported and annotated sequences, these lineage-specific ORFs have no homologues or orthologues in outlying species or lineages. Because their origins cannot easily be traced through common descent, they've received the moniker "ORFan" or "orphan" genes. They are genes with unknown ancestry.[26] More precisely, orphan genes are referred to as taxonomically restricted genes (TRGs),[27] which allows designation of the taxonomical levels defining their distributions (e.g., chordate-specific or primate-specific genes).

Each time a new genome sequence is reported sentiments of surprise are repeated whenever orphan gene analyses are included. In 2016, Richard Buggs, professor of evolutionary genomics at Queen Mary University of London, and his colleagues reported over 9,000 orphan genes identified in ash trees.[28] Buggs points out the ubiquity of orphan genes "has been one of the biggest surprises of genomics over the last 20 years." Rather than diminishing with more and more genome sequencing, as researchers expected them to, "orphan genes continue to comprise a sizable proportion of each new genome sequenced."[29] The range remains high, typically between 10–30 percent of genes.[30] A 2017 report on mammalian-specific TRGs echoes Buggs's observation:

> Genome and mRNA sequencing efforts of the last two decades have resulted in gene catalogues for a large number of species. This has spurred the comparison of genes across species and the identification of a surprisingly large number of proteins that appear to be limited to one species or lineage.[31]

Also noting a large proportion of orphan genes, a 2010 study on fungi noted, "It is believed that *de novo* creation of coding sequences is rare in comparison to mechanisms such as domain shuffling and gene duplication; hence, most sequences should have homologs in other genomes."[32]

These last two comments raise questions about the expression or functionality of identified orphans, as well as concerns about identifying or qualifying a gene as an orphan. Are TRGs transcribed and translated into proteins? Many scientists believe orphans are functionally relevant. Though the proteins themselves have gone undetected, RNA sequence analyses and ribosome profiling studies support this belief, since these assays indicate transcription and possible translation of the TRGs.

Orphans Everywhere, but Whence?

Buggs calls orphan genes "'the hard problem' for evolutionary genomics." He elaborates:

> Because we can't find other genes similar to them in other species, we can't build family trees for them. We cannot hypothesize their gradual evolution or their line of common descent; instead they seem to appear out of nowhere. Various attempts have been made at explaining their origins but . . . the problem remains unsolved.[33]

Do orphan genes arise *de novo* or are they variants of preexisting genetic sequences that were not previously associated with an ORF or were not previously annotated? Failure to compare potential orphan sequences to sequences from *whole* genomes of other organisms—and not just to the annotated gene regions—could inflate the number of orphan genes. Orphan gene sequences might exist, in part, in noncoding regions of other genomes, but not in sequences associated with a previously identified gene. Obviously, if subsequent analyses show these genes have arisen from previously unidentified homologous sequences, then they would no longer merit classification as orphans.[34]

If TRGs do not have homologues or orthologues in any other taxa, then how do they originate? Two evolutionary explanations are proposed most often: "Orphan genes . . . may arise by rearrangements of already existing coding sequences, often including partially duplicated genes and/or transposable (mobile DNA) elements, or completely *de novo* from previously noncoding genomic regions."[35] Still, many conceptual, mechanistic paths or combinations of mechanisms for originating orphan genes have been proposed:[36]

- Transcription first: a noncoding stretch of DNA acquires regulatory sequences. Such sequences may have previously been identified as noncoding RNAs (ncRNAs).
- Intergenic ORFs gain transcription or gradual extension of short reading frames that eventually gain structure and function. (*Intergenic* refers to regions between genes.)
- Parts of pseudogenized genes gain regulatory sequences.

Still, researchers note that "for all of these models, there are several consistent findings, but none of the models is, as yet, supported by a comprehensive set of data from diverse sources and corresponding experimental data."[37]

Despite the prevalence of orphan genes and the acknowledgment of their potential importance as discriminating features or providing functions unique to their particular taxa, TRGs are often neglected. The sentiments expressed in reports and commentaries signify that orphan sequences are unimportant—since they are not evolutionarily conserved elements. Although some researchers explore the significance of orphans, many attempt to dismiss them as nonfunctional or as irrelevant due to size (many orphans are small ORFs) or because they lack any sign of purifying selection. Attitudes that ignore or downplay the significance of TRGs suggest a bias against research on elements difficult to investigate and whose origins and existence somewhat challenge evolutionary explanations. They require experimental validations, not just conclusions drawn from bioinformatic analyses. Buggs makes a similar observation:[38]

Give[n] their ubiquity in all genome sequences orphan genes receive comparatively little attention from the research community. I suspect this is partly because they are such a difficult problem. Science is "the art of the soluble." It may be that little funding finds its way to the origin of orphan genes because it appears to be an insoluble problem.

Regardless of motivations, neglecting the study of orphan genes is short-sighted. Many TRGs that have been studied have been found to be functional or essential even in the relatively ideal environments of laboratory-controlled experiments. Functional significance is easily underdetermined when analyses are merely computational or take place in environmentally restricted conditions. Nevertheless, TRGs with no known homologues have been found to have functional significance in antimicrobial and immune responses, stress responses, regulation of DNA synthesis, and rapid adaptations to changing environments, as well as species-specific adaptations, and even in limb regeneration.[39] Even in the absence of protein translation, orphan RNA transcripts may also be of functional, regulatory significance (as are other conserved ncRNAs) and are largely unstudied in this capacity.

Storytelling in Evolution

Without a direct mechanistic pathway identified, explanations for increasing complexity seem more like persuasive rhetoric told to fit a predetermined materialistic worldview. (Recall my friend "Einstein" from "Is an Evolutionary Paradigm Truly Better?" on page 50.)

Campbell's Biology textbook, used in high school and university courses, demonstrates the importance in honing rhetorical skills.[40] It employs paradigm-developing exercises for "making connections." For example, the text describes a family of plants able to grow in soil that contains a toxic mineral called serpentine. "*Presumably,*" the text muses, "variants of ancestral, nonserpentine species arose that could survive in serpentine soils" and natural selection took things from there (emphasis added). Then the text prompts students to "explain how natural selection might have played a role in the evolution of species that are tolerant of serpentine soils." One could argue that students using *Campbell's Biology* are being taught the art of story development to fill gaps in the evolution narrative.

As Denton mentions time and again in *Evolution: Still a Theory in Crisis*, the challenge for any origination or innovation is how to incorporate the new function in proper context (timing, location, and pathway) in its intracellular or intra-organismal context. Merely speculating that it just somehow is incorporated, as the example from *Campbell's Biology* does, is insufficient.

Our Critiques

The preceding example from *Campbell's Biology* highlights one reason why scholars at Reasons to Believe criticize the modern synthesis. It fails to provide credible pathways for developing new complexity. Our critique is similar to that of structuralists such as Denton, as well as proponents of extended evolutionary synthesis (EES) and constructive neutral evolution theory (CNE). Moreover, we raise the criticisms for the same reasons: lack of supporting evidence for the sufficiency of natural selection and panadaptationism to drive major biological transitions or leaps in complexity.

A fair critique of an explanatory evolutionary paradigm should call for clarifications between interpretations driven by philosophical commitments to naturalism and interpretations necessitated by the data. When naturalists offer conditional or speculative explanations for innovations based on mechanistic processes, it is reasonable to request that they demonstrate empirical evidence supporting the scope and power of mechanistic processes. Even proponents of evolution remark on the need for evidentiary support. At the 2016 Royal Society of London meeting, modern synthesis advocate Douglas Futuyma stated that "empirical evidence is needed to evaluate enthusiastic speculation."[41] James Shapiro, EES proponent and originator of the theory of natural genetic engineering, acknowledged the same:

> How natural genetic engineering leads to major new inventions of adaptive use remains a central problem in evolution science. To address this problem experimentally, we need to do more ambitious laboratory evolution research looking for complex coordinated changes in the genome.

If we are able to observe cells coordinating NGE functions to make useful complex inventions in real time, major questions arise. How do they perceive what may be useful? We need to find out whether there are feedbacks between sensory inputs and genome changes. Is there any connection between the biological challenge and the NGE output? Cells can adjust other activities to meet the goals of survival, growth and reproduction. Can they do the same with DNA changes? We need to figure out how to do experiments on this.[42]

To CNE proponents we would say the same, "Empirical evidence is needed to evaluate enthusiastic speculation." Especially when part of the impetus behind advancing the CNE is to squelch antievolutionists rather than offer something verifiable or predictive within the evolutionary narrative. (See page 111, "What Can Natural Selection Accomplish?" and endnote 11.)

Summary

Acquiring new traits sometimes involves the introduction of new genes via gene flow or gene transfer into a population. In other cases, changes in gene sequences, allele frequencies, or epigenetic modifications—changes that are arguably reversible or fluid within a population—may suffice. Alterations in developmental timing and contexts or variations in gene expression and regulatory switches or pathways also produce new traits.

Despite these mechanisms for new trait acquisition (and even morphological rearrangements), many major biological transitions and leaps of increased complexity, which are needed to ascend an evolutionary tree of life, remain inexplicable. Likewise, despite an increased ability to understand and describe complex biological systems and population dynamics, as well as many adaptations and increases in biodiversity, we still lack plausible mechanisms to account for discontinuities between biological types and innovations (or origination) of new genes, pathways, systems, organs, and organisms. The problem of novelty persists despite the best explanatory efforts.

Discussion Questions

1. Using the way evolutionary biologists define *novelty*, does this explanation seem sufficient to drive large-scale evolutionary progressions? What questions should we ask to help make such a determination?

2. Consider the long-term evolution experiment (LTEE) and how it led to a novel trait. Is this result the same thing as innovation? Explain.

3. Does evolutionary developmental biology (evo-devo) generate true novelty? Why or why not?

4. Does extended evolutionary synthesis (EES) generate true novelty? Why or why not?

5. Of the evolutionary mechanisms that have been proposed to account for innovation, do any seem viable? Explain.

Chapter 11

What to Do with Teleology in Evolution?

by Anjeanette Roberts

There is, of course, nothing conscious or intentional in the action of natural selection. A biological species does not say to itself, "Let me try tomorrow (or one million years from now) to grow in a different soil, or use a different food . . . . " Natural selection is at one and the same time a blind and creative process.[1]

—Theodosius Dobzhansky

The word "teleology" has its roots in the Greek word *telos*, meaning "end" or "purpose." Evolution does not have any predetermined goal in mind. It is a series of processes that, all along the way, have no purpose driving it forward. At the heart of it, evolution has *purposeless* processes acting within populations on variations that emerge from random mutations and genome-altering mechanisms. A very basic description of evolution articulates the absence of teleology clearly: time + chance = change.

A common evolutionary claim asserts that more complex genomes and organisms emerge primarily from an accrual of random changes to genetic sequences and widespread neutral drift within populations. Yet, observed differences seem directed to increased complexity in system-level hierarchies (cellular, organismal, and ecological). The hierarchies are well-integrated and extremely unlikely to result from any series of random changes. Evolution is largely dysteleological (purposeless), yet organisms fit together in highly complex, purpose-filled systems. It seems evolution has a problem with teleology.

Evolution is largely dysteleological (purposeless), yet organisms fit together in highly complex, purpose-filled systems.

Randomness and Teleology

Within an evolutionary paradigm, the cause-and-effect mechanisms that generate genetic variation are blind to potential outcomes or functions. For this reason, many describe the mutational process as random. I tend to dislike this word. It is a perfectly good word—when it is referring to its probabilistic or mathematical meaning of independence between two variables (synonymous with *chance*). Sometimes, however, it is used carelessly and indicates a mere lack of causal understanding.

We now know that some biological changes once considered random are, at least sometimes, constrained and correlated with other characteristics of genome structure, biochemistry, function, or composition. In such cases, mutations themselves are random and independent of any relationship to final functional outcomes, *but* they are not necessarily random or independent in respect to structure, biochemistry, or composition at the site of mutation. So, care needs to be taken when using the word *random* in relationship to changes incurred by biological systems and the introduction of mutations to genetic sequences.

Care is also needed regarding causes that initiate mutational processes. Some causes are not necessarily random, although they may not be understood or identified in most instances. Many epigenetic and environmental factors trigger increased biomolecular/cellular activities that result in higher mutational rates. So, initiation of mutations may also be nonrandom phenomena.

Nuances aside, *random* is likely the best word for addressing the nature of biological mutations. Often used in place of *random* are words such as *chance* or *unguided* and less often, *unplanned*, *undirected*, or *unpredictable*. Use of these alternate terms can be helpful, but often they confound cause-and-effect mechanistic descriptions with philosophical implications.

In the absence of a supernatural reality, these words are grammatical and functional equivalents. But in a reality that entails the supernatural these words have different connotations and imply different potential causal relationships and explanations. In a theistic reality, *chance*, *unguided*, and *unplanned* all preclude any intent or intervention of a deity or designer.

Yet *randomness* need not exclude design. Randomness may be a feature of some processes employed in a designed system of greater structure and complexity. *Random*, therefore, may be the most neutral word in respect to metaphysical positions for describing the processes linking mutations and phenotypic outcomes. However, randomness and teleological processes are not intuitively compatible. Certainly, randomness does not entail teleology. Acknowledging this, many scientists end the conversation here.

Proponents of the modern synthesis tenaciously defend natural selection acting on random mutations as the driving force in evolutionary progressions. There is no room, no need for *telos*. They claim natural selection's iterative processes explain the accrual of functional complexity.

Appealing to Genetic Algorithms

Some evolutionists appeal to genetic algorithms (GAs) to demonstrate the sufficiency of basic evolutionary mechanisms to produce more complex outcomes from random iterative processes. However, GAs don't get us closer to producing complexity by means of natural selection. They only highlight the need for a goal (teleology) in order for evolutionary-like mechanisms to achieve anything significant.

GAs are computer programs designed to evolve solutions toward an end goal set by the programmer. Solutions are generated through iterations of the program that introduce manipulations of the input (usually strings of binary data). The manipulations are analogous to mutation, crossover, reproduction, inversions, duplications, and other evolutionary processes. Each modified string is evaluated based on a fitness or test function that selects the winners for subsequent rounds of manipulation. The fitness test selects those best able to reach the programmed goal. Therefore, it is not reflective of natural selection's blindness. Natural selection's only test function in each round is environmentally specified and based only on an ability to survive and reproduce.

In *Evolution 2.0*, Perry Marshall compares successful GAs to cheats "with preprogrammed parameters guiding the GA to a specific desired outcome. They always carefully protect the rest of the code from the same kind of random mutations that Darwinism claims cause evolution."[2] Genetic algorithms can be used to model multivariable system dynamics. They can even produce something new and valuable (analog circuits), but even then, successful GAs are designed with specific constraints or precise goals. So, GAs cannot save evolution from the teleological challenge; in fact, they highlight the problem.

Unlike successful GAs, natural selection cannot predict which mutations will *eventually* provide a survival advantage or which will offer future fitness for increasing complexity. It cannot help a cell or organism plan ahead for what will be beneficial in future environments or scenarios. It works only in current environments, applying selective pressures on organisms as they compete for survival. Preloading a genome for unforeseen challenges is some other kind of magic at work. Unless it turns out that there are universal rules woven into the fabric of nature—not just in chemistry or physics, but in the biological and biochemical realms of science—that dictate random changes toward an unseen, unknowable, unspecified goal, then an appeal to such power in nature is wishful storytelling. Any teleology (real or apparent) must be imposed from the outside or built into the system itself—or both.

What's Driving Evolution If Not Randomness and Natural Selection?
Recognizing that randomness and natural selection have yet to demonstrate any functionally complex outcomes (see chapter 10), others take a more deterministic view of nature. They appeal to a structuralist view (or natural biological law model). Those who adopt a natural law model similar to the anthropic principle for cosmology envision an underlying structure to the universe that heralds a biological anthropic principle. Just as there are physical and chemical laws, innate parameters of nature limit the potential paths and outcomes that govern biochemical systems. I became familiar with these concepts decades ago in the writings of Paul Davies (who postulated unidentified biochemical laws) and, then later, in the writings of structuralist Michael Denton.

Like those wielding the anthropic principle in cosmology, one can appeal to a structuralist model as directly pointing to a designer or lawgiver that set up and finely tuned the whole system to achieve a desired end. Or one can adopt a more materialistic approach, arguing these are just given characteristics for this universe that just happens to be this way. In either approach, designed or innate features constrain biological systems in a directive manner. Teleology is either intrinsic to the system or it is an illusion, inexplicable except for the chance (but fortunate for us) parameters accompanying this universe. Many evolutionary creationists or theists might adopt the intrinsic design argument within a structuralist view; nontheists or materialists, the latter.

Still others, often proponents of extended evolutionary synthesis (EES) or natural genetic engineering, take the puzzling position of endowing nature with anthropomorphic qualities, such as agency or volitional intent (e.g., selfish genes or clever viruses). (See "Cells as Agents of Change" on page 115.) Even modern synthesis proponents will adopt similar anthropomorphic language to describe natural selection or nature itself. Although many people who adopt this language say it's just a manner of speaking, it is not *just* a manner of speaking. It is language that skirts the difficult questions of cause-and-effect in complex biological systems and further highlights the teleology problem.

Why Anthropomorphize Nature?

The strong trend toward anthropomorphism is, in part, because cells and invading microbes *appear* clever and selfish. The dance between an organism's cells and invading microbes is extremely intricate and complex. It's hard to miss the choreography; therefore, it's relatively easy to get sucked into talking about microbes and cells in humanlike ways. This is another example where naturalists must, as Francis Crick admonished biologists, constantly tell themselves that the apparent design in nature is not real.[3] Invoking anthropomorphic language only exacerbates the issue.

Use of anthropomorphic language highlights how nonteleological, naturalistic evolutionary processes fail to account for relatively rapid changes and the prevalent discontinuities observed in the complexity and diversity of life. So, naturalists are forced to fall back on language that suggests purpose and volition as innate characteristics of biomolecules, cells, or nature itself. If one claims that life's history resulted from undirected evolutionary processes, one shouldn't use verbiage that implies intention or purpose of any kind.

Although some EES evolutionists go so far as to attribute intention and volition to cellular and biomolecular entities (see chapter 9), they admit ignorance as to how this might be possible. In *Evolution 2.0*, Marshall comments, "We don't know how cells make choices."[4] Perhaps that's because cells *don't make choices*. Viruses and cells do not choose, plan, or scheme. They are not volitional. They do not even evade attack, restrain abnormal or deleterious mutations, or preserve their own existence. Genes are not selfish. Viruses are not clever. Cells do not seek their own survival. Such whimsical language is widespread and difficult to avoid in published, peer-reviewed scientific works on evolution.

Whether as a literary flare or as real actions, one shouldn't endow cells and molecules with such capacity. I find this a disturbing trend that often obstructs discovery of, or belies, actual scientific mechanisms. It seems a bit like a regression to animistic concepts. Carried to an extreme, extrapolations become arguably *unscientific* and produce fringe theories such as the Gaia theory, whose proponents argue that Earth or its ecosystem is a self-regulating system directing its own development and experience.[5]

Reasoning to Best Explanation and Teleology

As we discuss in chapter 10, many scientists find natural selection and pan-adaptationism untenable. Despite a necessity for natural selection to work through gradual, stepwise advancements that demonstrate a basic continuum of adaptive survival of the fittest, nature is filled with persistent discontinuities and leaps in complexity. EES proponents, neutral theorists (including CNE proponents), and structuralists (not mutually exclusive categories) are equally harsh on the failure of natural selection to adequately provide or demonstrate plausible provisions for major biological transitions. But by abandoning the slow, functionally adaptive progressions (panadaptationism) of natural selection, these critics still face the same directional increase-in-complexity problem; they face a real or apparent teleology problem.

EES advocates fill the gaps by endowing molecules or cells with volitional agency. Structuralists insist the governing laws of the universe must be "directing" life's transitions according to set constraints. Others abandon natural selection's panadaptationism and instead adopt neutral theory, proposed and mathematically modeled by Motoo Kimura in 1968.

In neutral theory, it is primarily neutral mutations, especially large-scale neutral mutations occurring via macromutational mechanisms, accruing within populations over time that drive complexity and evolutionary progression. While neutral theory provides genetic grounds for *de novo* gene generation, constructive neutral evolution (CNE) in particular provides theoretical paths for apparent leaps in complexity. (See chapter 9, "Natural Selection in Developing Evolutionary Theories," "Cells as Agents of Change," and related endnotes.) These theoretical leaps result from neutral accrual of gradual changes and developmental shifts that result in large-scale, morphological changes. The conceptual pathways that CNE proponents propose lead to greater complexity through chance alone. Any teleology is mere illusion.

All these explanations face big challenges. To many critics, they seem more like wishful thinking and theory fitting than experimentally validated mechanisms. I wonder if it will ever be possible to demonstrate any proposed CNE pathway. Furthermore, CNE proponents herald their theory as a rival for intelligent design, rather than as anything demonstrably verifiable or as anything that offers predictive value to research. CNE is steeped in philosophy. It only seems scientific because it restricts itself to naturalistic descriptions. This is clearly seen in one of the CNE's seminal papers where one might read "case histories" as "just-so stories":

Continued failure to consider CNE alternatives impoverishes evolutionary discourse and, by oversimplification, actually makes us more vulnerable to critiques by antievolutionists, who like to see such complexity as "irreducible." Here, we expand on this idea by presenting in more detail "case histories" that illustrate how CNE might have operated in the emergence of several complex systems, including RNA editing, the spliceosome, and the ribosome, and how it might be invoked more broadly as an evolutionary paradigm underlying cellular complexity in general.[6]

Although naturalists try to fit mechanisms into plausible explanations, several conclusions drawn within an evolutionary paradigm in an attempt to deal with teleology are inconsistent with scientific inferences. Some observe that cells, viruses, and nature appear to be clever, and so leap to a conclusion that cells are volitional, self-aware, and intent on self-preservation. Some observe design in processes that appear purposefully directed toward meaningful (functional) goals and conclude these are only illusions. To claim as Crick once did that nature was not designed but rather evolved[7] asserts a belief, not a fact. Those who repeat an assertion of apparent-but-not-real design do not know whether the assertion is true or not. They are not better scientists than those who claim design; they are worse philosophers. They seem to abandon the broad powers of human reasoning and willingly restrict themselves to impoverished imaginings. Harvard biologist Richard Lewontin reflects on this idea (referring to astronomer Carl Sagan):

> We take the side of science in spite of the patent absurdity of some of its constructs, in spite of its failure to fulfill many of its extravagant promises of health and life, in spite of the tolerance of the scientific community for unsubstantiated just-so stories, because we have a prior commitment, a commitment to materialism. It is not that the methods and institutions of science somehow compel us to accept a material explanation of the phenomenal world, but, on the contrary, that we are forced by our a priori adherence to material causes to create an apparatus of investigation and a set of concepts that produce material explanations, no matter how counter-intuitive, no matter how mystifying to the uninitiated. Moreover,

that materialism is an absolute, for we cannot allow a Divine Foot in the door.[8]

I am among the scientifically initiated, yet I am mystified by such commitment and tolerance. And I echo claims of the patent absurdity of some of the constructs and arguments proposed by naturalists.

We see design everywhere; it is obvious. This is why Crick urges biologists to habitually deny *real* design and claim only *apparent* design. In addition to obvious design, much of nature is undeniably purposeful. It is primarily our limited knowledge that keeps us blind to greater purposes as yet undiscovered.

It seems odd to me that scientists whose work is grounded in making logical inferences from the data would continually deny the conclusion reached by many other rational people that design in nature is obvious. Observation gives rise to inferences. If even casual onlookers see design and purpose in complex, hierarchical, information-bearing systems, then surely the burden of proof is on the one who claims design and purpose are not *really* there. One cannot in good faith merely assert that something obvious is not obvious. Outside of evolutionary narratives, the rational conclusion is that design and purpose point to a creator.

Apparent Choice Points to Intricate Engineering

In a world rightly understood as the masterpiece of a brilliant Creator, volition and intent are not characteristics necessary for molecules, viruses, or cells. The Creator would have engineered and endowed living things with extremely complex capacities for adaptation.

Claims that volition and intent exist at molecular, viral, or cellular levels are so irrational as to venture toward the nonsensical. Defining self-replicating *molecules* as living entities and infusing them with teleological powers would solve the evolutionary problem, but the nature of reality and the nature of science would be fundamentally challenged. The order and foundation that secondary cause-and-effect relationships provide for successful scientific inquiry would dissolve into chaos as volition and subjectivity of selfish molecules comes to fruition.[9]

Evolutionary mechanisms are adaptive, but they are adaptive *because* the systems were created with plasticity and capacity to adapt, not because the cell is presciently creative or decisive. Scientists observe cellular responses to stimuli that may look like natural genetic engineering, but which are actually adaptive responses to molecular triggers that were preloaded into complex organismic systems. The distinction here is between a self-aware cell engineering its own fate and survival and an elaborate system engineered with a capacity to respond to environmental cues via myriad processes. The engineered system is far better equipped for adaptation than generally imagined but also has a finite capacity for adaptation. This certainly comports with observations in nature. Such processes function at adaptive levels up through and within speciation, but fail to accommodate extreme leaps in organismic types and result in multiple failures (extinction events throughout geological time) and true discontinuities.

The engineered system is far better equipped for adaptation than generally imagined but also has a finite capacity for adaptation.

Which Creation Model Gives Life Meaning?

For all but the panadaptationists of neo-Darwinism, teleology is a problem. Yet, panadaptationism is broadly denounced as a failed concept among EES and CNE biologists, structuralists, neutral theorists, and intelligent design and progressive creation proponents. Attempts to gloss over the teleology problem by endowing nature with intention or volition seem questionable as well. In stark contrast, the Christian worldview not only endows individual lives with meaning, but also manifests purpose in the divinely engineered design of every cell, creature, and ecosystem. Cells and organisms adapt *by design*—excellent design, in fact. The omniscient God presciently anticipated the types of environmental challenges, stresses, and pressures that would affect given organisms. Therefore, God intentionally endowed them with the mechanisms to survive, thrive, and adapt, not volitionally, but through extremely insightful engineering.

Only God has access to the future, knowing every possible environmental feature that creatures on Earth would face as Earth's ecosystems change through time. The divine Engineer used common designs of body plans, metabolic pathways, and biochemistry to form intricate networks of life, from the smallest cell to the grandest ecosystems. The shared biochemical and metabolic pathways allow experimentation and discovery in model organisms with applications across multiple phyla. Our discoveries in simple organisms have profound applications for human health and thriving and for creation care.

A progressive creation model holds that the ultimate purpose—the teleology—of all life is to show God's power and wisdom, to bless humanity, and in a profound act of love, to allow humanity to *see* the design and enjoy uncovering its wondrous manifestations in nature. A progressive creation model gives life *meaning*.

Life is not a happy accident of random or unguided secondary causes. Life comes only from life. For anything to arise out of a strictly materialistic universe and ask, "Why?" is a ludicrous concept. Human life is the pinnacle and intent of creation. All our longings and questions, together with all nature, point us to the personal Creator God of Christianity.

I have encountered many scientists and theologians who think evolution's greatest challenge to Christianity is to the concept of God creating humanity in his image. I think this is a major theological issue that needs addressing by those who espouse an evolutionary creationist position (see chapter 25). However, it is not the sole primary challenge facing integration between evolutionary theory and Christian orthodoxy. Another primary obstacle is the lack of purpose in evolutionary explanations. Evolutionary creationists must tackle both of these issues as they seek to harmonize God's revelation in nature and Scripture.

Discussion Questions

1. Define teleology and how it challenges evolution.

2. What philosophical implications do words like *chance, unguided,* and *unplanned* carry?

3. Do genetic algorithms (GAs) produce complexity by mechanisms similar to natural selection? Explain.

4. How do proponents of evolution employ anthropomorphism in their descriptions of evolutionary processes?

5. The author notes that "observation gives rise to inferences." If all

parties agree that there is at least *apparent* design, can scientists' observations test for whether the design is apparent or actual?

Chapter 12

Can Evolutionary Processes Generate New Information?

by Fazale Rana

Many intelligent design proponents and creationists challenge the validity of evolutionary theory by insisting that its mechanisms can't generate new information. In fact, these thinkers maintain that this problem is insurmountable—and, therefore, is the singular challenge confronting biological evolution.

Evolutionary mechanisms must generate new biological information to account for the origin and history of life (from simple to complex). Life scientists believe that evolutionary processes can do so.

So, which is it? Can evolution produce new information or not?

I agree with both positions. I think that, *in principle*, evolutionary mechanisms can create information. At the level of microevolution and microbial evolution, natural processes can account for the generation of new information. However, I question if these mechanisms can generate biochemical information *under the conditions of early Earth* in support of abiogenesis. I also question if these mechanisms can truly generate biological novelty. (See chapter 10.)

Because of space limitations, I am going to focus on the origin of biochemical systems. I am not going to address the capacity of evolutionary mechanisms to generate new information *after* biochemical systems are in place. (See chapter 10.) That is, I am not going to address the information question in the context of molecular evolution. There are two reasons why I have adopted this approach. First, my expertise is biochemistry and origin-of-life research. Second, I think this issue is much more foundational to the origin-of-life question than to the capacity of evolutionary processes to modify existing biochemical information, once it is in place.

Before anything, however, we need to define our terms. Remember, definitions matter.

What Do We Mean by *Information*?

In the same way that ambiguity surrounds key concepts such as *life, species, novelty,* and *evolution,* the definition of *information* can be equivocal. Many times, the dialogue regarding the capacity of evolutionary processes to generate information happens without participants taking the time to define what is meant by *information.*

> How do we define information in a biological context? In many respects, there is no singular answer.

So, how do we define *information* in a biological context? In many respects, there is no singular answer. In my view, the best way to answer this question is to turn to *Information and the Origin of Life* (1986).[1] In this classic book, renowned scientist Bernd-Olaf Küppers describes two distinct approaches for defining biological information.

The first approach relates the concept of biological information to Claude Shannon's classical information theory published in 1948. Concerned with problems in telecommunications, Shannon was interested in the storage, transmission, and loss of character sequences (alphabets, numbers, ones, and zeroes) when transmitted electronically. He wanted to monitor the loss quantitatively during data transmission. He wasn't concerned about the *meaning* ascribed to the sequence or the loss of that meaning.

Shannon defined information (sometimes called Shannon information or syntactic information) as a sequence of characters, with the information content of the sequence inversely related to the probability of assembling the sequence by chance. Specifically, the lower the probability of forming the sequence by chance, the greater the information content.

As a case in point, the sequence of nucleotides (abbreviated as A, G, C, and T) that comprise a region of DNA corresponds to syntactic information, regardless of whether the sequence is functional. If the probability of forming an encoding DNA sequence is the same as the probability of assembling a junk DNA region, then sequences harbor the same amount of syntactic information.

Information in nucleic acids (or proteins) consists of nucleotides (or amino acids), but some sequences direct biochemical activities and others don't. In other words, some of these sequences harbor "meaning." This important point brings us to back to Küppers's scheme for defining biological information.

According to Küppers's first approach, biological information also consists of two additional dimensions beyond the syntactic level. He dubs these two levels "semantic" and "pragmatic." The semantic dimension refers to the meaning ascribed to a sequence and the pragmatic dimension refers to the action that the information elicits, activities "agreed upon" ahead of time by the sender and recipient. In this scheme, semantic information includes the syntactic dimension, while pragmatic information includes both the semantic and syntactic. It is challenging to quantify semantic and pragmatic information. At the cellular level both dimensions are defined by the genetic code and the processes of transcription, translation, and the folding and post-translational modification of proteins.

According to Küppers, the second way to think about biological information is to recognize that the information in biochemical systems consists of a set of instructions instantiated within the biomolecules themselves. These instructions direct biomolecular activities and, hence, the cell's operations. This is called algorithmic information.

From an algorithmic standpoint, the more complex the instructions, the greater the information content. Consider a DNA sequence of alternating nucleotides—AGAGAGAG and so on. The instructions needed to generate this sequence are:

1. Add an A,
2. Add a G,
3. Repeat first and second steps x number of times, where x corresponds to the length of the DNA sequence divided by two.

What about a DNA sequence that corresponds to a typical gene? In effect, because there is no pattern to that sequence, the instructions needed to create it are the sequence itself. In other words, a much greater amount of algorithmic information resides in a gene than in a repetitive DNA sequence.

Is Biochemical Information Digital or Analog?
Another question we must consider centers around the nature of biochemical information. Does it have an analog or digital format? The answer is both.

Biochemists have long recognized that nucleotide sequences encode digital information. So, too, do amino acid sequences that make up proteins. Digital information refers to the discrete, discontinuous representation of information. Both the nucleotide and amino acid sequences represent a succession of discrete units just like ones and zeroes. In this framework, the messenger RNA transcribed from a gene consists of an isolated piece of code specifying the digital information (i.e., amino acid sequence), which the cell's machinery uses to build a specific protein.

Biochemists Georgi Muskhelishvili and Andrew Travers pointed out that the information harbored in DNA also shows analog characteristics. Analog information is the representation of information in continuously varying format.[2] They note that nucleotide sequences not only encode information to make proteins, but also impact the higher order architecture of DNA, which houses the analog information.

Most people recognize DNA's iconic double-helical structure. What may not be well-known is that the double helix can adopt a variety of higher order shapes. And these higher order shapes influence gene expression.

Muskhelishvili and Travers point out that the digital and analog information are coupled intrinsically through the nucleotide sequence. That is, the nucleotide sequence simultaneously specifies the digital information of the gene and the higher order architectures of the genome, which in turn influence the expression of the digital information found in the gene.

They also note that proteins that interact with DNA aid in the coupling of digital and analog information. Proteins bind to specific nucleotide sequences. Once bound, these biomolecules help to promote and stabilize higher order architectures. In other cases, bound proteins destabilize the double helix. Basically, proteins play a role in regulating the expression of the digital information in the genome through the analog component.

Proteins also contain analog information in the higher order structures that form when protein chains fold. Protein analog and digital information is coupled through the amino acid sequence. The amino acid sequence determines the three-dimensional structures of proteins. It is the protein's overall three-dimensional shape that is a key contributor to its function, or the functional expression of the information encoded in DNA. The three-dimensional structure gives the information in proteins—and, ultimately, the information in the DNA sequences that encode the information to make proteins—meaning.

In isolation, nucleotide sequences have no meaning in and of themselves. The meaning ascribed to DNA sequences is established through codes, such as the genetic code, the histone binding code, and so on.

The point of this discussion is to illustrate just how nuanced the concepts of information can be and how challenging it can be to apply these concepts to biochemical information. Biochemical information is complex. So, now let's turn our attention to the question: does evolution have a problem explaining the origin of information?

Can Evolutionary Mechanisms Generate Information?

Often, when creationists and intelligent design proponents explore the capacity of evolutionary mechanisms to create biochemical information, they portray the question as a probability problem. They usually focus on proteins. The question becomes, what is the likelihood that the proteins needed to carry out essential life functions could form through random assembly of amino acids?

Whether they realize it or not, creationists and intelligent design proponents are treating biochemical information as syntactic information when they ask this question. Let me explain. The cell employs 20 different genetically encoded amino acids to make proteins. These amino acids possess a range of chemical and physical properties. In principle, the 20 amino acids can link up in any of the possible sequence combinations.

Each amino acid sequence gives the protein chain a specific chemical and physical profile along its length. The amino acids in a protein chain interact with one another in three-dimensional space. Some amino acids attract while others repel. Because of these interactions, the amino acid sequence and the overall chemical and physical properties along the chain fold the protein into a uniquely complex and precise three-dimensional structure. The protein's three-dimensional architecture determines the function it assumes in the cell. To summarize, the protein's amino acid sequence determines its structure and, hence, function.

Not all hypothetical amino acid sequences are equal. Presumably, some will form proteins with useful functions. Others would produce proteins that are "junk" to the cell. These junk proteins adopt three-dimensional shapes that have no biochemical utility. The question then becomes, when treated as a probability problem, what is the likelihood that the proteins needed to carry out essential life functions could form through random assembly of amino acids?

In their book, *The Mystery of Life's Origin*, chemists Charles Thaxton, Walter Bradley, and Roger Olsen argue that, in the absence of any chemical competition with other chemical compounds and biologically irrelevant amino acids, the probability of getting the right amino acid in a specific position in a protein molecule is 1.25 percent. (There is a 50 percent chance of natural processes randomly selecting a left-handed amino acid; a 50 percent chance of joining the two amino acids in the appropriate chemical bond; and a roughly 5 percent chance of selecting the right amino acid.) Therefore, the probability of undirected processes assembling a protein 100 amino acids in length becomes roughly one chance in 10^{191}. It should be noted that typical proteins are several hundred amino acids in length.

In effect, there is no chance that undirected processes could assemble even a relatively small protein made up of a specified sequence. Bradley and Thaxton put it this way:

> If we assume that all carbon on earth exists in the form of amino acids and that the amino acids are allowed to chemically react at the maximum possible rate of 10^{12}/s for one billion years (the greatest possible time between the cooling of the earth and the appearance of life), we must still conclude that it is incredibly improbable ($\sim 10^{-65}$) that even one functional protein would be made.[3]

This seems like a sufficiently compelling argument—but it has one chief failing. It doesn't consider the semantic properties of amino acid sequences. These properties are influenced by the functional equivalency of amino acids in the protein's structure, the physicochemical constraints on protein structures, and the structure of protein space.

Functional Equivalency

Probability calculations of this sort neglect the fact that some proteins with different amino acid sequences share the same structure and activity (i.e., proteins with different amino acid syntactic information have the same semantic information). This similarity stems from the fact that some amino acid positions can be varied freely with no observed effect on the protein's structure and function, others can be varied to a limited extent, and some cannot be varied at all. This means that a number of amino acid sequences can be biologically indistinguishable. Biochemists refer to this phenomenon as functional equivalency. When functional equivalency is accounted for, the analysis asks, what is the probability that a protein of a specific *function* (not sequence) and three-dimensional structure would have emerged through undirected processes?

Biochemists can't properly determine this type of probability. We simply lack a full understanding of the relationship among amino acid sequence, protein structure, and protein function. In the absence of full knowledge, biophysicist Hubert Yockey estimated this probability for the protein cytochrome C.[4]

Cytochrome C, which is involved in energy-harvesting pathways, contains about 110 amino acids. It is found throughout the living realm and is thought to be one of the most evolutionarily ancient proteins. Biochemists have determined the cytochrome C amino acid sequence for numerous organisms. Yockey used this sequence data to estimate the range of variability for each amino acid position in this protein by aligning and comparing all known cytochrome C sequences.

With some understanding of functional equivalency in hand, Yockey determined that the probability of random chemical events stumbling upon a *functionally equivalent* cytochrome C to be on the order of one chance in 10^{75}.

So, by simply considering functional equivalency, the probability of producing a functional cytochrome C plummets from one chance in 10^{191} to one chance in 10^{75}.

Protein Sequence Space

Protein sequence space refers to all possible amino acid sequence combinations that conceivably exist. Of all those sequences, some are functional, others are not. Some people compare protein sequence space to the ocean and the functional sequences to islands. How many "islands" are in sequence space and what is the separation among them?

Many people assume that the population of functional islands in protein sequence space is sparse because proteins are intolerant to a number of changes in amino acid composition (substitutions cause loss in function). So, not only was sequence space assumed to be lightly populated, the islands also appeared to feature steep cliffs.

No one knows what protein space really looks like. The popular conception may well be incorrect. For example, in 2010, scientists from Spain reported that while the islands do possess steep cliffs, the ocean is richly populated with functional regions.[5] The researchers showed that at any point in time 98 percent of amino acid positions cannot be substituted without the protein losing function, but eventually greater than 90 percent of the amino acid residues in a protein can be altered. This seeming paradox is explained as follows: Once one amino acid is changed, it allows invariant positions to become tolerant to changes and freely altered positions to become invariant.

Instead of an ocean populated with a few islands, the researchers believe that protein sequence space is occupied by a "wide-mesh net spanning a large part of sequence space." If these results stand up, it means the likelihood of evolution randomly building functional, information-rich molecules may not be that unthinkable.

Physicochemical Constraints

In effect, it may not matter what protein sequence space looks like. Even though protein sequence space might be vast, physicochemical constraints may limit the number of ways proteins can fold into three-dimensional structures.

If a protein consists of 150 amino acids, then there are 20^{150} possible sequences. (This represents a vast amount of syntactic information in the amino acid sequence.) Biochemists estimate that a protein made of 150 amino acids can fold in 10^{68} possible ways. The possibilities seem endless—$(20^{150})^{68}$ potential three-dimensional structures. Yet, biochemists have found that there are only 10^3 protein folds that exist in nature because of physicochemical constraints on protein folding.[6] The basis for the restricted folding is complex and is beyond the scope of this chapter. Suffice it to say, this observation alone makes random assembly of functional proteins a distinct possibility.

> **We really don't have enough fundamental understanding of the relationship between amino acid sequence, protein structure, and function to perform proper probability calculations.**

We really don't have enough fundamental understanding of the relationship between amino acid sequence (syntactic information), protein structure (analog information), and function (semantic information) to perform proper probability calculations. Based on what we do understand, the probability of random assembly could be easier than most people imagine.

Can Origin-of-Life Mechanisms Generate Information?

In reality, biochemical information's origin is not a probability problem. Evolutionary biologists do not think that subunit molecules randomly assembled into information-rich molecules. (Such a scenario would be properly modeled as a probability problem.) Instead, they argue, chemical selection is at work. Chemical selection is a collection of complex processes that researchers believe drove and dictated the origin-of-life process on early Earth. Scientists studying life's genesis view these processes as nonrandom. This means that we cannot treat the origin of information-rich molecules as a probability problem.

In the lab, origin-of-life researchers have observed the effects of chemical selection in abiotic (nonbiological) systems throughout the building of proteins and RNA molecules. It is not clear, however, if these selection effects are adequate to yield the full breadth of necessary bio-information molecules. This is still an outstanding question in origin-of-life research.

Still, scientists hold out hope for an affirmative answer based on *in vitro* evolution laboratory studies. Their optimism has been fueled by the success of laboratory studies in which origin-of-life researchers have evolved a wide range of functional ribozymes from random RNA sequences. (See chapter 6.) Based on these types of studies, researchers infer information-rich molecules could have evolved.

As we pointed out in chapter 6, lab studies don't prove that evolutionary processes generated these types of molecular systems *under the conditions of early Earth*. In other words, these studies lack historical geochemical relevance. To be fair, however, we must acknowledge that, *in principle*, evolutionary mechanisms can generate semantic biochemical information.

Can Evolutionary Mechanisms Generate Algorithmic Information?

In my opinion, the proper approach to address evolution's information problem is to view biochemical information as algorithmic. In effect, biochemical systems consist of instructions (algorithms) instantiated in matter and these algorithms tell the matter how to behave. So, the question becomes, can evolutionary mechanisms generate algorithmic information?

Sara Imari Walker and Paul Davies agree with this approach. These two scientists argue that the origin-of-life community has focused wrongly on the genesis of syntactical information in molecules, which Walker and Davies deem as trivial. While Darwinian processes can, *in principle*, produce molecules with syntactical and semantic information, these mechanisms cannot account for the important information that manages and controls biochemical systems.[7]

So, does the evolutionary paradigm have an information problem? In our attempts to respond to this question, it becomes evident just how important it is to carefully define the terms we use. Depending on how we think about the concept of information, we could easily conclude that evolutionary processes can generate information in the context of the origin of life. Yet, *when we view biochemical information as algorithmic information* it becomes evident that evolution does, indeed, have an information problem.

Discussion Questions

1. Define syntactic information and algorithmic information. Why is it important to distinguish between the two?

2. When accounting for biochemical information, is a probability approach the best way to discern whether evolution can generate information? Why or why not?

3. How does functional equivalency affect the likelihood that evolution can produce information?

4. Does evolution indeed have an information problem? Explain.

Chapter 13

Does Evolution Explain
the Fossil Record?

by Sue Dykes

In order to show that a hypothesis is evident, it does not suffice that all the phenomena follow from it; instead, if it leads
to something contrary to a single one of the phenomena, that
suffices to establish its falsity.
—Blaise Pascal (1647)[1]

Perhaps the most contentious prediction of the modern synthesis is the idea
that the fossil record displays gradual diversification from a sequential series of most recent common ancestors. If the prediction were to prove true,
then we should expect to see a combination of two things in the fossil record:

1. We should see gradual acquisition of new traits and gradual diversi-
    fication into new species. This trait acquisition should appear even
    more gradual for species with a long generation time (the time to
    reach sexual maturity) because it takes many generations for muta-
    tions to occur by chance and then become fixed in a whole population.
2. We should see many transitional forms leading up to speciation events,
    following a branch-like pattern and showing clear ancestor-descen-
    dant lineages. Moreover, this should be seen repeatedly, for all lineages,
    not just in a few instances.

The reality is quite different. What we see in the fossil record is more
like a picture of numerous and divergent new species appearing so rapidly
that it is difficult to reconcile their phylogenies (evolutionary histories and

> **Darwin acknowledged that if further research failed to recover transitional forms . . . then his theory, underpinned as it was by gradualism, would be falsified.**

relationships), followed by stasis (no significant evolution) once they are there.

Charles Darwin himself recognized this discontinuous pattern and he was honest about its repercussions. Darwin acknowledged that if further research failed to recover transitional forms—particularly for species that seemingly appear out of nowhere in the fossil record—then his theory, underpinned as it was by gradualism, would be falsified.

In 1972, Niles Eldredge and Stephen Jay Gould proposed a theory of punctuated equilibria[2] as an alternative to Darwin's gradual approach. According to this theory, geological stability and species stasis are the norm for most of Earth's history, but occasionally a major geological or environmental event occurs. The resulting instability and pressures produce rapid splitting of species into new forms that leaves virtually no trace of transition. Punctuated equilibria certainly describes the observed *patterns* of stasis and saltations in the record, but it fails to provide a biologically plausible *mechanism* for achieving the patterns. Nevertheless, many evolutionary biologists still appeal to punctuated equilibria to explain the lack of gradualism in the fossil record.

The Cambrian Explosion

The puzzle that contributed to Darwin's concern about gradualism and the falsification of his theory was a massive discontinuity in the fossil record known as the Cambrian explosion. For about the first 4 billion years of Earth's history (the Precambrian), there was no sign of the animal life we know today. Then, in a short period of geological history, new marine animals representing almost all body plans existing today appeared. They were fully formed and fully complex. Cambrian rocks are dated from about 541 million years ago to about 485 million years ago. They are found all around the world, including in Europe, North America, Siberia, China, and Africa. (Although these sites are now located on dry land, at the time they were covered by seawater.) Darwin had hoped that transitional fossils would be discovered in geological sequences below the Cambrian, and that over time more geological discoveries would solve his dilemma about this abrupt appearance of hugely disparate, fully formed, fully complex body plans.

To appreciate the significance of this dilemma, we need to realize what is meant by "body plan." Different plans involve different arrangements of tissues (e.g., epidural, exoskeletal, muscle, etc.) and body parts (e.g., legs, wings, antenna, etc.). Each novel body plan requires novel proteins regulated by novel genes and novel genomic arrangements. Theoretically, it should take thousands of generations for these processes to occur. The fossil record should show a slow diversification process of speciation from a common ancestor and then branching out from there, until groups of species diverge so much that each group can be classified into different genera, then different genera are grouped into families, families split away into orders, then classes, then phyla.

In reality, from the start of the Cambrian, new body plans were so disparate from each other that they were already separated at the phylum level. More than 20 new phyla can be identified from this period, with no way to link the new life-forms via a branching structure. More problematically for the evolutionary paradigm, there are no evident precursors in the rocks below the Cambrian in any locale across the globe. Evolutionary biologists initially believed that the layer below the Cambrian, known as the Ediacaran, would be loaded with species identifiable as ancestors to the Cambrian fauna, but this is not the case. During the Ediacaran, a few very enigmatic species appeared (also explosively)—including sponges, some segmented, elongated creatures, and fossils argued by some to be primitive mollusks. None, however, are plausible ancestor candidates for any Cambrian species.[3]

Some researchers have also suggested that soft-bodied Cambrian precursors might have existed but would not have preserved well. Thus, their absence from the record might not reflect absence in real life. However, paleontologists have identified soft-bodied specimens in the Ediacaran strata, such as sponge embryos; so, it is highly unlikely that every single soft-bodied precursor, if they had existed, would be absent.

Some researchers try to downplay the explosiveness of the discontinuity. They suggest that life-forms first started appearing late into the Cambrian period (which would have given the Ediacaran biota time to evolve) or that the appearances of the majority of new life-forms were spread over tens of millions of years. They also argue that the length of time taken for new phyla to appear was stretched over a long time. Radioactive dating results do not support these arguments. Not only has uranium-lead dating put the start of the Cambrian faunal explosion at 538.5 million years ago,[4] but research also seems to indicate that the majority of the new animal phyla appeared during a period of about 10 million years in the *middle* of the Cambrian.[5] For comparison, 10 million years is the same amount of time evolutionary biologists presume it took for modern humans to diverge from the chimpanzee and gorilla lineages, which is evolution at the level of family, not order, class, or phylum. No matter how short the generation time must have been for some of these species, it is difficult for biologists to explain the lack of diversification (a slow, branching process) that should normally precede such disparity between high-level taxonomic groups.

Chronology is a problem as well. Following the same neo-Darwinian prediction for diversification, evolutionary scientists expect basal primitive forms in a presumed lineage to appear first, followed by derived (more complex) forms ultimately branching away to form their own phyla or subphyla. In other words, the fossil record should show a logical ancestor-descendant sequential order. Presumed ancestors and descendants should not appear simultaneously with each other.

Many Sudden Appearances

The Cambrian explosion is not the only "biological big bang" (though it is the most rapid and comprehensive). Major extinction events are typically followed by "radiations" of new families or orders of life-forms. Some gradual speciation might be expected in the case of preexisting species that survived the extinction event, if environmental niches suddenly become available, but evolutionary theories do not predict abrupt radiations. Even if such an event occurred only once in history, it would be notably unusual. The fossil record shows *many* radiations:

- Vascular land plants appear explosively about 423 million years ago (mya).
- Flying insects appear, with no precursors, during the Upper Carboniferous period (about 310–290 mya).
- The Permian-Triassic extinction event (about 252–251 mya) wipes out approximately 96 percent of known marine species and about 70 percent of terrestrial forms. Then, in a short period of the early Triassic, new families and orders of life-forms (including novel insect orders, such as beetles and flies) appear on land, sea, and air, replacing almost

all of the wiped-out creatures.

- Flowering plants (angiosperms) appear suddenly during the Cretaceous period (145–65 mya). This event stands as one of the many major transitions in life's history with which evolutionary biologists grapple. Darwin himself called it his "abominable mystery."
- Approximately 97 percent of all angiosperms make their first appearance within a period of about 5 million years.[6]
- Whole orders of modern placental mammals and almost all orders of modern birds appeared within 15 million years of the last dinosaurs being wiped out (about 65 million years ago).[7]

This is only a partial list of dramatic appearances by groups with disparate body forms. Likewise, there are discontinuities in most presumed phylogenetic lineages, which also bear witness to extinctions followed by sudden appearances. Scientists represent the gaps between these periodic turnovers as "ghost lineages." These *inferred* lines of descent are based on the presumption of common ancestry. Researchers build these lines by comparing new traits appearing (or disappearing) over time or computing similarities of sequence at the molecular level. Usually missing along the inferred lines of descent are intermediates that would confirm the presumption.

This absence might be readily explainable if the lineage in question is ancient and if there is very patchy representation of specimens attributed to it. But for recent lineages with good representation of species along them, sudden appearances of new genera require explanation that is plausible from a biological mechanism point of view. Take, for example, human lineage. It is presumed that we descended from a chimpanzee-modern human common ancestor, but inexplicable jumps occur at the genus level. Gaps between genera like *Ardipithecus*, *Australopithecus*, and *Homo ergaster/erectus*, as well as features unique to modern humans (e.g., globular brain shape[8] with novel genes to regulate its function[9]) are significant and require explanation.

So, too, does the recent emergence of language[10] and symbolic behavior, which is currently undisputedly a feature only of modern *Homo sapiens* (see chapter 17.)

Transitional Forms
Despite the lack of evidence in the fossil record for transitional forms (as Darwin would have defined them), paleoanthropologists often claim an abundance of transitional forms. This seeming paradox revolves around the definition of

"transitional forms." Darwin expected to find innumerable transitional forms, appearing in a stepwise manner, with slight modifications to their morphology, leading from a basal species to a new species, and similarly to the next. This should be the pattern for all lineages throughout the fossil record—and it should be the rule, not the exception. We have already seen that this pattern does not exist.

Most paleontologists overlook this issue. They then take the entire ensemble of species from one point in the fossil record to another and define these as transitions, whether or not direct ancestor-descendant lineages can be inferred between fossils. Their reasoning is that species in the fossil record have already branched away from a main, evolving lineage. That lineage itself is not represented by actual fossils. They then appeal to one or two cases where fossils are interpreted as being transitional forms in the Darwinian sense of the word. Such cases are widely used for educational purposes.

These would include the "fishapod" series that documents the presumed sequential transition from lobe-finned fishes to land vertebrates. One of the transitional forms, called *Tiktaalik*, is often held up as a proof of biological evolution (the right transition at the right time). However, the fishapod series has sequence problems. When placed in order of age, features like fins (the ancestral state) and digits (the derived state) should appear in the "right order"—but they don't.

In 2010, paleontologists in Poland discovered a set of footprints that testifies to the emergence of land vertebrates 10 million years *prior* to the first intermediate in the fishapod series to have legs.[11] The footprints also predate the first fishapod thought to have emerged onto land by about 30 million years. An argument could be made that the fishapod species were all present in their "correct" order, but what we observe is simply an artifact of the imperfect fossil record, resulting in the few out-of-order specimens that date later than they should. The fossil record can be patchy. A first or last date of appearance does not always mean that the species concerned was not present for much longer periods of time. This may be the case for fishapods (although 30 million years is a long time for all the later species in the series to be absent). Ideally, evolutionary biologists should refrain from using the fishapod series for educational purposes and should not hold it up as undisputed evidence for evolution, at least until more fossils are discovered and the situation is resolved, if it ever is.

The whale series is the most recent evolutionary icon to appear in textbooks and other educational materials. Modern land mammals started diversifying about 65 million years ago. Yet by about 42 million years ago, the first

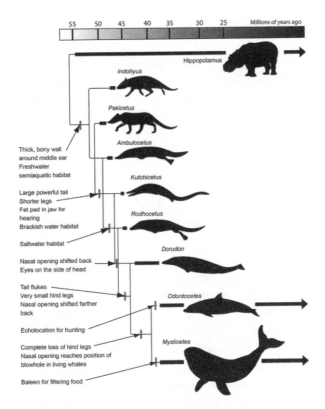

Figure 13: A Pictorial Representation of Whale Evolution

fully aquatic, now-extinct family of whales, called basilosaurids (e.g., *Dorudon* and *Basilosaurus*), were prolific. How a fully terrestrial land mammal evolved into a fully aquatic marine mammal has puzzled researchers from Darwin's day onward. Then some potential intermediates were discovered, predominantly in a floodplain basin in modern-day Pakistan. Not all researchers agree on the original terrestrial mammal in the series; some posit a wolf-like ancestor, others a deer-like ancestor. Most museums and textbooks display specimens such as *Pakicetus* (a wolf-like species) and *Ambulocetus* (the "walking whale") together with protocetids like *Rodhocetus* or *Maiacetus*, all appearing in the record during the period from about 53–47 mya, prior to the generally accepted dates of the first appearance of *Durodon* and *Basilosaurus*. Visual reconstructions of these series are easily accessible.[12]

The trouble with this particular series is that the pre-basilosaurid intermediaries were simple semi-aquatic mammals, no more aquatic perhaps than a giant otter. Their osteological proportions most resembles a putative protocetid like *Maiacetus* (as do those of *Rodhocetus*). *Maiacetus* had weight-bearing hips, strong hind limbs, and "hooflets" at the end of its digits. It certainly had no flippers, tail flukes, or other whale-like features. It lived primarily on land and gave birth on land.[13] Furthermore, researchers have recently become aware of a probable "temporal paradox" with a discovery of a jawbone belonging to a *Basilosaurus* in Antarctica. Several lines of geological evidence suggest that it dates to 49 mya.[14] It is already difficult to argue for the massive body plan changes (both soft and hard tissues, and involving all body systems, not just respiration) necessary for a land mammal to evolve into an aquatic one. If there is almost no time in which to do so—*plus* taking into account the relatively long generation times in whale species—this question would appear unresolvable.

Many More Troubles for Evolutionary Lineages

Other presumed lineages face similar problems, and attempts to draw simple, easily resolvable phylogenies are beset with issues, like saltations (sudden appearances) and temporal paradoxes.

Biogeographic paradoxes occur when species believed to have diverged *after* continents or islands became isolated, somehow appear in areas separated by thousands of kilometers of ocean. The existence of monkeys (known as platyrrhines) in South America is a prominent example. South America split from Africa some 180 mya, well before any monkeys existed. The earliest monkey fossil in South America is from 26 mya. (In Africa, monkeys known as catarrhines are found from about 34 mya.) The only way to explain this is to appeal to "floating islands"—fully equipped with food, water, and shelter—that successfully transported a mating pair of monkeys (or a fortuitously pregnant female) between the two continents.[15]

Evolution of certain complex features occurring even once in any given lineage might be difficult to explain. Morphological inconsistencies give rise to presumed reversals and repetitions of certain tricky traits. Some examples include wings evolving several times in the stick insect family,[16] the re-evolution of mandibular teeth in frogs,[17] and the repeated evolution, in lizards, of giving birth to live young after having laid eggs.[18]

Very similar, highly complex features (e.g., echolocation) have been known to emerge in unrelated species exploiting distinct environments (e.g., dolphins and bats), at all levels of the organism.[19] This is known as convergence (see chapter 19). Finally, some organisms, such as the octopus, simply do not fit genetically into the phylogeny to which scientists believe they belong.[20]

The anticipated Darwinian pattern of transitional forms is not found in the natural world. There is no record of the expected series of slowly modifying intermediate fossils for each lineage. Scientists rightly work to make sense of the record in nature and the model proposed for the origin and development of life. Yet, multiple issues concerning phylogenies—issues that we propose are model-based—have led to unusual conclusions about how morphological transitions can be explained.

Where Do We Stand?

The record of nature shows numerous examples of abrupt, near-simultaneous appearances of disparate new groups of organisms at the level of phylum, order, class, and family. These life-forms are fully complex and fully formed and seem to be without precursors or intermediates. Theories abound that link the patterns of extinctions and replacements to environmental changes,[21] but they lack evidentiary support. Experimental proofs at the genetic level have yet to find viable biological mechanisms that generate the underlying specified complex information required to drive such major innovations in short time frames (see chapter 9).

The biological big bangs observed in the fossil record—which include the origins of life, of biochemical systems, and, as discussed here, of animal life[22]—are well recognized. They provide important discussion points, not only among scientists, but also for those debating evolution and creation. The sudden proliferations of new life-forms seem to be more in keeping with the events described in progressive creation models, both in the details provided and in the order in which they are presented.[23]

> **The sudden proliferations of new life-forms seem to be more in keeping with the events described in progressive creation models.**

For scientists involved in interrogating these "major transitions," research into plausible mechanisms to explain them is of paramount importance and a great deal of work is now being done in this area. Evolutionary biologists are currently working in epigenetics, developmental biology, inheritance mechanisms, the interaction between ecological niches and evolution, and many new areas that they expect will "extend" the modern synthesis.[24] (See "Natural Selection in Developing Evolutionary Theories" and "Cells as Agents of Change" in chapter 9 and "Getting a Leg Up the Tree" and "Can an Extended Evolutionary Synthesis Get Us Any Closer to True Novelty" in chapter 10.) It is still not clear if these explorations will solve the enigma the fossil record represents for the evolutionary paradigm.

Discussion Questions

1. Describe the challenges the Cambrian explosion poses for Darwinian diversification predictions.

2. Summarize six additional dramatic appearances by groups with disparate body forms ("biological big bangs") and how evolutionary models explain them.

3. Do the mechanisms for "transitional forms" such as *Tiktaalik* and whale intermediates seem plausible? Explain.

4. Given the various sudden proliferations of new life-forms in the fossil record, do they fit better in evolutionary or progressive creation models?

Chapter 14

What about the Genetic Similarity between Humans and Chimps?

by Sue Dykes

"Psst, the human genome was never fully sequenced. Some scientists say it should be." So read a June 20, 2017 headline in *Stat News*, an online life sciences magazine.[1] My coauthor Anjeanette Roberts drew similar conclusions in 2015 and 2016.[2] She estimated that about 10 percent of the human genome was not captured in the human reference genome. Experts interviewed for the *Stat News* article estimated that up to 9 percent remained unassembled.

What are we to make, then, of the well-established idea that we are "99 percent chimpanzee"? This iconic precept in evolutionary biology is repeated in most scientific magazines, textbooks, and educational websites. It turns out that when missing sequences and other details are considered the actual similarity appears to be significantly lower.[3]

What Do the Similarities Indicate?

Most evolutionary biologists still appeal to high degrees of sequence similarity and almost identical chromosomal banding patterns to show that the "nested hierarchies" of novel mutations and altered sequence arrangements generally appear in the order predicted of human and primate kinships and the kinships with these groups and other mammals. In the eyes of many people, the similarities are persuasive confirmation of evolutionary relationships.

Evolutionary biologists expect high rates of conservation in the protein-coding regions of related organisms. These sequences should remain largely unchanged by random mutations and should be almost identical in sequence and location along the genome. Thus, when chromosomes are compared and sequences aligned between primate species, there seems to be a confirmation of common ancestry. On the understanding that most proteins that make up the bodies of mammals are similar in their genetic coding and that genomes are fully "functional," strong similarities between the genomes of chimpanzees and humans are not unexpected, whether in coding or noncoding stretches of the genome.

Differences Are Far More Interesting

Ideas that challenge well-entrenched theories invariably take a good deal of time to gain traction. For evolutionary biologists, a 99 percent similarity between the chimpanzee and human genomes is very comforting. It confirms the basic predictions of their guiding theory. Closely related species should show closely matched genetics. And they do! No need to look any deeper?

However, the statistical similarity between the genomes is proving to have less and less biological relevance than might be expected at first glance. As we are about to find out, it is the difference in the way that genes are ultimately expressed—and in the tissues in which they are expressed—that accounts for the high level of phenotypic, cognitive, and behavioral difference between chimpanzees and humans.

Copy Number Variations

The difference in copy number variations (CNVs) still presents a problem for calculating the statistical difference in human and chimp genomes. CNVs refer to sections of the genome that are repeated, with the repetitious sequences varying from individual to individual and even from tissue to tissue for an individual. CNVs comprised of highly repetitive sequences pose an exceptional challenge for statistical comparisons of genome sequences.[3] Some CNVs are specific to chimps; others are specific to humans. Sometimes, whole genes occur in differing numbers of copies. Researchers are just beginning to study the relevance of CNVs to the human-chimp relationship. These gene copies may have even greater impact on differences between chimpanzees and humans than currently imagined.

Many of the human-specific CNVs appear to be involved in brain function, size, and development,[4] and these extra copies are mostly expressed in areas that "make us human." They include genes that code for high neuro-adaptive function involved in brain development and in the complex formation of the cerebral cortex, which supports complex thought.[5] For example, some CNVs are specific to neurons found in the human frontal cortex, which controls motor functions, problem solving, language, social behavior, and other functions.[6]

There are instances where humans have reduced copy numbers of genes that are in higher number in chimpanzees and other primates. For example, chimps carry more copies of a gene that causes reduced growth of the forebrain than do humans.[7] With extra (or fewer) copies of genes being expressed in areas of the brain that control function for cognitive capacities, it is understandable that CNVs alone account for many of the behavioral and cognitive differences between humans and chimpanzees. This is true of other body systems as well. Extra copies of immunity-related genes in humans are thought to provide a more diverse reservoir of sequences that enable rapid adaptation to disease.

In the case of some CNVs, one-on-one alignments of the respective human and chimp genes will show identical or near-identical sequences. This contributes to the 99 percent idea, but if, as I've pointed out, additional or fewer copy numbers up- or down-regulate gene expression, *particularly in the brain*, then it is this gene expression that accounts for major differences between humans and chimpanzees. Percentages of similarity then become less relevant.

Insertions and Deletions
Known as indels, the insertions and deletions of DNA segments within genomes also account for genetic differences between humans and chimps. Many of these indels are small (less than 100 base pairs in length) and affect only parts of genes and noncoding regulatory regions. One study identified over 840,000 small, human-specific indels that affect over 7,000 genes and about seven times as many pseudogenes. (See chapter 23.) In sequences surrounding the genes affected by these human-specific indels, the researchers also identified an enrichment of regulatory factors that impact transcription and translation.[8] Other studies have concentrated on larger indels, particularly insertions that effectively account for brand-new gene sequences, sometimes called "orphan genes," found only in the human genome. (The conservative estimate for these novel genes is 300.) It is significant to note that orphan genes are primarily expressed in the brain, particularly the prefrontal cortex, and in the testes.[9] (See chapter 10 for more on orphan genes.)

Research suggests that the testes may well be a "crucible" for new gene evolution. Once formed in the testes as "young retrogenes," the new genes are believed to be transmitted to offspring and then retrotransposed into other areas of the autosomal nuclear genome.[10] Although these novel protein-coding sequences number only in the hundreds, there are over 20,000 human-specific insertions involving these limited number of sequences in non-protein-coding regions, most of which scientists believe are involved in regulation.[11]

Indels account for only a small percentage of the difference in nuclear DNA sequence between chimpanzees and humans. However, when we consider the actual tissues in which human-specific genes are expressed, a small statistical divergence translates into important physiological and cognitive differences.

The same holds true for mitochondrial DNA (mtDNA). Here the one-on-one percentage sequence similarity has been recalculated to be at 91.1 percent.[12] The degree of difference in mtDNA is significant because the mitochondria are the "workhorses" of the cell, responsible for energy metabolism. Clinical studies imply that mutations to this genome lead to neurological- and muscular-degenerative conditions.[13]

Differences in Gene Expression

Differential gene expression also accounts for disparities (mainly in the brain). Even if corresponding genes in humans and chimps are identical (or nearly identical), the way these genes are deployed in the two species may differ. Other sequences code for proteins that interact with these genes and are instrumental in turning them on and off, so that more or less of the relevant proteins are produced. These proteins are called transcription factors. To exert their influence, they must bind to DNA near the gene they regulate. The transcription factor binding sites often have numerous *Alu* sequences (short, repetitive nuclear sequences). (Geneticists initially considered these *Alu* sequences nonfunctional junk. They now have evidence that these sequences play a role in developmental processes.) *Alu* sequences are primate specific and play critical roles in the formation of neurological networks.[14] Even small differences in the numbers of interacting transcription factors in humans and chimps may coordinate big differences in gene expression in the brains of the two species.[15] Other sequences previously thought to be noncoding also affect gene expression differences between humans and the great apes, including certain pseudogenes, endogenous retroviruses, short and long interspersed nuclear elements, and other noncoding RNAs.[16]

Splicing also contributes to genetic complexity and the differences between humans and primates. A gene is made up of exons and introns. Exons are sections that code for regions of the final protein products; introns are

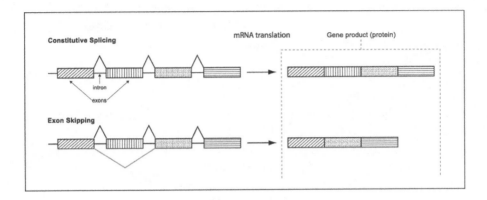

Figure 14: Gene Structure and Alternate Splicing

noncoding sections. After DNA is transcribed into RNA, a molecular machine called a spliceosome cuts out the introns and then "stitches together" the exons. Alternative splicing occurs when exons are stitched together in variant combinations. This allows one gene to produce several different proteins. Additionally, genes can sometimes also be "read" in both directions along the DNA strand, potentially doubling the number of proteins that any single gene can produce. This means that the same genes in humans and chimps can be spliced differently to produce different proteins.

Almost half of the genes examined for a 2012 study[17] showed evidence of alternative splicing between chimpanzees and humans. Moreover, alternative splicing sites are often tissue specific. In the same study, the most common cases of alternative splicing between humans and primates were found in the cerebellum, the part of the brain that not only controls all motor functions and motor learning, but is also believed to have a role in higher cognitive functioning and language.[18]

Epigenetics is the study of features that do not involve any changes to the sequence of the genome itself, but, instead, act "over and above" the DNA code (see chapter 7). One of the epigenetic mechanisms that plays a vital role in gene expression is methylation, which involves the addition of a methyl group (CH_3) to nucleotides at strategic sites along the DNA. Each methylation site acts like an off switch that prevents expression of a specific gene. Methylation patterns are tissue-specific and, once again, one of the main organs showing differences in methylation sites between chimpanzees and humans is the brain.[19]

Methylation also affects the way chromosomes are "packaged up," which also influences gene expression. For example, methylation sites can alter the binding activity of histones. Histones are alkaline proteins that bind to the genome and behave like the bobbin on a sewing machine, winding up a strand of DNA into coils so that it can eventually be packaged into more and more complex three-dimensional structures that ultimately make up chromosomes (see figure 7.1). In areas where there is high binding of histones, genes tend to be inactivated, while genes that need to be expressed at greater levels have less histone binding. Geneticists have conducted genome-wide comparisons of prefrontal cortex brain cells in chimpanzees and humans. Their results showed that humans have a starkly different amount of a methylated histone that affects regulation of transcription start sites for genes known to have clinical implications in neuropsychiatric conditions.[20] Researchers believe these human-specific modifications play an important role in the gene networks affecting cognitive functions that differentiate humans from chimpanzees.

Cell-Surface Sugars and Brain Biochemistry

There are also biochemical factors believed to cause marked differences between the brains of humans and chimpanzees. As in most mammals, chimp cells have sugars that attach to their surfaces. Biologists think these sugars play a big role in several physiological processes (including immunological responses) and may affect development. In other vertebrates, there are low levels of these surface sugars on brain cells. Humans, however, totally lack a particular type of surface sugar, called GL-neur or Neu5Gc. In other animals, GL-neur ultimately plays a critical role in the development of neural plasticity, outgrowth, and myelination. It is thought that the total absence of this brain-surface sugar may promote larger, more complex, and more plastic brains in humans.[21]

Chromosome 2

Another stark difference between chimpanzees and humans is that the former have 24 pairs of chromosomes, while the latter have 23. Evolutionary scientists hypothesize that at some stage in the human lineage ancestral chromosomes 2A and 2B fused to form human chromosome 2 (see chapter 22). Meanwhile, these chromosomes remained distinct in the chimpanzee lineage. Regardless of how human chromosome 2 came to be different from that of the chimp, genes located along this chromosome are of special interest when it comes to explaining some of the more important disparities between chimpanzees and humans.[22]

The long (q) arm of human chromosome 2 is sensitive to change. Clinical studies have demonstrated that mutations or deletions have direct impact on human intellectual capacities, combined with other problems such as developmental delays, impaired speech, and skeletal abnormalities.[23] Researchers have also identified differences of over 10 percent in sequences found at this chromosome's "relic centromere" (the adjoining point accounting for the chromosome's X shape), which has been the focus of most research. One study reported a mismatch of almost 150,000 base pairs between chimpanzees and humans on the q arm of this chromosome. Substitutions accounted for 1.69 percent of the difference and indels accounted for another 3.58 percent.[24] The relic centromere's position on chromosome 2 is close to the presumed fusion point where changes in sequence affect neurological and behavioral functions.[25]

Brain Shape and Genetic Network Features

Some of these functional differences—particularly those affecting the brain and the testes—are now known to be present only in modern humans and not in earlier hominins. This presents astounding implications for the evolutionary paradigm. First, it means that a very recent change occurred in brain size, shape, and functional capacity between Neanderthals and other Middle Paleolithic hominins on the one hand and modern humans on the other.[26] Second, it means that to achieve such change, a whole network of genes and significant regulatory areas would have been rapidly sequenced in a completely novel way in the genomes of modern humans alone. This entire process would have required highly coordinated physiological and genetic changes[27] in a quick time frame. (Chapter 16 discusses these human-specific variations in more detail.)

Small Differences Make All the Difference

The percentage similarity between the chimp and human genomes is misleading in terms

The percentage similarity between the chimp and human genomes is misleading.

of biological relevance. DNA sequences—indeed, genes themselves—may display identical coding, but a host of factors lead to widely varied expression of genes and pseudogenes. Where there are detectable differences in DNA sequences, such as in the case of indels, these may appear statistically small in the context of genome-wide comparisons of chimpanzees and humans. However, they translate into significant disparity, particularly regarding novel genes, largely expressed in the brain and unique to humans. When added together, the genome-wide differences affect thousands of genes and even more non-coding sequences. They account for the general physiological, behavioral, and intellectual differences between chimpanzees and humans.[28]

Many of the chimp-human genetic disparities related to cognitive functions are also applicable to the Neanderthals and Denisovans. These uniquely human sequences pose a challenge to evolutionary time lines and mechanisms. These human-specific sequences must have emerged rapidly and achieved a high level of coordinated activity to explain the novel brain structure and behavior of modern humans. It's true that, statistically, there are high levels of similarity between the genomes of humans and chimpanzees—and even higher degrees of similarity between Neanderthals and humans. The quantitative differences are small, but the qualitative differences are big. In the case of humans, a little goes a long way.

Research into this interesting area will surely continue. Work in epigenetics is also progressing, including work on microRNAs and exosomes and their effects.[29] An improved understanding of protein space is also needed to complement these discoveries.

What is becoming clear is that the more we do know, the more we don't know. We can hope that, as more papers report "surprising" or "unexpected" results that seem to fly in the face of evolutionary expectations, scientists will resist falling prey to the temptation of summarily rejecting new ideas. We hope they will instead accept the challenges posed by discoveries in genetics and genomics with a good measure of humility and a desire to see science progress—even if that requires a paradigm shift.

Discussion Questions

1. What does the oft-reported 99 percent genetic similarity between humans and chimps really mean?

2. How do indels affect human-chimp genetic comparisons?

3. From an evolutionary perspective, what is required to obtain modern human brain size, shape, and functional capacity? Does the pathway seem viable?

Chapter 15

Are the Hominin Fossils Evidence for Human Evolution?

by Sue Dykes

Nothing frustrates a paleontologist more than discontinuities in an evolutionary tree. The goal of constructing a phylogeny (evolutionary tree) is to connect species together into a tidy, evolving lineage, showing neatly stacked, nested hierarchies. Unexpected discoveries are part of science. But, when it becomes commonplace for new fossil finds to "shake up" evolutionary trees,[1] it is not unusual for behind-closed-doors discussions among experts in the field to become heated.

Some of these discussions—for instance, the recent "rewriting" of the dinosaur family tree[2]—have led to lively debates that tend to be welcomed for their role in reviving interest in the field.[3] Human evolution is another story. With a wealth of fossil evidence available, the discussions about humanity's lineage can become quite serious, because anything that derails the expected patterns of hominin evolution wreaks havoc on attempts to draw firm phylogenetic relationships between species. It seems that the more we discover and the more we test, the more frustrated paleontologists become. New discoveries regularly undermine the ideal of a clear, single evolving lineage leading to modern humankind.

The Changing Tune of the March of Progress

Until the late 1960s, it was well accepted that hominin fossils fit into a clear progression of a single, evolving species, first represented by Thomas Huxley in his book *Evidence as to Man's Place in Nature* (1863)[4] as a series of primate skeletons leading to humanity. Anthropologist Francis Clark Howell expanded on Huxley's imagery in his 1965 classic work, *Early Man*,[5] to include some Miocene apes progressing via certain hominins—such as *Australopithecus*,

New discoveries undermine this most intuitive and logical "model" for human evolution.

Homo habilis, *Homo erectus*, and Neanderthals—to "Modern Man." Known as *The March of Progress*, this iconic image serves as shorthand for human evolution. Paleoanthropologists themselves would like to see *The March of Progress* dispensed with because the anticipated single lineage with clear transitional forms has failed to appear in the evidence. Instead, new discoveries undermine this most intuitive and logical "model" for human evolution.

Initially, the "single species lineage" hypothesis for human origins anticipated some variability due to sexual dimorphism, normal variability within a species, or variation over time due to evolutionary processes. However, the hypothesis was effectively falsified in 1976 when paleoanthropologists in Kenya unearthed an early *Homo erectus* cranium (KNM-ER 3733) and a *Paranthropus boisei* cranium (KNM-ER 406) in the same layer. Both skulls dated to about 1.7 million years ago.[6] Such was the divergence between these two contemporaneous crania that it could no longer be argued that every fossil find would fit within a single, evolving lineage. The straight line changed to a tree, but this soon morphed into a multitrunked bush. Fossils of several different hominins with bipedal capabilities appear in the fossil record at a time that corresponds to the presumed "root" of the human evolutionary tree. This positioning makes these creatures almost concurrent with the proposed time of divergence of chimpanzees and humans from their common ancestor (around 6 to 8 million years ago). More recent studies have suggested that modern humans may have interbred with some hominin species. Thus, paleoanthropologists proposed a new lineage model, likened to a "braided stream,"[7] to incorporate the possibility for endless permutations of divergence and reconvergence of hominins, plus any number of "side streams" (representing species) at any given moment in time. (This will be addressed in the next chapter.)

Still, each new discovery raises fundamental questions. For instance, how did bipedalism evolve so rapidly after the divergence from a human-chimp ancestor? Can evolution explain major transitions in the hominin fossil record (e.g., the change in body shape and size between *Australopithecus* and *Homo erectus*)?

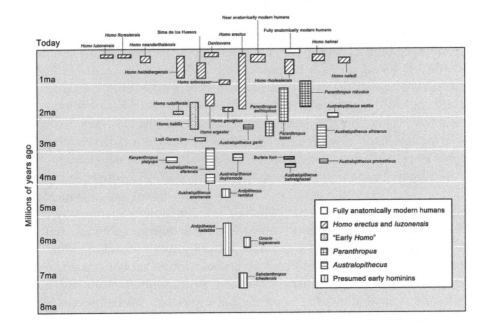

Figure 15: Representation of the Hominin Fossil Record

Major Transitions in Human Evolution

Despite the prevalence of diagrams showing phylogenetic relationships among hominins, in reality it is difficult to draw firm inferences from the hominin fossil record about human ancestry and descent. All inferred phylogenetic diagrams are peppered with question marks at vital nodes, dotted lines indicating uncertainty, and "floating" branches.[8] The best diagrams, in fact, are those that show no inferred lines of ancestry at all, such as the one shown in figure 1.[9] The following sections of this chapter discuss the abrupt "transitions" and temporal paradoxes in the human origins story.

From a Common Ancestor to Bipedal Hominin

Three genera of early bipedal hominins (see figure 15) appear in the record from 7.2 million years ago to about 4.3 million years ago. The first of these fossils, a cranium from Chad in central Africa, is attributed to *Sahelanthropus tchadensis* and dated to 7.2–6.8 million years ago (mya).[10] It shows signs of bipedalism in that its foramen magnum (the hole at the base of the skull where the spinal column joins the brain) indicates a more upright-standing hominin. It is further distinguished by its "non-chimp-like" teeth.[11] Similar, but different enough to be classified into its own genus, is *Orrorin tugenensis*, represented by a series of fossils found in Kenya and dated to 6.0–5.2 mya. These fossils do not include a full cranium. Paleoanthropologists describe the creature's dentition as being "ape-like,"[12] but the angle of the head of the femur (where it joins the pelvic bones) is such that researchers believe it reflects a bipedal stance.

Lastly, we have *Ardipithecus kadabba* (6.3–5.2 mya) and *Ardipithecus ramidus* (4.51–4.3 mya), both found in Ethiopia. *A. kadabba* consists of craniodental fragments and a few postcranial bones, including a toe bone from which bipedalism is inferred.[13] The most comprehensive *A. ramidus* specimen, dubbed Ardi, was discovered in 1994 and includes 125 pieces of fossilized bone. By itself, *A. kadabba* makes it difficult for paleoanthropologists to be dogmatic about the similarities and differences between other hominin species and about *A. kadabba*'s attribution to a completely different genera. Paleoanthropologists gain a little more clarity about the locomotion of *Ardipithecus* if they consider *A. kadabba* together with Ardi. Even so, the Ardi find was so brittle and chalky that it took scientists 15 years to excavate and describe it in publications. Just touching some of the bones turned them to dust. The pelvis even required extensive reconstruction.

Nevertheless, paleoanthropologists have been able to make some clear inferences about *Ardipithecus*. Firstly, its teeth (enamel thickness, size, and shape) indicate that it is not an ape. The thickness of the enamel does indicate that it is still more primitive than *Australopithecus afarensis*, which makes its first appearance some 3.7 mya. Researchers infer *Ardipithecus's* locomotion from the pelvis reconstruction, foot, and upper body. They concluded that *Ardipithecus* did not drag its knuckles like an ape.[14] Instead, it likely moved via a mixture of tree-climbing and bipedalism. Although researchers are uncertain as to what kind of gait *Ardipithecus* may have had due to a divergent big toe for branch-grasping and a rigid foot. A recent paper suggests that the locomotion of *A. ramidus* would have been a form of early, rudimentary bipedalism. The authors noted that, compared to African great apes, *Ardipithecus* has a larger midfoot and smaller toes, which would have given these hominins slightly more propulsion than chimpanzees and gorillas can produce.[15]

These three genera of fossil hominins pose important questions about the rapid transition from a knuckle-walking, chimp-like ancestor to a bipedal hominin. Indeed, they raise additional questions about the actual timing of the hominin divergence. The date for the common ancestor of the human and chimpanzee varies according to the method used to calculate it. The presumed mutation rates are usually based primarily on fossil evidence in the first place, together with calibrations of the genomes of great apes and macaques. Estimates range from about 4–4.5 mya[16] to 7.5 mya.[17] A 2012 attempt to recalibrate the human-chimp divergence used current mutation rates per generation, and extended the time to 7–13 million years.[18] However, the current mutation rate is very low compared to previous rates,[19] so paleoanthropologists seem to favor the range of 4–7 mya.

If bipedal hominins were already in Africa by 7 million years or more ago, then paleoanthropologists must explain the rapid transition to bipedalism. Bipedalism requires highly coordinated changes to the anatomy and, as a result, changes to genetic regulatory networks that control such adjustments. Even just the first steps toward bipedalism would involve complex changes:

- The foramen magnum must relocate from the back of the skull base to a position more centrally below it, so that the head will be carried in an upright position. (This appears to have happened as early as 7 mya, if the evidence from *Sahelanthropus tchadensis* has been interpreted correctly.)
- The inner ear bones need to be repositioned to maintain balance.
- The pelvis must become more bowl-shaped and oriented horizontally.
- The femur needs to be angled inwards, requiring a new shape for the femoral head (as claimed for *Orrorin tugenensis*).
- The shins need to be vertical above the ankles to provide a center of gravity and an ability to retain balance as one foot moves in front of the other.
- Joints must enlarge to withstand the greater stress of weight-bearing in the hip, knees, and ankles.
- The calcaneus (heel bone) must reorient itself so that it has its main "plantar" surface flat on the ground, rather than at an angle, which in chimpanzees allows for the grasping of tree branches.
- Musculature in general needs to be reorganized to accommodate not only the skeletal changes, but also to allow for posture changes, upright walking, and running.

These changes would not only be extensive but also need to happen in a highly coordinated way. Even a few generations from divergence would not be long enough to start toward bipedalism—yet this is what proponents of evolution claim for all three of these hominin genera. This contradiction forms the basis of the challenges that paleoanthropologists raise in response to papers characterizing such early hominin species, no matter how rigorous the research in describing the finds. For the time being, the scientific community takes a cautious approach toward these fossils and tends to classify them as "possible" early hominins.[20]

From "Apelike" to "Humanlike" in One Simple Step?

One difficult transition to explain is the shift between apelike australopithecines and the more humanlike Homo genus. Paleoanthropologists believe this change took place about 2 million years ago with "significant changes."[21]

The australopithecines persist in the record until about 1.98 mya[22] and had small brains (about 466 cubic centimeters[23] on average; chimp brains average 360 cc). The early Homo species date from about 2.8 mya[24] and averaged a brain size of 658 cc. (Early Homo erectus dates from about 1.85 mya[25] and averages 758 cc.) For comparison, a modern human brain averages about 1,330 cc.[26] Apelike characteristics of australopithecines included long, curved finger and toe bones for climbing (Australopithecus sediba was an exception to this rule); Homo digits tended to be flat. The australopithecines had an apelike orientation of the ear canal; later Homo specimens reflect a humanlike, upright stance.[27] The australopithecines had long arm bones relative to the body and relatively short legs. In most species of Homo, this is reversed—the arms are shorter compared to the legs, which have more humanlike proportions.

The australopithecine ribcage was inverted and funnel-shaped with highly mobile shoulders for climbing, compared to Homo species' more barrel-shaped chests, pinched in at a waist to allow the hips to swivel while running. The australopithecines had small, flared hips, while Homo erectus had very humanlike, bowl-shaped hips. The spine of the australopithecines was straighter than that of Homo species, which becomes increasingly S-shaped to provide a correct center of gravity for a fully upright back. For height, A. afarensis and A. africanus came in at about 138–151 centimeters for males and 105–115 centimeters for females. Homo ergaster (the African H. erectus) averaged 180 cm for males and 160 cm for females.[28] From these height differences, it can be seen that sexual dimorphism was more pronounced in the australopithecines than in Homo species.

Progressing from a facultative biped (e.g., *Australopithecus*, *Paranthropus*, and possibly *Homo habilis/rudolfensis*) to an obligate biped (e.g., *Homo ergaster/erectus* and later *Homo* species) is a very large step indeed. The many musculoskeletal changes must also coordinate with genetic and developmental adjustments.

One would also expect a lot of time and many generations of gradual evolution with slight modifications to pass before the crossover could be achieved—but *Australopithecus*, *Paranthropus*, *H. habilis*, *H. rudolfensis*, and *H. erectus* (in the form of *H. georgicus*) all existed in a similar time frame to each other. *H. georgicus* is the first example of *H. erectus* found outside of Africa. (Presumably it originated in Africa concurrently with *H. rudolfensis* and *H. habilis*, then migrated, reaching Georgia 1.85 mya.) Some researchers consider *H. habilis* and *H. rudolfensis* to be transitional species and propose these be reassigned to the *Australopithecus* genus.[29] Even if we accept this proposal, the timing for this radical transition remains very tight, and there appears to be no real consensus as to what might have been the driving force behind this shift.[30]

Brain Evolution and Temporal Paradoxes
For decades, paleoanthropologists looked at the somewhat gradual increase in brain sizes as a clear demonstration of human evolution from hominins. In fact, brain size was a main criteria for deciding whether a fossil specimen should be attributed to *Australopithecus* or *Homo*—until 1964, when Louis Leakey and his colleagues reduced the "qualification size" of the *Homo* brain to 600 cc to accommodate his new discovery. Leakey dubbed his find *Homo habilis* (meaning "handyman") because he assumed that this species was the maker of Mode I stone tools that had already been discovered in the Olduvai Gorge of Tanzania.[31]

A 2018 paper attempted to demonstrate a near-straight line increase in brain size from "archaic" hominins (australopithecines, etc.) to "pre-modern *Homo*" (late *Homo* species that existed just prior to 500,000 years ago).[32] The research team used a logarithmic scale to measure the endocranial volume on the y-axis, which gives the impression that late *Homo* brain sizes were nicely grouped together in a slowly increasing sequence while there was a relatively broad range of size differences between australopithecines and early *Homo*. A careful look at the samples included in the study reveals anything but a gradual increase in size. What the data actually show is a rather chaotic pattern of brain sizes across species and genera over time. The brain sizes of the "pre-modern *Homo*" included in the study range from 546 cc to 1,390 cc, while the australopithecines range is 385–555 cc, the paranthropines range is 400–800 cc, and *Homo habilis* and *Homo rudolfensis* (referred to by the study as transitional species) range is 509–805 cc.[33] Moreover, this study excludes some key species, such as Neanderthals and modern humans, which would have only increased the vast range of values.

The study also left out three diminutive species—*Homo floresiensis* (sometimes called hobbits), *Homo naledi*, and *Homo luzonensis*—that effectively put an end to the idea of a gradual "evolution" of brain size.[34] These species have small bodies to go along with their small brains. An argument might be made that their encephalization quotient (the size of the brain measured against the size of their body) is in proportion to other (larger) concurrent species, thus rendering it redundant to point out the lack of a gradual progression in brain size. However, there are more interesting anomalies at play here: all three species are examples of "temporal paradoxes." Each retains a blend of features from across the hominin genera. For example, they possess curled, apelike digits for climbing that show affinities with *Australopithecus* (or even earlier genera), features akin to early *Homo* species, and some features considered "modern" to the point of having similarities with *Homo sapiens*.[35]

Not only is it difficult to classify these three species, but they also fail to appear in the "correct" order predicted by evolutionary theories. *H. naledi* was discovered in a cave system of the Highveld (plateau grassland) of South Africa. Radiometric dating puts it at about 300,000 years old,[36] making it a contemporary of the first Neanderthals in Europe. *H. floresiensis*, found on the Indonesian island of Flores, is dated to 100,000–60,000 years old.[37] (Some hominin material on the same island dates back to as early as 700,000 years ago.[38]) Finally, *H. luzonensis* from Luzon Island in the Philippines dates to about 67,000 years old.[39] (There is also some evidence of hominin activity on this island, in the form of butchered bones and stone tools, that dates back 700,000 years.[40]) Both islands are located within a biogeographical area called Wallacea. Due to fluctuating sea levels in the past (e.g., 160,000 years ago),[41] the islands of Wallacea were intermittently connected by land bridges, which allowed for various fauna, including hominins, to colonize the area.

Paleoanthropologists have attempted to explain how such primitive hominins might have made an early exit from Africa, and why they remained so "unevolved," compared to other species in the hominin fossil record. Insular dwarfism (a phenomenon whereby species become smaller on islands if there are fewer resources than on the mainland) has been cited to explain the size of *H. floresiensis*. It would appear, however, that this creature was not simply a small version of *H. erectus*, as researchers initially proposed. It has too many pre-*erectus* features to make it a derivative of this species.[42]

Meanwhile, no appeal could ever be made to insular dwarfism to explain the primitive features and small size of *H. naledi*. Its location in an open grassland environment, where several other hominin species appear at more "predictable" times, make it difficult to interpret *H. naledi* as its own species. (As an example, *Homo helmei*, only slightly more recent than *H. naledi*, had a brain size of about 1,400 cc and a morphology approaching that of modern humans.[43]) The only evolutionary explanation for *H. floresiensis*, *H. naledi*, and *H. luzonensis* might be that they evolved early (perhaps as early as several million years ago, judging by their most primitive features), then did not evolve significantly from that time onward. They persisted in their primitive form while the hominin lineage was presumably evolving in leaps and bounds around them.

Does Brain Size Matter?

The brain size of hominin fossil craniums is not the only factor paleoanthropologists turn to when considering the idea of brain evolution. More recently, the actual arrangement of the brain has taken center stage thanks to studies into the differences between Neanderthal and modern human brains. We have not only a growing number of Neanderthal endocrania to study (plus the technology to do so more accurately), but we are also now learning that the genetic differences between the two species often relate to brain function.

On average, Neanderthal brains are marginally larger than the average modern human's brain (though there is a vast range of size in modern human brains).[44] It appears, however, that it is not the size of the brain that matters—rather, it is the arrangement of the brain and the proportional amount of tissue (and genes expressed in these tissues) dedicated to specific functional areas that make all the difference. Studies have shown that the globular shape of the modern human brain differs noticeably from those of all species that precede it.[45] Chapter 16 covers the differences from Neanderthal brains in detail, but they are worth summarizing here:

- Immediately after birth, Neanderthals and modern humans begin a different trajectory of brain development. The globularization process occurs in the first two years of human infancy, resulting in high foreheads and large frontal lobes.[46]
- Areas of the brain that are enlarged in modern humans (e.g., the cerebellum, the parietal lobe, temporal lobes, and the frontal cortex) all

deal with higher levels of cognitive functions, information processing, language processing, creativity, and other functions that "make us human."

- There are large areas of the Neanderthal genome, called "Neanderthal deserts," where it largely follows the chimpanzee sequence. In these same places, the modern human genome has unique sequences. Most Neanderthal deserts reside in "functionally important regions"[47] related to cognitive capacities and cranial formation.[48]

- Geneticists are discovering that genes that differ in sequence between Neanderthals and modern humans are linked to the capacity for language and symbolic thought.[49]

It seems there is no easy evolutionary explanation for the complex cognitive skills unique to the human species.[50]

> **It seems there is no easy evolutionary explanation for the complex cognitive skills unique to the human species.**

The Last Word in Human Evolution

Despite a plethora of imagery in textbooks, museum displays, and educational websites depicting human evolution as an orderly, gradual process, the hominin fossil record shows no such clearly discernable "lineage." There is no well-defined, hierarchically nested progression of creatures with ever more modern traits leading to our species. Instead, saltations and "out-of-order" species produce a chaotic picture with no possibility to discern even the major nodes of a lineage, let alone obtain a firm handle on which species of *Australopithecus* (from East Africa or from South Africa) was the true "ancestor" to us all. Not least of the saltations is the advent of symbolic behavior—sometimes called the "cultural big bang"—evidenced by art and artifacts incontrovertibly associated with modern humans. This unique cognitive leap goes together with the humanity's globular brain and novel genetic networks specific to our species. (See chapter 17.)

The truth of the hominin fossil record is that it does not fulfill the evolutionary paradigm's predictions. Reasons to Believe's progressive creation model provides a more plausible explanation of the evidence. We propose that the common factor among primates, extinct and extant, is their Creator. If one God is responsible for all life, as the Bible states, then it makes sense that groups of organisms (like apes, hominins, and humans) would share similar traits. Scripture also makes better sense of humanity's uniqueness, attributing it to God creating men and women in his image (Genesis 1:26–27).

Discussion Questions

1. What events led to a human evolutionary trajectory from "line" to "tree" to "multitrunked bush" to "braided stream"?

2. Review and discuss the complex changes required for the emergence of hominin bipedalism. Does an evolutionary explanation seem reasonable?

3. Evaluate the steps involved in a transition from australopithecines to the *Homo* genus. Does evolution adequately explain the transition?

4. According to the author, what scientific evidence has "effectively put an end to the idea of a gradual 'evolution' of brain size"?

5. Does human origins research show an "orderly, gradual process" for human evolution or does it reveal leaps and temporal challenges? Explain.

Chapter 16

Did Humans and Neanderthals Interbreed?

by Sue Dykes

I f a Neanderthal, dressed in a suit and carrying a briefcase, were traveling alongside you in the subway, would you have any difficulty distinguishing him from all the other commuters? This hypothetical scenario is part of a growing narrative that presumes a real lack of difference between hominin species such as Neanderthals and modern humankind. But were Neanderthals really the same as "us"?

Who Were the Neanderthals?

Homo neanderthalensis was a species of hominin that is thought to have lived from approximately 200,000 years ago until about 40,000 years ago.[1] Neanderthal fossils with "classical" features date from about 135,000 years ago. Prior to this, "proto-Neanderthals" (those that shared traits with *Homo heidelbergensis*) existed from about 250,000 years ago. Classic Neanderthals have been found at dozens of sites from Siberia and Uzbekistan to eastern, southern, and western parts of Europe to multiple locations in the Middle East (Israel, Turkey, Lebanon, Syria, Iraq, and Iran). These sites have variously produced Neanderthal tools and remains, ranging from near-complete skeletons to partial skeletons, skulls, jaw fragments, and isolated bone fragments. The finds include infants, children, adolescents, and adults.

A closely related species, known as the Denisovans (named after the cave in the Altai mountains in Siberia where the first specimen was found) may have persisted from about 160,000 to 50,000 years ago.[2] There is not a sufficient sample of specimens to be able to tell what Denisovans looked like and how comparable they were to Neanderthals anatomically. However, their DNA and much larger tooth size imply that Denisovans were different from

There are significant diagnostic differences between modern humans and Neanderthals.

Neanderthals at the species level.

Both species are distinct from modern humans (*Homo sapiens*). Not only is this determined genetically (both mitochondrial and nuclear DNA fall within separate ranges), but also developmentally and morphologically. There are significant diagnostic differences between modern humans and Neanderthals.[3] Paleoanthropologists believe modern humans emerged in Africa too recently to be the direct descendants of Neanderthals and Denisovans, whose presumed common ancestor (*H. heidelbergensis*) is thought to have evolved from a Eurasian branch of *Homo erectus*.

Morphological and Developmental Differences

On comparing the anatomies of Neanderthal and modern human skeletons, it can immediately be seen that Neanderthals were much more robust, but shorter in stature. Their ankle and knee joints were larger, the tibia (shinbone) was shorter and flatter, the hip joint was larger, and the pelvis more "flaring" than the narrower modern human hipbone. This wide hip arrangement provided support for a stout upper body, including a bell-shaped ribcage (modern humans have a barrel-shaped ribcage), together with distinctly large, strong collarbones, shoulder joints, and elbow joints. The outer structural walls of the limb bones themselves are thicker in composition. These are just a few of the diagnostic differences between the two species.[4]

All these features are diagnostic on their own, but it is in the craniodental features where the most significant differences lie. The modern human face is small and flat in the mid-face, with a uniquely prominent chin bone (no other hominin has this feature). Neanderthals had robust, forward-projecting mid-faces with large nasal cavities, a receding chin, and prominent brow-ridges above the eye sockets. The facial differences become apparent during development. Bone was added to the upper jaw of the Neanderthal as the face grew downwards, but was resorbed in modern humans.[5]

The dentition of these two species differs, as well. Neanderthals had uniquely shaped incisors, large pulp chambers in the premolars and molars, and a noticeable gap behind the third molars ("wisdom teeth").[6] There is also a very important difference in tooth eruption patterns between the two species. Age at weaning can be determined from tooth chemistry,[7] as can tooth eruption stages. Neanderthal teeth follow an earlier eruption pattern like other hominins and extant hominoids like chimpanzees, indicating a short childhood. Human teeth take many more years to finish erupting. A prolonged childhood is one of the features that make modern humans unique among all species (extant and extinct).

There are also significant differences in the shape of the skullcap and the brain. In the Neanderthal, these features have more in common with other *Homo* species. Immediately above the brow ridge in the Neanderthal, the skull recedes backward very quickly. Toward the rear, the skull is flat and extremely elongated, with a distinct bump or ridge (known as the occipital bun) at the back of the skull base. The braincase is wider than that of modern *H. sapiens*. Modern human brains are uniquely "globular," which means that the brain rises immediately above the eye sockets, behind a very high, vertical forehead. It is round and high, and narrow from side to side.[8] Most importantly, there is again a developmental difference in the stages of brain growth during the early childhoods of both species. Infant brains in both species do not differ significantly in size and shape. However, as all new parents are very aware, human babies are born with a large opening at the top of the skull called the fontanel. This soft spot provides room for the globularization process to be completed within the first two years of life.[9] In other words, the brain has room to grow upward above the eyes, rather than backward and outward, providing for a large frontal cortex (the part of the brain behind the high forehead).

These shape differences are not merely cosmetic. Areas that are enlarged in the human brain include the cerebellum[10] (at the base of the brain, to the rear), the parietal lobes[11] (at the top), the frontal cortex and orbito-frontal lobes[12] (forehead area), and temporal lobes[13] (on each side). These are key areas that control cognitive flexibility, fine motor control, episodic and working memory capacity, attention span, social abilities, self-representation, creativity, abstract thinking, and language processing, to name a few. These major structural differences are also matched by differences at the molecular level. Novel gene networks in humans control these vital areas of our "language-ready" brain.[14]

Do We Have Neanderthal DNA in our Genomes?

The study of ancient DNA (aDNA) has progressed in leaps and bounds of late. Rapid sequencing techniques allow for quick alignments of short sequences of highly degraded DNA. And these advances have paved the way for paleoanthropologists to sequence the genomes of Neanderthals and Denisovans and compare them to modern human genomes. The most shocking outcome of these comparisons is the claim that these hominins interbred with modern humans, leaving behind contributions to our genomes. However, one thing to know before analyzing papers on this subject is that most comparative studies between archaic hominin species and modern humans rely on matching very small aDNA fragments (between 35 and 50 base pairs in length) against human "reference genomes" (approximately 3.2 billion base pairs). Research indicates that this practice leads to "pervasive reference genome bias."[15]

This means that the smaller the fragment of aDNA, the more often geneticists would expect it to match up or overlap with other fragments at multiple sites along the modern reference genome. This expectation often leads to spurious results in the form of higher coverage (many overlapping alignments), apparently longer segments of sequence match (implying lower levels of linkage disequilibrium and more recent divergence dates), and higher overall statistical sequence similarity. Scientists have even found signals of interbreeding between Neanderthals and modern human populations where this would not have been possible.[16]

When analyzed with this caveat in mind, these aDNA studies have provided extremely important information about ancient and modern species. They've given us valuable insights into similarities and, perhaps more importantly, dissimilarities between them.

Statistical Similarities and Differences

From an evolutionary standpoint, when the genomes of chimpanzees, Neanderthals (or Denisovans), and modern humans are compared, researchers are looking for two things.

First, researchers are searching for sites ("loci") along the Neanderthal genome where it has sequences that are novel or "derived" compared to the chimpanzee genome, which are matched in the human reference genomes. Any genes related to these loci are dubbed "Neanderthal genes." Second, they are looking for areas where the Neanderthal genome matches the chimpanzee genome, but where all human groups have novel polymorphisms (so-called "Neanderthal deserts").

Theoretically speaking, there could be three reasons for similarities between (derived) Neanderthal sequences/genes and modern human sequences/genes. Modern humans either have (1) direct Neanderthal ancestry, (2) introgression of Neanderthal sequences through interbreeding, or (3) parallel/convergent

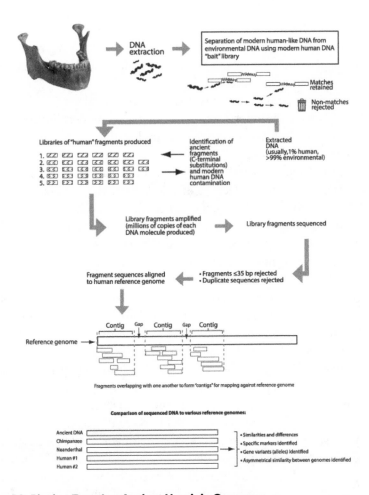

Figure 16: Piecing Together Ancient Hominin Genomes

evolution with Neanderthals. Since Neanderthals are no longer believed to be direct progenitors of modern humans,[17] ancestry is not normally considered.

The Interbreeding Question

The inference of introgression of Neanderthal sequences due to interbreeding is based on some underlying assumptions. First, evolutionary biologists assume that modern human populations have experienced random mutations at similar rates globally throughout history. Second, they must assume that selection is completely neutral, meaning that nothing drives positive, negative, or background selection differently between groups worldwide. *Then* if geneticists match a Neanderthal genome to any modern human reference genome, they could expect the genomes to be fairly identical, no matter which human population was being compared.

What has been found, however, is the opposite. The degree of similarity between derived loci in Neanderthals and non-African modern humans is about 2 percent. (The highest percentages are found in the Far East rather than in Europe.) These similarities are absent in sub-Saharan African populations. Between Far East Denisovans and modern Melanesian and Oceanic groups there is a 2–4 percent similarity.[18] Because of this "asymmetry" among modern human groups, and given the underlying assumptions, introgression of sequences through interbreeding appears to be the most logical conclusion, particularly as neither Neanderthals nor Denisovans are known to have ranged into Africa. There are, however, some challenges to this conclusion:

- To date, no evidence of Neanderthals has been found in East Asia. This makes the higher similarity to modern East Asian sequences (compared to modern European sequences)[19] counterintuitive. This has led to speculation that any putative interbreeding events—which must have been exceedingly rare[20]—occurred *before* human migration began, but did not reoccur when the two species met up again in Europe.[21]
- Contrary to evidence on the nuclear DNA, mitochondrial DNA (mtDNA) shows no evidence of interbreeding as measured in extant populations and in fossils of modern humans. (Mitochondrial DNA is passed down along the maternal line.) This implies that there was almost complete sterility between Neanderthal females and modern human males. This confirms that the two are distinct biological species.[22]
- Evidence from the Y chromosome of a Neanderthal from Spain shows major genetic incompatibilities (antigen-related "H-Y" genes) with modern humans. So, it is highly doubtful that a human mother could carry a male hybrid to full term.[23]

Had a male hybrid survived gestation, studies of the human X chromosome suggest he would likely have been sterile.[24] All in all, it seems Neanderthals, Denisovans, and modern humans would have been "at the edge of biological compatibility,"[25] which gives some pause in accepting the conclusion of interbreeding without reservation.[26]

Neanderthal Deserts

There is also the question of Neanderthal (and Denisovan) deserts, often neglected when discussing the interbreeding issue. Neanderthal deserts remain an outstanding question for researchers.[27] They are found in "functionally important regions" of the genome and, unlike the areas where sequences overlap, they are in very specific locations,[28] which is unusual under neutral models.[29]

Many of the genes unique to modern humans often come as a "package," linked together in networks (e.g., neural gene networks).[30] Neanderthal deserts are predominantly linked with cognitive capacities and cranial formation,[31] the testes,[32] X-chromosome male sterility genes,[33] brain functions,[34] and nervous system development.[35]

Of special interest is a massive Neanderthal desert, approximately 17 million base pairs long, on the q arm of chromosome 7, which encompasses the FOXP2 gene. In humans, this vital gene helps regulate language and many other brain functions, in addition to its own regulatory area.[36] The human genome also has unique substitutions that affect a binding site for a FOXP2 transcription factor.[37]

The genetic discontinuity between humans and Neanderthals appears to have occurred concurrently with the reorganization of the human brain. The implications are tantamount to "an improbable behaviorally modern human transition through a long-standing 'psychological evolutionary barrier.'"[38]

Neanderthal deserts overlap with Denisovan deserts (where the Denisovan, Neanderthal, and chimp sequences all match, but the human sequences are "novel") more often than would be expected by chance. Again, it implies that the same specific targets for negative selection (which ought to be "neutral" across populations) would have needed to act identically across diverse populations on introgressed sequences from completely independent, putative interbreeding events.[39] This high improbability leads us to consider an alternate explanation for the genomic evidence available.

The Alternative Conclusion: Convergent Adaptive Evolution

It has become apparent that the principal genes situated at loci where modern human mutations match with Neanderthal genes (or the Denisovan genes[40]) are all confirmed to be what could be termed "adaptive" genes (unlike the Neanderthal deserts). These genes mainly code for immune responses (including toll-like receptor [TLR] genes,[41] human leucocyte antigen [HLA] genes[42]), keratin-related genes,[43] fat metabolism (Europeans only),[44] high-altitude respiration (Tibetans only),[45] and skin pigmentation genes. A 2016 study into the highest frequency of "putative targets of adaptive introgression"[46] confirmed that the 126 loci with the highest similarities were related to, or spanned, areas enriched for immune-related genes (31 genes) and for skin pigmentation adaptations (seven genes).

If this conclusion were preferable to the interbreeding conclusion, some questions would need answering. Is the underlying assumption of global neutral selection favoring the interbreeding conclusion correct? Did modern humans acquire these adaptations, differentially around the world, without any "help" from introgression?

Is the underlying assumption of global neutral selection favoring the interbreeding conclusion correct?

Examining the Underlying Assumptions for Introgression

Research into neutral theory is showing that adaptive evolution is the norm. Mutation rates not only differ across time and geographical regions, but within a genome itself at sites that are highly susceptible to mutations and strong selection.[47] Moreover, as one gene is modified, the surrounding areas, together with the gene's "network," are often selected as a package alongside a beneficial mutation.[48] This is called "linked selection."[49] Direct selection alone may account for a small part of total selection, but when all types of linked and background selection are accounted for, only 5 percent of the genome actually evolves neutrally or by chance.[50] So, which kinds of sequences are targets for the strongest selection?

How Adaptable Are Modern Humans?

As modern humans have migrated and changed subsistence strategies over time, they have experienced genetic mutations providing adaptations for all sorts of challenges, through selection, at a local level:[51]

- UV radiation and temperature-related stimuli drove recent skin lightening[52] as well as hair and eye pigmentation adaptations[53] and hair follicle adaptations.[54]
- Novel food sources[55] (particularly since the Neolithic period) drove

adaptations for fat metabolism, lactase persistence into adulthood, mannose metabolism, and alcohol metabolism.

- Extreme environmental conditions drove adaptations for high altitude, extreme cold, and even breath-holding for deep free diving.[56]

Of all these adaptations, the strongest selection seems to occur in genes related to immune responses.[57] Not only are some genes—like *HLA*, *TLR*, interleukin (*IL*), and immunoglobulin-related (*Ig* and *KIR*) genes—more susceptible to strong selection for disease response, but they are also driven directly by the pathogens themselves, in terms of variability (mutation variability is correlated to pathogen richness in the environment)[58] and in terms of their specificity.[59] According to research, viruses account for around 30 percent of direct adaptive amino acid mutations in the human proteome.[60] The strongest selection pressure is directly on *HLA* and *TLR* genes.[61]

Parasites have also driven strong selection for mutations on various genes. For instance, the malaria parasite[62] (affecting *HLA*, β-globulin, and *G6PD* genes) and helminths (parasitic worms) have imposed strong selection on interleukin genes in hunter-gatherer societies (mainly living in sub-Saharan Africa and Australia today).[63] In immune-related genes, therefore, a large degree of regional difference in mutation sites—as well as asymmetry in selection from area to area—is to be expected without any appeal to Neanderthal or Denisovan introgression.

Similar asymmetry applies to skin and hair pigmentation adaptations around the world. The underlying causes for these are very simple and do not require interbreeding to explain. Many endothermic species follow a well-known law called Gloger's rule.[64] In a nutshell, the rule is that birds and mammals will tend to have lighter pigmentations in colder climates (closer to the poles) and darker pigmentation in warmer climates (closer to the tropics). Low UV radiation levels and the need to maximize vitamin D metabolism drive this phenomenon in mammals (including extinct species like Neanderthals).[65] Mammals adjust vitamin D metabolism by down-regulating melanin production near the poles or up-regulating eumelanin-rich pigmentation near the equator.

Many of the human-specific adaptations that have occurred independently from area to area are a form of convergent evolution within the human species. Most have occurred within the past 5,000–18,000 years,[66] which clashes with the timing of presumed interbreeding events (around 50,000–60,000 years ago).[67]

The fact is that humans, like all other species, have adapted locally to different challenges throughout their global migration and in the face of specific stimuli. When these adaptations have taken place in areas sans Neanderthals or Denisovans, evolutionary biologists make no appeal to interbreeding, and evidence of genetic similarity is simply discounted and removed from the analysis.[68] Yet, if modern human adaptations mirror Neanderthal or Denisovan adaptations (in Eurasia alone), then introgression is inevitably cited as the origin for such.

The Bottom Line on Interbreeding

Why, despite the apparent challenges enumerated above, is it a well-entrenched fact within the scientific community that modern humans interbred with Neanderthals or Denisovans? The reason is that current bioinformatics models are usually based on specific assumptions, particularly neutral selection (homogeneously between groups around the world). Conclusions of introgression from interbreeding events then become almost inevitable. While many adaptations detailed in this chapter appear to be too recent in modern humans to be attributed to introgression from interbreeding, the case is not closed. Fractions of possibility remain that warrant an open mind on the matter.

For the time being, the Reasons to Believe model is provisionally entertaining the prevailing view of interbreeding. As science progresses, we continue to assess the merits of alternatives by monitoring research into neutral theory, aDNA analysis, adaptive evolution, and other relevant fields.

So, How Similar Are Neanderthals and Humans, Really?

Neanderthals were morphologically, developmentally, and genetically distinct from anatomically modern *Homo sapiens*. The starkest differences have been identified in brain arrangement and in the gene networks regulating brain development and function. Linked to parts of the brain affecting higher functions (e.g., language, cognitive capability, and symbolic behavior), these differences coincide with the appearance of artifacts attesting to symbolic activity, which modern humans brought with them as they migrated around the globe. This hallmark of human behavior is discussed in the next chapter.

Discussion Questions

1. In what ways are humans distinct from Neanderthals and Denisovans?

2. Do the craniodental differences between Neanderthals and humans seem compelling? How so?

3. Explain the differences in brain size, shape, and growth between humans and hominins. What do these differences mean?

4. How does "pervasive reference genome bias" affect human-hominin comparisons?

5. Where does scientific research appear to land on the question of human-Neanderthal interbreeding?

Chapter 17

Did Neanderthals Create Art?

by Sue Dykes

I f you had to name behavioral characteristics that "make us human," distinct from animals, what would top your list? How about art, music, or spirituality? All these behaviors require the ability to think and communicate symbolically. One of the most interesting debates in paleoanthropology today centers around whether modern humans are the only hominins to ever use symbolism.

Evidence in the fossil record suggests the abrupt appearance of symbolic, even ritual, behavior. This event is known as the cultural big bang or "the dawn of human culture."[1] Which hominin species was the first to progress from rudimentary tool use to the creation of art, music, jewelry, and funerary goods? Was it modern humans—or did Neanderthals and other archaic hominins engage in these activities, too?

Fueling this lively debate are questions related to human exceptionalism, gradualism in the evolutionary process, and the cognitive capacity for language, which is intrinsically linked to the ability to think symbolically.[2] To answer these questions, it is necessary to first evaluate each claim of symbolic behavior in Neanderthals and other archaic species. And to do that, we must keep the following issues in mind.

How would symbolic behavior be recognized as such in the artifacts found at dig sites? There is a difference between the ability to craft utilitarian artifacts for expedient use (e.g., tools for gathering food or harnessing fire) and engaging in true symbolism (e.g., ritual behavior showing a curiosity about the afterlife). We must also unequivocally rule out cases where a natural cause can explain an inferred symbolic behavior (e.g., deliberate burial vs. natural burial).

Additionally, the dating of artifacts must be closely examined. We need to know if researchers dated the artifact itself directly or indirectly, using

Some dating methods can give a very secure date, but others are far less reliable.

surrounding sediments or nearby datable samples. If the latter, can we be confident with the methodology and prove unbroken association between the artifact and surrounding sediments? Is it possible that an indirectly dated artifact was simply dropped on top of cave sediments already millennia old? Furthermore, some dating methods can give a very secure date, but others are far less reliable.

Once a date is firmly established as being "secure," is there any ambiguity of association between the artifact and the hominin species to which it is attributed? For instance, if an artifact found in Europe is dated at about 40,000–50,000 years ago, can it be securely associated with Neanderthals or other hominin groups at the site—or could modern humans have been the authors of the artifact instead?

Neanderthal Burials

The late Harold Dibble was an expert in paleoanthropology and worked at many of the sites where symbolic behavior has been claimed in association with Neanderthal burials. For Dibble, it was important to distinguish between a burial and a funeral. Plainly put, a burial is a simple disposal of a body. A funeral, on the other hand, involves ritual or symbolic behavior and would presumably be accompanied by funeral rites as well.[3]

The most commonly accepted markers of a simple burial are: (a) a skeleton in full articulation and (b) a pit that was dug deliberately. Paleoanthropologists consider these conditions as evidence of a rapid burial of some sort, as otherwise signs of scavenging would normally be present (e.g., tooth marks, disarticulation of bones, and evidence of consumption). Burial, however, does not necessarily indicate symbolic behavior. Evidence of symbolism includes: (a) deliberate positioning of a body, usually inferred if legs and arms are flexed; and more particularly, (b) the placement of funerary items or grave goods directly with the body (flowers, jewels, weapons, items of value or evident cultural significance, etc.).

There are approximately 20 Neanderthal sites that paleoanthropologists interpret as deliberate, if not ritual, burial sites. The best-known sites are all located in France: La Ferrassie and the nearby Roc de Marsal, as well as La Chapelle-aux-Saints and Le Moustier. At La Ferrassie, a number of individual near-complete or fragmentary skeletons have been found, sometimes well-articulated and sometimes within large pits; at Roc de Marsal, the skeleton of a child was found in a pit. Most of these sites were excavated in the early days of paleoanthropology when documentation was not as meticulous as it is today. Thus, present-day researchers have reexamined these sites using new techniques to establish whether pits were preexisting or dug deliberately. They also want to know whether the sediments on top of the skeletal remains were likely due to normal cave sedimentation processes (such as rockfall, frost, earthquake, etc.) and whether other indications of deliberate burial were present at the sites (deliberate placement of body, etc.). In all four instances, natural causes are quite possible to explain the remains[4] and any claim of symbolic behavior is highly disputed.[5]

In the French cases cited thus far, the best evidence for purposeful burial is the near-complete state of some of the skeletons. However, since the discovery of fully articulated skeletons in cave sites in South Africa and elsewhere (e.g., "Little Foot," dated at around 3 million years ago or more,[6] or *Australopithecus sediba*, dated at nearly 2 million years ago[7]), such evidence no longer constitutes irrefutable proof of deliberate burial. With these sites under question,[8] serious doubt must remain as to the conclusion of purposeful burial, and certainly any symbolic behaviors inferred are speculative at best.

Very few cases of supposed purposeful burial at Neanderthal sites include anything resembling grave goods. Of these, two have more persuasive evidence: Shanidar in Iraq and Teshik-Tash in eastern Uzbekistan.

Shanidar Cave has produced many Neanderthal fossils, including near-complete skeletons. Paleoanthropologists have interpreted the best preserved specimen, labeled Shanidar IV, as a ritual burial even though it was found beneath rubble that seems more consistent with a roof fall.[9] The cave is subject to tectonism (rock instability, movement, and faulting) and the presence of an additional four partial skeletons beneath the same rubble could indicate a catastrophic burial, rather than a ritual one. In fact, the site's original researcher and others initially recognized the rockfall as the reason why the remains were crushed and so rapidly buried and preserved.[10] Three of the bodies are represented by just a few bone fragments, and Shanidar IV is the only individual that appears to have been fully engulfed by the rubble. Thus, a natural cause for these burials cannot be firmly ruled out.

What has elevated Shanidar IV to become the "poster boy" for Neanderthal ritual burial is the presence of pollen clumps found in two soil samples collected at the site. (These were routine samples taken from "about the same level"[11] as Shanidar IV.) It appeared that full flower heads had been buried near Shanidar IV. Moreover, some of the plant specimens are known to possess medicinal properties, leading some people to conclude that those who buried Shanidar IV were "practicing naturalists"[12] or shamans. Unfortunately for claims of Neanderthal spirituality, these pollens came from flowers abounding on the surface outside of the cave today. Gerbil-like rodents known as Persian jirds (*Meriones persicus*) carried the pollen into the cave.[13] This animal is endemic to the area and is known to store large accumulations of seeds and flowers at intervals along its burrow system. Other accumulators of pollen have been found at the site, including wind and insects. All but one of the pollens in the soil samples are found today at the surface and in the soil throughout the site.[14] Any deliberate placing of flowers at the site has been convincingly ruled out.[15]

The assemblage in a cave at Teshik-Tash in Uzbekistan was likewise reported as a Neanderthal ritual burial with grave goods. This site consists only of a shattered skull (broken into about 150 pieces) and some postcranial bone fragments of a Neanderthal child. A number of goat horn cores lay on the ground around the remains. Reports described the horn cores as "encircling" the body—in reality most of the horn cores are located near to skull and rib fragments, while the scant long bone elements are well outside of the "circle." Examining the site in even greater detail makes the few horn cores near the remains pale into insignificance. A vast number of identifiable goat horn cores, as well as goat bones, are strewn around the site in no particular pattern. These remains make up such a large proportion of the assemblage that chance alone can account for the six horns lying nearby the skeleton.[16]

Additionally, paleoanthropologists noted that several blocks of rock had fallen from the vault of the cave down onto the remains,[17] providing a possible natural cause of death for the individual taking shelter there. It could also account for the high degree of fragmentation of the cranium, which is not as evident in other bone elements at the site. The presence of gnaw marks on the femur indicate that researchers did not find the bones in their original positions. So, a deliberate burial cannot be inferred based on body arrangement because the original position is unknowable. The whole assemblage, including the numbers of goat remains, is in keeping with it having been an animal den for a considerable period of time.[18]

Although the narrative of Neanderthal burials seems firmly entrenched, there is no single burial site that provides adequate evidence for symbolic behavior in Neanderthals. What little provisional evidence there is proves to be highly dubious upon balanced review. Based on current findings, anyone arguing for human exceptionalism has good grounds upon which to challenge true symbolic behavior in Neanderthals, at least as far as burials are concerned.

Neanderthal Art
Every now and again, people will claim that Neanderthals produced works of art, crafted jewelry and musical instruments, and even that they adorned themselves with wings from birds of prey.[19] Art is undisputedly symbolic. When researchers encounter it at a fossil site, they almost always associate it with the creative cognition functions that accompany a language-capable brain. What constitutes such art, however, becomes a matter of some contention.

Again, there are key questions to ask when evaluating any claims of art at fossil sites. Has a natural cause been ruled out? Is the dating method reliable and the date secure? Have modern humans been firmly ruled out as authors of the art? It is also important to note if there is evidence of a repeated pattern of behavior. A case for Neanderthal art would be stronger if it could be shown that these hominins regularly produced art or other items of symbolic significance. We also need to ask if an artifact really constitutes symbolism or if it serves a utilitarian function (e.g., the use of ochre to treat animal hides as a mosquito repellant or to protect the skin from the sun[20]).

For our purposes here, we'll examine three prominent claims for art associated with archaic hominin species:

1. Scratches on a 500,000-year-old shell from Java attributed to *Homo erectus*[21]
2. Cave paintings in Spain dated to approximately 80,000 years ago and attributed to Neanderthals[22]
3. A "hashtag engraving" on the cave floor of a site in Gibraltar, also attributed to Neanderthals[23]

Trinil Shell
In the case of the shell from Java, natural causes were almost certainly at play. The Trinil shell, as it's called, is from a freshwater mussel. The scratches on its surface are fine (a fraction of a millimeter wide), multidirectional, and appear to have been made over the course of time. If *H. erectus* did make the scratches, they would have been using Acheulean hand-axes—large stones chiseled to a sharp point at one end and known to be used by *H. erectus*. These tools would likely be too cumbersome for such fine motor work.

The scratches on the Trinil shell are very like those on a 7 million-year-old piece of bone found lying on gravel substrate in Concud, Spain.[24] No hominins were known to be ranging in this area at that time (from an evolutionary point of view, the split between a chimpanzee-human common ancestor might not yet have occurred), so there is no problem attributing *these* scratches to natural causes. This implies that the Trinil shell might be a similar case. And since the Trinil shell is the sole "evidence" for *H. erectus* art—a species that persisted for approximately 1.5 million years without any other artwork attributed to it—it seems a stretch to claim that this artifact attests to the necessary level of cognitive hard-wiring being present in *H. erectus*.

The Cave of La Pasiega

In 1911, archaeologists in Spain discovered several galleries of paintings in a cave network called La Pasiega. The site features a plethora of figures, including bison, horses, deer, geometric designs, and possible symbolic images, painted with red and black pigments. It has been a rich research site for over a century now.

There has been debate about attributing at least some of the art to Neanderthals. The most strident claim for Neanderthal art centers around one vertical line that forms an integral part of a larger painting. The complete image depicts three cattle pens, one below the other, with animal symbols in two of the pens. The pigment appears cohesively constant throughout the whole image and the painting makes sense as a "whole." In 2018, researchers reported using uranium-thorium (U-Th) radiometric dating to measure the proportion of parent-daughter isotopes in various calcite plaques that have accumulated over the cave paintings. The calcite plaque over the vertical line delineating the left-hand side of the three cattle pens dates to 50,000–80,000 years ago, a time before modern humans arrived in that area. Thus, Neanderthals were credited as the artists of this specific drawing.

However, the claim seems to fall apart upon close inspection of the individual dates of plaques covering other areas of the painting. Calcite plaque covering the vertical line marking the right-hand side of the same cattle pens is dated to a mere 3,000 years ago. A plaque over one of a series of dots above the cattle pens dates to 2,000 years ago. Why such a divergence in dates? Wherever you have water trickling down a cave wall, you have what is called an open system. Water dissolves and leaches away uranium (the parent isotope in this instance) from the calcite being measured, leaving a disproportionate amount of thorium (the daughter isotope) to give the impression of radioactive decay over a much longer period of time. U-Th dating should only be used in closed systems (like the inner cores of stalagmites), where water cannot dilute or concentrate either of the isotopes.[25]

A more critical evaluation of all the sites that returned early dates of these paintings determined that the reliably dated plaques all center around a period of approximately 47,000 years ago,[26] which might well coincide with new dates calculated for the arrival of modern humans in Spain, prior to 44,000 years ago.[27] Despite the inaccuracy of the U-Th method in an open system, more and more researchers are dating artifacts in caves using this technique. Therefore, it is always wise to check the original papers to see which technique is used for dating.

Gibraltar Hashtag

In 2014, science news sites reported the finding of a 40,000-year-old hashtag sign scratched on a cave floor in Gibraltar. The mark was attributed to Neanderthals and claimed as evidence of symbolic thought—but this conclusion is questionable on several fronts.

To begin, the date is hardly firm. The hashtag is at the far back of the cave beneath a thin covering of sand, which itself dates to between 38,500 and 30,500 years old. There is no way to ascertain when the sand began to accumulate on top of the hashtag after it was scratched into the surface. The association with Neanderthals is, therefore, tenuous. Modern humans were ubiquitous in western Europe by this time, while the presence of Neanderthals is only conjectured. Recent firm isotopic dates have put the last Neanderthals in southern Iberia to closer to 40,000 years ago.[28]

More pertinently, it is difficult to interpret random scratches like this as art. The floor at the back of a cave is not somewhere "art" would be expected to be admired, interpreted, and preserved. Furthermore, despite attempts by the researchers involved to show that only stone tools would likely have made the marks, the scratches are of the exact dimensions one would expect of a bear's claws. Deep, multidirectional bear scratches are common on the floors of caves, as they routinely clear out hollows for hibernation sites. Lastly, even if the scratches were made with tools, it is far more likely they were made in the process of butchering meat or disarticulating birds for consumption. A nonartistic interpretation of this hashtag is a much stronger inference.

Shell Jewelry

Crediting Neanderthals and other Middle Paleolithic hominins with the creation of shell jewelry is likewise open to dispute. In certain instances, the U-Th dating is debatable. For example, this dating method put an ochre-covered shell found in an open system between 115,000–200,000 years old—but direct carbon dating on the same shell showed it to be only 50,000 years old.[29] Other claims of Neanderthal jewelry rest on tenuous evidence of "polishing" on the shells (implying that the shells were rubbing against skin or each other), scratches, and piercing (presumably for threading on to strings for use as a necklace).[30]

It cannot be overemphasized that the first rule of interpretation would be to rule out possible natural causes, rather than claim evidence of symbolism. Many obvious natural occurrences can account for scratch marks on shells. The shell might have rubbed against a gritty substrate, like gravel or other marine debris.[31] Polishing could well be due to the shells being used to line the nests of bird like the brown noddy tern, a habitual accumulator of marine debris and shells in elevated sheltered coastal overhangs.[32]

Collections of small shells at coastal cave sites, like Grotte des Pigeons in Morocco and Blombos in South Africa, are often associated with hominin jewelry. One reason is because the location—away from the beach in elevated rock shelters—implies deliberate accumulation at these sites. Another reason is the conclusion that the animals housed in the shells were too small to be used for food (e.g., *Nassarius* shells); ergo, the shells must have been sought out for personal adornment. Moreover, these shells often bear holes and markings that archaeologists interpret as efforts to fashion the shells into wearable beads. However, upon further inspection, such holes in the shells appear large, irregularly shaped, and lacking any uniform pattern. This would be more in keeping with natural damage than with deliberate piercing.

Most interesting of all are the piercings on the mollusk shells found at Blombos. The perforations are perfectly round and deliberate—and are directly attributable to a predator of this mollusk (*Natica tecta*).[33] Predators of mollusks are known to create a wide variety of piercing shapes that closely mimic what archaeologists expect anthropogenic piercings to look like. So, care should be taken when interpreting shell accumulations.[34]

Musical Instruments

There is no doubt that music requires symbolic thought. Were musical instruments to be incontrovertibly linked to Neanderthal sites, it would be logical to conclude that this species was capable of symbolic thought, highly sociable, and almost certainly language-ready.

Archaeologists have been finding Paleolithic "bone flutes" since the 1920s.

These supposed instruments are typically made from the femora of young cave bears. Regularly spaced piercings on the bones are presumed to be finger holes. Many claims have been made in favor of crediting Neanderthals with the creation of these flutes, but none of these claims have stuck. Among the most famous examples is a "bone flute" found at Divje Babe I Cave, Slovenia, in 1995. The find sparked a lot of excitement—even discourse about the music scales the flute might have produced.

However, like many, if not all, of the bone flutes attributed to Neanderthal musicians, the Divje Babe flute was incorrectly identified. Closer inspection of the bones and a knowledge of Ice Age animals in that area show that hyena scavenging, not music-making hominins, are the source of the holes. The punctures in the bear cub femora precisely match the spacing and the shape of this extinct predator's premolar crushing teeth.[35]

The Latest Word in Language

Modern *Homo sapiens* have been described as the only species alive today that "mentally dissects the world into a multitude of discrete symbols and combines and recombines those symbols in our minds, to produce hypotheses of alternative possibilities."[36] New research emerging from ancient DNA studies is providing insight into the very wiring of the human brain. In particular, we are learning more about the sequences and whole gene networks, exclusive to modern humans, that affect language capacities and the cognition required for symbolic behavior. These genetic features accompany a brain shape arrangement that exists only in modern humans.[37] (See chapters 14 and 16.)

The so-called language gene, *FOXP2*, is among the most notable genetic differences that distinguish humans from Neanderthals and other hominins. The gene is part of a large sequence (17 million base pairs long), where the Neanderthals' version follows the chimpanzee sequence more closely, while the modern human version does not.[38] This would seem to confirm that modern humans are indeed unique in possessing full language capabilities. No doubt Neanderthals had a high cognition level, adept as they were, for instance, at hunting in groups.[39] However, language requires more than intelligence—it requires a different *type* of cognition that allows for the expression of abstract ideas and symbols and the ability to master grammar and syntax. Until recently, it was thought that language evolved gradually throughout the *Homo* lineage, but new research is providing insights into the need for the syntax-capable, language-ready brain to have been in place *before* language could be acquired.[40] We will probably never really know what form of communication

Neanderthals and other Middle Paleolithic groups possessed, but it seems unlikely that they had the capacity for language as we know it in our species.

Were Neanderthals Truly Symbolic Thinkers?

To sum up, every claim of symbolic capacities in Neanderthals based on art, jewelry, musical instruments, and all kinds of putative symbolic artifacts is disputed. I cannot stress enough the importance of this point. Most people ("laymen" and scientists alike) are convinced that Neanderthals used symbolism based on numerous "examples" that they believe have been well-evidenced. Once two or three or more papers are published with the same claim, the science is considered to have built its case. This confidence transfers to popular science in the form of misleading headlines, textbooks, museum displays, and more.

This confidence transfers to popular science in the form of misleading headlines, textbooks, museum displays, and more.

Nevertheless, each case needs to be evaluated on its own merits, not merely assumed as another arrow in the quiver of evidence for Neanderthal symbolism. Ideally, when a claim of Neanderthal symbolism surfaces, the scientific community should show more caution and interrogate the claim before forming a consensus. They should question why there is only one case of symbolic behavior for a region, manifest by a species present in the fossil record for such a long time. And each time a claim is validly disputed, new papers would reset the evidence back to n = 1, and recall that "one swallow [bird] does not a summer make."[41]

Unfortunately, many evolutionary biologists are keen to minimize differences between our species and extinct hominins. They are known in the field as "Neanderthal Champions."[42] There are several, however, who reject these efforts. Jean-Jacques Hublin, a leading paleoanthropologist, has described these Neanderthal champions (ironically) as being "on a mission from God," and accused them of trying to "deny any evidence not matching with their personal crusade." Further, Hublin states, "The latest debates on Neanderthal abilities are one of the worst examples in which ideological issues have overshadowed scientific evidence."[43]

Consensus science today agrees that hominin species such as Neanderthals were highly advanced in cognition and intelligence. For example, there is evidence at certain Neanderthal sites that these hominins used hearths during temperate periods when they could harness naturally occurring fire.[44] Data shows that Neanderthals could control and use natural fires for long periods at a time, even if they lacked the technological skill to make fire on demand.[45] Their toolkit was more advanced than the hand-ax biface tools used by *H. erectus*. Neanderthals produced comparatively much smaller tools, such as stone scrapers and spear points, up until their extinction. They survived in the face of bitter glacial conditions for well over 100,000 years (or more, if earlier dates for Neanderthals are accepted). In the view of Harold Dibble, they used many kinds of adaptations to survive, and their ability to survive so long was "pretty successful, better than we've done so far."[46]

Advanced as Neanderthal cognition may have been, there is still a *qualitative* difference between the types of cognition displayed by Neanderthals and modern humans. The last word on language and symbolism should go to paleoanthropologist Ian Tattersall:

> We find nothing in the technological record of the Neanderthals to suggest that they were symbolic thinkers. Skillful, yes; complex, certainly. But not in the way that we are . . . behaviorally there was no qualitative break with the past; the Neanderthals were simply doing what their predecessor had done, if apparently better. In other words, they were like their ancestors, only more so. We are not. We are symbolic.[47]

Discussion Questions

1. What kinds of questions should one ask when considering whether artifacts at dig sites represent symbolic behavior?

2. Review the evidence for Neanderthal burials. Do the burials seem catastrophic or ritualistic, and why?

3. How does the evidence for hominin cave scratches, paintings, and "hashtag engraving" fare?

4. Does the evidence show that Neanderthals created "bone flutes"? Explain.

5. How do claims of hominin symbolism follow a trajectory to scientific consensus? Would a minority view be more consistent with the evidence?

Chapter 18

Can Evolutionary Processes Explain the Origin of Eukaryotic Cells?

by Fazale Rana

Whenever I speak on university campuses, presenting scientific evidence for design and raising scientific challenges to the evolutionary paradigm, it isn't uncommon for students to challenge me with the idea that symbiosis among single-cell organisms gave rise to eukaryotic (or complex) cells. This is known as symbiogenesis or the endosymbiont hypothesis. It is an important facet of the evolutionary paradigm because it offers an explanation for the origin of eukaryotes.

Many people find the endosymbiont hypothesis, and its attending evidence, compelling. They believe it provides broad support for evolutionary explanations for the origin, history, and design of life. Nevertheless, I am going to argue that it is equally reasonable to view eukaryotic cells (and, therefore, life) as the product of a Creator's handiwork. First, let me detail the endosymbiont hypothesis, what it is, and why evolutionary biologists accept this idea.

Endosymbiont Hypothesis
Many evolutionary biologists believe that eukaryotic cells originated when free-living bacterial and/or archaeal cells engulfed another microbe, leading to a symbiotic relationship. This process is known as endosymbiosis. Once engulfed, the ingested cell (endosymbionts) established a permanent relationship with the host; presumably, the endosymbiont provided the host with metabolic benefits and the host provided the endosymbiont with a safe environment in which to grow and divide. Over time, the two cells became mutually interdependent.

This theory also suggests that some organelles, such as mitochondria, were once endosymbionts. According to this model, the endosymbionts gradually

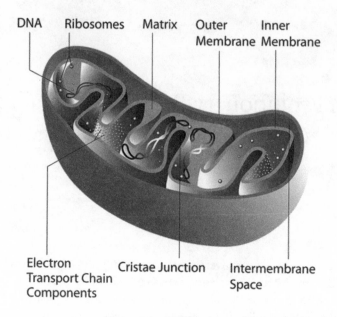

DNA   Ribosomes   Matrix   Outer   Inner
                              Membrane Membrane

Electron   Cristae Junction   Intermembrane
Transport Chain   Space
Components

Figure 18.1: Illustration of a Typical Mitochondrion

evolved into organelles via genome reduction. This reduction resulted when some of the genes from the endosymbionts' genomes were transferred into the genome of the host organism. During the transformation from endosymbiont into organelle, the genome reduction was extreme. For example, mitochondrial genomes, typically around 20,000 base pairs, encode 35–40 proteins. The group of bacteria that biologists think gave rise to mitochondria has a genome of over 1 million base pairs. Over time, evolutionary processes developed the machinery to produce the proteins endosymbionts required in the cytoplasm and to transport those proteins into the mitochondria.

Evidence for the Endosymbiont Hypothesis
One main line of evidence for endosymbiosis is the similarity between some organelles and bacteria. For example, evolutionary biologists believe mitochondria descended from a group of bacteria called alphaproteobacteria (specifically bacteria that align with the Rickettsiales). Mitochondria are similar in size and shape to a typical bacterium and have a double membrane structure like alphaproteobacteria. These organelles also divide in a way that is reminiscent of bacterial cells.

Another piece of evidence is the presence of DNA in mitochondria. Evolutionary biologists view the existence of the diminutive mitochondrial genome as a vestige of the organelle's evolutionary history. Additionally, the biochemical similarities between mitochondrial and bacterial genomes are taken as further evidence for the evolutionary origin of these organelles.

The genomes of mitochondria could be viewed as transitional in nature. Some biologists believe that, given more time, the transfer of mitochondrial genes into the host cell's nucleus will be completed. After all, there are other organelles—such as the highly unusual mitosomes and hydrogenosomes—found in single-celled eukaryotes that lack genomes entirely. Apparently, the gene transfer process has reached fruition in these endosymbionts-turned-organelles.

Yet another piece of evidence for endosymbiosis is a unique lipid in the mitochondrial inner membrane. This lipid (cardiolipin) is an important component of bacterial inner membranes, yet it is not found in the membranes of eukaryotic cells—*except* for the inner membranes of mitochondria. Biochemists consider it a signature lipid for mitochondria and a vestige of this organelle's evolutionary history.

Despite the seemingly compelling evidence for the endosymbiont hypothesis, I contend that evolutionary biologists lack a genuine explanation for the origin of mitochondria and, in a broader context, the origin of eukaryotic cells. In a review article critical of the endosymbiont hypothesis, Hungarian biologists István Zachar and Eörs Szathmáry point out that evolutionary biologists have proposed over 20 different evolutionary scenarios for the mitochondrial origins that fall underneath the umbrella of the endosymbiont hypothesis. And all of them fail to adequately account for the origin of mitochondria.[1]

> **Evolutionary biologists lack a genuine explanation for the origin of mitochondria and, in a broader context, the origin of eukaryotic cells.**

The Challenge of Protein Transport into Mitochondria

Similarities between mitochondria and alphaproteobacteria are not enough

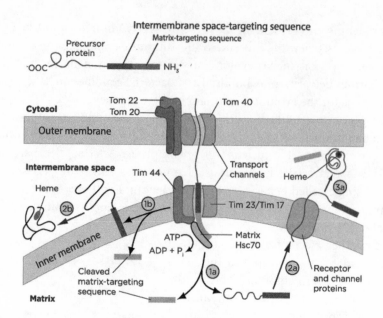

Figure 18.2: An Overview of Protein Targeting and Transport into Mitochondria

to establish the validity of the endosymbiont hypothesis. Evolutionary biologists must also explain how mitochondria became fully integrated into the host cell's metabolic systems. Even though biochemists have made significant strides toward understanding how the process of protein transport works for mitochondria, they still must identify a plausible pathway that can adequately account for the evolution of this biochemical operation, if the endosymbiont hypothesis is to be accepted.

Except for select exceptions, most mitochondrial proteins are made in the cytosol of the cell and transported into the mitochondria. The overall process of mitochondrial protein biogenesis consists of four stages: (1) protein synthesis, (2) targeting the protein to the mitochondria, (3) transporting the protein into the mitochondrial lumen, and (4) targeting the protein to its destination within the organelle.

The cell's machinery makes mitochondrial proteins as pre-proteins with a signal sequence at one of its ends (the N terminus). The signal sequence has a specialized structure (an amphipathic alpha-helix) that serves to target the proteins to mitochondria. Think of the signal sequence as analogous to an address label that tells the post office where to deliver a letter.

Receptor proteins that are part of the outer membrane (TOM) complex recognize the signal sequence and transport the protein through a channel into the intermembrane space (the region between the mitochondria's inner and outer membranes). Protein chaperones keep the mitochondrial proteins unfolded and stabilized throughout this process.

Once in the intermembrane space, two different translocase of the inner membrane (TIM) complexes (TIM22 and TIM23) work together to take the protein "baton" from the translocase of TOM complex and usher it into the lumen (or the matrix) of the mitochondria. If the protein is to remain within the lumen (because that's where it performs its work), then proteins called peptidases remove the signal sequence and the protein adopts its intended three-dimensional shape. If the protein is to be incorporated into the inner membrane, then it possesses an additional targeting sequence that is recognized by another protein complex dubbed OXA (oxidase assembly). This biomolecular ensemble inserts the protein into the inner membrane. If the protein is to carry out its work in the intermembrane space, then the OXA complex will transport the protein back across the inner membrane.

Alternatively, some proteins destined to operate in the inner membrane space possess a stop signal sequence. These sequences prevent the TIM22 and TIM23 complexes from transporting it across the inner membrane into the lumen. Instead, peptidases in the intermembrane space remove the signal sequence, allowing the protein to adopt its operational structure. Finally, if the protein is to be incorporated into the outer membrane, then another complex referred to as SAM inserts it into the outer membrane.

Each stage of mitochondrial protein biogenesis involves a series of irreducibly complex biochemical systems that, in turn, integrate with each other to form the complex, integrative process of mitochondrial protein biogenesis. Moreover, each step of the process must precisely interact with the other steps. If not, the entire process fails. For natural mechanism to produce such a complex process, several biochemical systems had to evolve *simultaneously* and integrate with one another. For example, once mitochondrial genes became incorporated into the host genome, DNA sequences specifying the various signal sequences had to simultaneously evolve and become precisely appended to every one of the mitochondrial DNA sequences with the final, correct target specified for each protein upon translation. The TOM, TIM22, and TIM23 complexes had to evolve simultaneously to recognize mitochondrial proteins and work in tandem to move proteins into the mitochondria. In addition, chaperones had to emerge that would recognize mitochondrial proteins and keep them unfolded during the transport process. Signal peptidases had to evolve to remove signal sequences from mitochondrial proteins with exacting precision. Finally, stop sequences and additional targeting sequences had to evolve and become precisely positioned within the mitochondrial protein genes.

Though some researchers have suggested that TIM may have emerged through co-option, in reality, no one knows how mitochondrial protein biogenesis could have evolved.[2] Cell biologist Franklin Harold sums up the situation:

> The origin of the machinery for protein import is more complicated [than the origin of the ATP/ADP antiporter] and is subject to much debate. . . . Most of the transferred genes continue to support mitochondrial functions, having somehow acquired the targeting sequences that allow their protein products to be recognized by TOM and TIM and imported into the organelle.[3]

To say that such a complicated system "somehow" evolved is not a scientific explanation. It is little better than a just-so story. In the absence of a plausible evolutionary route for mitochondrial protein transport, it is reasonable to question the explanatory power of the endosymbiont hypothesis. If there is any real evidence for the endosymbiont hypothesis, it is the morphological and biochemical features shared by mitochondria and gram-negative bacteria.

Still, evolutionary biologists remain convinced that this model accounts for the origin of eukaryotic cells. These life scientists have a philosophical precommitment to the evolutionary paradigm that compels them to seek natural explanations for shared features—even if said features could just as easily be interpreted from a creation model perspective.

A Creation Model Perspective on Mitochondria

It is reasonable to view eukaryotic cells as the work of a Creator, wherein the shared similarities between mitochondria and bacteria reflect common design rather than common descent. However, to legitimately interpret mitochondrial origins as creation, there must be a reason for the biochemical similarities between mitochondria and bacteria. Thanks to recent research advances, an explanation now exists for why mitochondria have their own genomes and why the mitochondrial inner membranes harbor cardiolipin.

In 2016, biochemists reported on a survey of over 2,000 mitochondrial genomes representing a wide range of eukaryotic organisms. They have discovered three properties that are common to the genes found in these organelles.[4] These properties are the key to why mitochondria have their own genomes and also argue against the complete reduction of the mitochondrial genome over time.

1. Many of the proteins encoded by mitochondrial genomes are associated with the organelle's membranes. These proteins consist of myriad hydrophobic amino acids. If these proteins were encoded in the nuclear genome and produced in the cytoplasm—instead of in the lumen of mitochondria—the mitochondrial proteins would be misdirected to the endoplasmic reticulum (ER) instead of the mitochondria. The cell's machinery that directs proteins to the ER can't discriminate between the proteins of the ER and those that should be targeted to mitochondria. To avoid misdirection, these proteins must be produced in the interior of mitochondria.

2. Proteins encoded by mitochondrial genomes form the core components of the electron transport chain (ETC). The ETC is part of an elaborate energy-harvesting operation that takes place in the inner membranes of mitochondria. Encoding ETC proteins within the mitochondrial genome, instead of the nuclear genome, affords the cell more efficient regulatory control over its energy metabolism.

3. Protein-coding genes in mitochondrial genomes have a high guanine-cytosine (GC) content. The higher the GC content of a region of DNA, the more stable it is. The interiors of mitochondria are harsh environments due to the presence of reactive oxygen species (by-products of energy metabolism). Thus, the high GC content serves as an elegant design feature, ensuring the genes' durability in the organelle interior.

Cardiolipin's Function

There is a close association between cardiolipin and several proteins found in the mitochondrial inner membrane. These proteins help harvest energy. Compared to other lipid components in the inner membrane, cardiolipin appears to associate preferentially with these proteins. Evidence indicates that cardiolipin helps to stabilize the structures of these proteins and serves to organize them into larger functional complexes within the membrane.[5] In fact, several studies have implicated defective cardiolipin metabolism in the onset of some neuromuscular disorders.

For example, cardiolipin closely interacts with the F_1-F_0 ATPase. This complex is a biomolecular rotary motor that produces the compound ATP—an energy storage material used to power cellular operations. Like other proteins found in the inner membrane, cardiolipin forms a close association with F_1-F_0 ATPase. However, instead of binding permanently to the surface of the protein complex, cardiolipin interacts with it dynamically. Biochemists think that this dynamic association and the unusual chemical structure of cardiolipin (which gives it the flexibility to interact with a protein surface) are critical for its role within the mitochondrial inner membrane. As it turns out, cardiolipin not only stabilizes the F_1-F_0 ATPase complex (as it does for other inner membrane proteins), but it also lubricates the protein's rotor, allowing it to turn in the viscous cell membrane environment. Additionally, cardiolipin's unique structure helps move protons that provide the electrical power to operate the F_1-F_0 ATPase motor.

Why Do Mitochondria Have Their Own Genetic Code?

There is at least one other feature of mitochondrial genomes that requires an explanation if we are to legitimatize a creation view of these organelles and that is the mitochondrial genetic code.

Mitochondria possess deviant, nonuniversal genetic codes that at first blush seem to reflect an evolutionary origin. To understand why this seems so, a little background information is in order. To a first approximation, all life on Earth possesses the same genetic code. To put it another way, the genetic code is universal. However, there are organisms that possess a genetic code that deviates from the universal code in one or two of the coding assignments. (Genetic code consists of coding units, called codons, where each codon corresponds to one of the 20 amino acids found in proteins.) Presumably, these deviant codes originate when the universal genetic code evolves, altering coding assignments.

Quite frequently, mitochondrial genomes employ deviant codes. One of the most common differences between the universal code and the mitochondrial code is the reassignment of a codon that specifies isoleucine in the universal code, so that it specifies methionine in mitochondria. In fact, evolutionary biologists believe that this evolutionary transition happened five times in independent mitochondrial lineages. (See chapter 19.)

So, while many biologists believe that mitochondria's deviant codes can be explained through evolutionary mechanisms, creationists must show a compelling reason for a Creator to design an alternative genetic code in these organelles. Work by a team of German biochemists provides insight for just such a purpose—one that underscores elegant molecular logic.

These researchers provide evidence that the reassignment of the isoleucine codon for methionine protects proteins in the inner membrane of mitochondria from oxidative damage.[6] Metabolic reactions that take place in mitochondria during the energy-harvesting process generate high levels of reactive oxygen species (ROS). These compounds are highly corrosive and will damage the lipids and the proteins of the mitochondrial inner membranes. The amino acid methionine is also readily oxidized by ROS to form methionine sulfoxide. Once this happens, the enzyme methionine sulfoxide reductase (MSR) reverses the oxidation reaction by reconverting the oxidized amino acid to methionine.

Creationists must show a compelling reason for a Creator to design an alternative genetic code in these organelles.

Because of reassigning the isoleucine codon, methionine replaces isoleucine in the proteins encoded by the mitochondrial genome. Many of these proteins reside in the mitochondrial inner membrane. Interestingly, many of the isoleucine residues of the inner mitochondrial membrane proteins are located on the surfaces of the biomolecules. The replacement has minimal effect on the structure and function of these proteins because these two amino acids possess a similar size, shape, and hydrophobicity. But because methionine can react with ROS to form methionine sulfoxide and then be converted back to methionine by MSR, the mitochondrial inner membrane proteins and lipids are protected from oxidative damage. To put it another way, the codon reassignment results in a highly efficient antioxidant system for mitochondrial inner membranes.

However, this codon reassignment is not universally found in the mitochondria of all organisms. As it turns out, this codon reassignment occurs only in active animals that place a high metabolic demand on mitochondria (and with it, concomitantly elevated production of ROS). On the other hand, this codon reassignment does not occur in Platyhelminthes (flatworms, which live without requiring oxygen) and inactive animals (such as sponges and echinoderms).

From a creation viewpoint, there are good reasons why mitochondrial biochemistry is the way it is. Understanding the rationale for the design of mitochondria reveals an ingenuity to all life's designs. At the end of the day, one could legitimately embrace either the endosymbiont hypothesis or the creation model explanation for the origin of eukaryotic cells. For me, the common design model makes better sense, particularly considering the recent insights into the exquisite molecular rationale that undergirds the biochemical features of mitochondria.

Discussion Questions

1. From an evolutionary perspective, does the evidence for the endosymbiont hypothesis seem compelling? Discuss.

2. What three properties are key to understanding why mitochondria have their own genomes? What bearing does this knowledge have on mitochondrial origins?

3. How does a creation perspective account for the mitochondrial genetic code?

Chapter 19

Can Evolution Repeat Outcomes?

by Fazale Rana

A s you have probably gathered by this point in the book, I am skeptical that evolutionary processes can *fully* account for life's origin, history, and design. This view puts me at odds with "mainstream" scientists who view evolution as *the* organizing principle in biology. Because I am a biochemist, my critics accuse me of being either dishonest or incompetent. Why else would I question the "fact" of evolution in the face of the overwhelming evidence for common descent? They claim that theological motivations fuel my skepticism.

I agree with that assessment—partially. I find it hard to square certain features of the evolutionary framework with some of Christianity's most important biblical and theological ideas (see chapter 5). However, I also think that evolution faces some very real scientific problems.

The deficiencies are best exposed by evolution's failed scientific predictions. Like all scientific theories, the theory of biological evolution makes predictions. Predictions are one of the most important features of a scientific model. They are the expected entailments that logically flow out of a theory. If a theory is valid, then researchers should observe certain things and they should obtain certain results when they perform specific experiments. One failed prediction of the evolutionary paradigm is the unexpected pervasiveness of convergence.

What Is Convergence?
Quite often, organisms that cluster into distinct and disparate groups share identical (or nearly identical) biological systems. Evolutionary biologists believe that these shared features evolved independently and repeatedly. Presumably, evolutionary mechanisms channeled separate evolutionary pathways toward the same endpoint. That is to say, the evolutionary process independently

Given the nature of evolutionary processes, we wouldn't expect convergence to be so pervasive.

converged on highly similar systems in distinct lineages of organisms.

This phenomenon is widespread. Evolutionary biologists Simon Conway Morris and George McGhee detail many examples of convergence in their respective books, *Life's Solution* and *Convergent Evolution*. Both demonstrate that identical evolutionary outcomes are a characteristic feature of the biological realm.[1]

Scientists see these repeated outcomes at the ecological, organismal, biochemical, and genetic levels. (To illustrate the pervasiveness of convergence, I describe 100 examples of it at the biochemical level in my book *The Cell's Design*.)[2] But given the nature of evolutionary processes, we wouldn't expect convergence to be so pervasive. In fact, we would expect it to be an oddity, not commonplace.

Historical Contingency

To appreciate why wide-scale convergence creates problems for the evolutionary paradigm, it is necessary to think a little bit about the nature of evolutionary mechanisms.

According to the late evolutionary biologist Stephen Jay Gould, evolutionary mechanisms are best described as historically contingent.[3] The evolutionary process consists of an extended sequence of unpredictable, chance events. If any of these events were altered, it would send evolution down a different trajectory. To help clarify this concept, Gould used the metaphor of "replaying life's tape." If one were to push the rewind button, erase life's history, and then let the tape run again, the results would be completely different each time. In other words, the evolutionary process shouldn't repeat itself and rarely should it arrive at the same end.

Gould based the concept of historical contingency on his understanding of the evolutionary process. Since he proposed his original description of historical contingency, several studies have affirmed his view. For example, in 2002, two Canadian investigators carried out a landmark study that simulated macroevolutionary processes using autonomously replicating computer programs that operated like digital organisms.[4] These programs can be placed into different "ecosystems" and because they replicate autonomously, they can evolve.

By monitoring the long-term evolution of these digital organisms, these two researchers determined that evolutionary outcomes are historically contingent and unpredictable. Every time they placed the same digital organism in the same environment, it evolved along a unique trajectory.

A 2008 study that was part of the long-term evolution experiment (LTEE) demonstrates that evolutionary processes are historically contingent.[5] As discussed in chapters 8 and 10, the LTEE began in February 1988 with a single cell of *E. coli* that was used to generate 12 genetically identical lines of cells. Throughout the experiment, samples of cells have been frozen every 500 generations. These frozen cells represent a "fossil record" of sorts that can be thawed out and compared to current and other past generations of cells. Around 32,000 generations into the LTEE, *E. coli* started utilizing citrate in the growth media as a carbon source. Experiment leader Richard Lenski and his coworkers determined that a sequence of mutations formed an evolutionary pathway that culminated in the ability to use citrate. (For more information see chapters 8 and 10.)

The evolved ability presented Lenski's team with a rare opportunity to test the notion of historical contingency. The results indicate that a potentiating series of unidentified mutational changes made it possible for *E. coli* to grow on citrate. Cells that did not experience that same pathway of changes could not evolve citrate-utilizing capabilities. In other words, historical contingency characterized the evolution of the citrate-growing strains.

Can Evolution Replicate Its Results?

Though confronted with two disparate observations—evolutionary processes are historically contingent, but convergence is widespread—evolutionary biologists brush them aside. They insist that if organisms face similar challenges, the forces of natural selection will funnel evolutionary trajectories down the same pathway toward the same endpoint.

But this scenario can't explain the instances in which convergence occurs in organisms from radically different environments (and distinct lineages). Under these circumstances, the forces that comprise natural selection must, by definition, be different.

A remarkable example of this type of convergence can be seen in the sand lance (fish) and the chameleon (reptile). Biologists have uncovered an extraordinary similarity in the visual systems and behavior for these two creatures. Both the chameleon and the sand lance move their eyes independently of one another in a jerky manner, rather than in concert. While one eye is in motion, the other is motionless. Moreover, both animals use the cornea of the eye to focus on objects. All other reptiles and fish use the lens of the eye to focus images on the retina. The chameleon and sand lance both rely on a specialized muscle (the cornealis muscle) to adjust the focusing of the cornea. The chameleon determines depth perception using a single eye. Scientists believe the sand lance does the same. Both animals have skin coverings over their eyes to prevent them from being conspicuous to both predators and prey.

The feeding behavior of sand lances and chameleons is also the same. The trajectory that the chameleon tongue takes when attacking its prey is the same as that taken by the sand lance when it lunges for its prey. (The sand lance buries itself in sand beds with its eyes above the surface and waits for tiny crustaceans to pass by.)

The words of the researchers who were among the first to discover this convergence are compelling: "When faced with a beautifully coordinated optical system such as this, it is a challenge to provide an explanation for the convergence of so many different finely-tuned mechanisms."[6]

An Arresting Example of Convergence

One of the most startling examples of convergence uncovered so far is the independent origins of DNA replication in bacteria and archaea/eukaryotes. This single example illustrates how remarkable molecular convergence is from an evolutionary standpoint.

DNA replication—the process of generating two daughter molecules identical to the parent molecule—is essential for life. This duplication plays a central role in reproduction by inaugurating cell division. Once DNA is replicated, a complex ensemble of enzymes distributes the two new molecules between the emerging daughter cells.

Because DNA replication is so complicated, most biochemists thought it arose only once, prior to the origin of the last universal common ancestor (LUCA). In fact, they long regarded the close functional similarity of DNA replication, observed in all life, as evidence for this single origin event. The common features of DNA replication include:

1.   Semi-conservative replication;
2.   Initiation at a defined origin by an origin-replication complex;
3.   Bidirectional movement of the replication fork;
4.   Continuous (leading strand) replication for one DNA strand and discontinuous (lagging strand) replication for the other DNA strand;

5. Use of RNA primers; and
6. The use of nucleases, polymerases, and ligases to replace RNA primer with DNA (see "The Process of DNA Replication").

Then, in 1999, researchers from the National Institutes of Health demonstrated that the core enzymes in the DNA replication machinery of bacteria and archaea/eukaryotes (the two major trunks of the evolutionary tree of life) did *not* share a common evolutionary origin. It appears as if two identical DNA replication systems emerged independently in bacteria and archaea—*after* these two evolutionary lineages supposedly diverged from the LUCA.[7] Considering the concept of historical contingency, it is most reasonable to expect evolutionary processes to produce two *different* forms of DNA replication in archaea and bacteria.

To appreciate why this is the case, it is helpful to review the mechanism of DNA replication.

The Process of DNA Replication

DNA consists of two polynucleotide chains aligned in antiparallel fashion. The two strands are arranged alongside one another with the starting point (5′) of one strand in the polynucleotide duplex located next to the ending point (3′) of the other strand and vice versa. The chains twist around each other, forming the well-known DNA double helix. Four different nucleotides—adenosine (A), guanosine (G), cytidine (C), and thymidine (T)—comprise the chain sequences.

The nucleotide sequences of the two DNA strands are complementary. When the strands align, the A side chains of one strand always pair with T side chains from the other strand. Likewise, G side chains pair with C side chains. Biochemists refer to these relationships as Watson-Crick base-pairing rules. Thus, if biochemists know the sequence of one DNA strand, they can determine the sequence of the other. Base pairing plays a critical role in DNA replication.

Conceptually, template-directed, semi-conservative DNA replication entails splitting the parent DNA into two single strands. According to the base-pairing rules, each strand serves as a template for the cell's machinery to follow as it forms a new DNA strand with a nucleotide sequence complementary to the parent strand. Because each strand of the parent DNA molecule directs the production of a new DNA strand, the result is two daughter molecules. Each possesses an original strand from the parent molecule and a newly formed

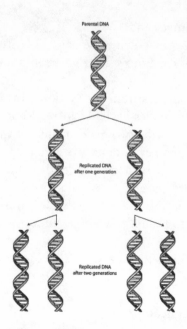

Figure 19.1: Semiconservative DNA Replication

DNA strand produced by a template-directed synthetic process.

DNA replication begins at specific sites along the double helix. Typically, prokaryotic cells have only a single origin of replication; more complex eukaryotic cells have multiple origins. The double helix unwinds locally at the origin of replication to produce a replication bubble, which will expand in both directions during replication. Once unwound and exposed within the replication bubble, the parent strands are available to direct the production of the daughter strand. The site where the double helix continuously unwinds is the replication fork. Because DNA replication proceeds in both directions away from the origin, each bubble contains two replication forks.

Top-to-Bottom Replication

Replication can only proceed in a single direction, from the top of the DNA strand to the bottom ($5'$ to $3'$). Because of the DNA's antiparallel alignment, only one strand at each replication fork has the proper orientation (bottom-to-top) to direct the assembly of a new strand in the top-to-bottom direction. For this leading strand, DNA replication proceeds rapidly and continuously in the direction of the advancing replication fork. Replication can't proceed along the

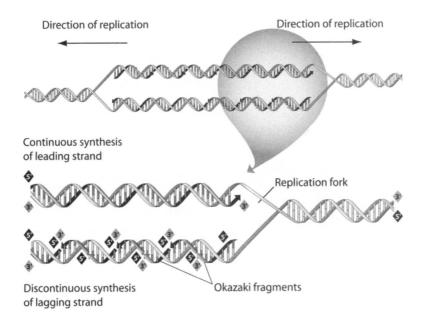

Figure 19.2: DNA Replication Bubble

strand with the top-to-bottom orientation until the bubble expands enough to expose a sizable stretch of DNA. When this happens, DNA replication moves away from the advancing replication fork. It proceeds a short distance along before stopping to wait for more of the parent DNA strand to unwind. The replication process repeats these steps as many times as necessary, until the entire strand is replicated. The small DNA fragments produced in this start-stop fashion are called Okazaki fragments, after the biochemist who discovered them.

The strand produced discontinuously lags behind the replication of the continuously produced leading strand. But the leading strand at one replication fork is the lagging strand at the other replication fork because the replication diverges as the two ends of the replication bubble advance in opposite directions.

The Proteins of DNA Replication
DNA replication requires an ensemble of proteins to carry it out. First, a complex of several different proteins identifies the replication origin; then a protein called helicase unwinds the DNA double helix to form the replication fork. Unwinding introduces torsional stress in the DNA helix downstream from the

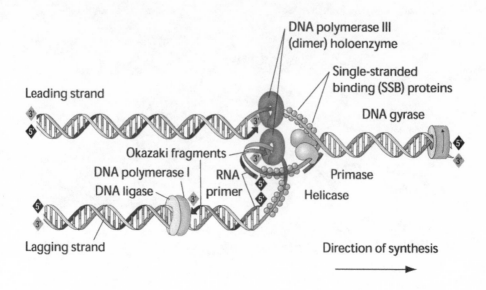

Figure 19.3: The Proteins of DNA Replication

replication fork. Two other proteins (topoisomerase and gyrase) relieve the stress, thus preventing the DNA molecule from supercoiling. Single-strand binding proteins fasten themselves to the exposed strands to keep them from breaking apart.

Once the replication fork is established and stabilized, DNA replication can begin. However, the protein that synthesizes new DNA by reading the parent template strand (DNA polymerase) cannot start from scratch. It must be primed. The primosome, a massive complex consisting of over 7 different proteins, produces the RNA primer required.

After priming, DNA polymerase will produce DNA continuously along the leading strand. For the lagging strand, DNA polymerase can only generate DNA in spurts to produce Okazaki fragments, and each time it does so the primosome complex must produce a new primer. Once replication is complete, a protein called a 3'-5' exonuclease removes the RNA primers from both the continuous DNA and the Okazaki fragments, and a different DNA polymerase then fills in the gaps left behind. Finally, a ligase protein connects all the Okazaki fragments together to form a continuous piece of DNA out of the lagging strand.

This is a cursory description of DNA replication, but even so it clearly illustrates the complexity and intricacies of the process. It is phenomenal to think this biochemical system evolved a single time, let alone twice. There is no obvious reason for DNA replication to take place the way that it does. Even if the process could have evolved independently on two separate occasions, it is reasonable to expect that functionally distinct processes would emerge for bacteria and archaea/eukaryotes, given their idiosyncrasies. But this is not what happened.

It is phenomenal to think this biochemical system evolved a single time, let alone twice.

Paleobiologist J. William Schopf, one of the world's leading authorities on early life, put it this way:

> Because biochemical systems comprise many intricately interlinked pieces, any particular full-blown system can only arise once. . . . Since any complete biochemical system is far too elaborate to have evolved more than once in the history of life, it is safe to assume that microbes of the primal LCA [last common ancestor] cell line had the same traits that characterize all its present-day descendants.[8]

The single origin Schopf and other evolutionary biologists expected and predicted is simply not observed for the earliest complex, fully formed biological systems necessary for basic DNA replication. We can consider this a failed prediction of evolution.

Convergence and the Case for a Creator

Prior to Charles Darwin, biologists used the term *analogies* to refer to shared biological features found in organisms that cluster into disparate groups. They believed analogous systems were designs conceived by the Creator and then physically manifested in the biological realm.

If we take this historical concept of biological analogies together with evolutionary theory's failed prediction, we find convergence fits awkwardly within the naturalistic framework but makes perfect sense within creationism. Convergent features can be understood as reflecting the work of a divine, intelligent mind employing a common set of solutions to address a common set of problems facing unrelated organisms.

Convergent features have the added benefit of making biology possible as a scientific discipline. They allow us to apply what we learn about one organism to others. If God created every life to be uniquely distinct, then what we learn for that life-form would apply to it alone. Shared features enable us to generalize insights we gain from studying a single biological system. To put it differently, shared biological features have been designed for discovery.

This discoverability of biochemical systems reflects God's providence and care for humanity. If not for the shared features, it would be nearly impossible for us to learn enough about the living realm for our benefit without resorting to unethical experimentation on our fellow humans. Where would biomedical science be without model organisms such as yeast, fruit flies, and mice standing in for people?

Discoverability also makes it easier to appreciate God's glory and grandeur, as evinced in biochemical systems by their elegance, sophistication, and ingenuity.

Discussion Questions

1. The author notes how convergence is pervasive in the biological realm. From an evolutionary view, does historical contingency explain this observation?

2. Discuss how the independent origins of DNA replication in bacteria and archaea affect an evolutionary explanation (thus, prediction) for their origin.

3. From a creation model perspective, how can convergent features be understood? What benefit(s) do they provide humanity?

Chapter 20

Can Evolutionary Co-option Explain the Irreducible Complexity of Biochemical Systems?

by Fazale Rana

During the mid-1980s, I was a graduate student at Ohio University, studying biochemistry. I began to develop a real appreciation for the chemical structures and processes that take place in living systems. Their elegance, sophistication, and ingenuity impressed me, to say the least.

The more I marveled at biochemical systems, the more I began to wonder how life scientists explain their origins. This is known as the origin-of-life problem. So, on top of my responsibilities as a graduate student, I began to study the different origin-of-life scenarios posited by researchers in this field, driven solely by my curiosity.

What I learned left me disappointed. I was quickly reaching the conclusion that chemical evolution could not account for the origin of biochemical systems and, hence, the origin of life. It was at this point that I developed the conviction that a Creator of some sort had to be responsible for the origin and design of life—at least at the molecular level. (It was later that I accepted the truth of the Bible.)

As a graduate student, I saw numerous problems with chemical evolution. I still do (see chapter 6). One of my concerns had to do with the interdependency of the proteins that make up biochemical systems. Every operation in the cell involves an ensemble of proteins that work collaboratively. I saw this codependence as a problem for chemical evolution. Even if chemical selection generated a functional biomolecule, it wouldn't be of any use if its protein partners didn't also arise at the same time. And, even if all the proteins did emerge simultaneously, this biochemical system would be of little value in isolation because a cell consists of an integrated network of systems. In short, biochemical systems are nested in an interdependent hierarchy. It seemed to me that a core set of biochemical systems (each one comprised of a distinct set of proteins) had to originate all at once. It turns out that my intuition as a graduate student had merit. In recent years, biochemists have focused quite a bit of attention on trying to determine life's bare minimum biochemical requirements. Using a variety of approaches, biochemists have concluded that for a cell-like entity to be a bona fide life-form, it must have the capacity for:

- DNA replication
- Cell division
- Protein synthesis
- Cell membrane assembly
- Energy extraction pathways

These insights into life's minimum biochemical complexity cause problems for chemical evolutionary scenarios.

Researchers think that these requirements necessitate somewhere between 200 to 500 different proteins.[1] If all of these different proteins don't come into existence all at once, the protocellular entity comprised of these partial and incomplete systems wouldn't be alive. I think it is obvious that these insights into life's minimum biochemical complexity cause problems for chemical evolutionary scenarios.

Irreducible Complexity

As a graduate student, I intuitively recognized that life in its most basic form was irreducibly complex, though I doubt that I could have ever described the concept as well as biochemist Michael Behe. He articulated the concept of irreducible complexity in his classic work *Darwin's Black Box*, as a "a single system composed of several well-matched, interacting parts that contribute to basic function, wherein removal of any one of the parts causes the system to effectively cease functioning."[2] Behe makes the case that a protosystem produced by Darwinian process of slight, incremental, iterative change cannot lead to irreducibly complex systems. Any protosystem lacking even one part that contributes to "basic function" is nonfunctional. The same conclusion stands even if all the essential components are present but do not interact with one another in a just-so fashion. If the protosystem doesn't have function, then natural selection can't operate on it to produce an improved system and natural selection has nothing to select. Irreducibly complex systems must come into existence complete and fully operational. It makes sense that they reflect the work of an intelligent Agent—all the more so, given the many irreducibly complex systems that human designers produce!

As a biochemist, I can attest that virtually every biochemical system is irreducibly complex. Therefore, it is reasonable to question the assumption that evolutionary processes could truly account for these phenomena.

At this juncture, it is critical to make an important, yet subtle, distinction between Behe's application of irreducible complexity and mine (both when I was a burgeoning biochemistry student and still to this day). I focus on the problems irreducible complexity causes for the origin of life, whereas Behe's emphasis is on the origin of new biochemical systems once life has already originated.

The Bacterial Flagellum

The bacterial flagellum is an iconic example of an irreducibly complex biochemical machine. This massive protein complex looks like a whip extending from the bacterial cell surface. Some bacteria have only a single flagellum, while others possess several flagella. Rotation of the flagellum allows the bacterial cell to navigate its environment in response to various chemical signals.

An ensemble of over 40 different kinds of proteins makes up the typical bacterial flagellum, and these proteins function in concert as a literal rotary motor. The flagellum's components include a rotor, stator, drive shaft, bushing, universal joint, and propeller. It is essentially a molecular-sized electrical motor directly analogous to human-made rotary motors. The flow of positively charged hydrogen ions through the motor proteins embedded in the bacterial inner membrane powers rotation.

According to Behe, evolutionary mechanisms can't explain the origin of the flagellum because it is irreducibly complex. If any of the myriad proteins that comprise it are unavailable, then the flagellum won't function. And what good is that for the cell?

Is Co-Option an Evolutionary Pathway to Irreducible Complexity?

Evolutionary biologists have challenged Behe's argument by claiming that irreducibly complex systems can evolve in a stepwise manner through a process called co-option (or exaptation).[3] According to this model, the biomolecules of irreducibly complex systems originally played other roles in the cell and later

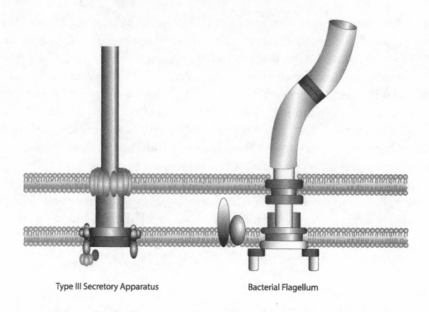

Type III Secretory Apparatus   Bacterial Flagellum

Figure 20.1: Comparison of Bacterial Flagellum and Type III Secretory Apparatus

were recruited, or co-opted, one-by-one, to be part of transitional systems that eventually led to the irreducibly complex systems of contemporary biochemical operations. These transitional systems likely performed functions that were distinct from those performed today.

As a case in point, some evolutionary biologists claim that the bacterial flagellum evolved from the type III secretory apparatus through the process of co-option.[4] Pathogenic bacteria use the type III secretory system (T3SS) to export proteins into the cells of the host organism. The molecular architecture of the T3SS closely resembles the portion of the flagellum embedded in the bacterial cell envelope.[5] Evolutionary biologists speculate that the first flagellum arose from the merger of the T3SS apparatus and a filamentous protein system. Presumably, both structures provided the microbe with prior services, neither of which had anything to do with motility.

This explanation is not without its problems. For example, when viewed from an evolutionary standpoint, it is not clear which came first: the flagellum or the T3SS machine. According to Milton Saier, a biologist from the University of California, San Diego, insufficient information exists to determine whether one came first or if neither came first, or if both structures evolved from the same precursor system.[6] If evolutionary analyses indicate that the T3SS machine emerged from the flagellum, it thoroughly undermines the co-option explanation.

And, of course, the T3SS secretory apparatus is itself irreducibly complex. Moreover, the flagellar systems in bacteria and archaea are highly similar and appear to have emerged independently, serving as yet another remarkable example of convergence.[7] (See chapter 19.)

Despite these problems, co-option remains plausible—at least *in principle*. In fact, this mechanism defines the very nature of the evolutionary process. Evolutionary biologists view biological systems as the outworking of random, historically contingent processes that co-opt preexisting designs to cobble together new systems.

Still, at this juncture the evolutionary explanation for the bacterial flagellum and most other biochemical systems appears to be no more than evolutionary just-so stories. Invariably, the naturalistic scenarios proposed to account for the origin of irreducibly complex systems are highly speculative and lack any type of detailed mechanistic undergirding. This is clearly the case for all the evolutionary explanations offered to account for the emergence of the bacterial flagellum. Biologists Mark Pallen and Nicholas Matzke make this very point: "The flagellar research community has scarcely begun to consider how these systems have evolved. This neglect probably stems from a reluctance to engage in the 'armchair speculation' inherent in building evolutionary models."[8]

In other words, just because evolutionary biologists have proposed a mechanism to explain the origin of irreducibly complex systems doesn't mean that these mechanisms work. This concern has already been identified for evolutionary explanations built around constructive neutral evolution irremedial complexity theory. This approach is overrun with these types of "explanations."[9] (See "Persistent Paradigm" in chapter 2, "Cells as Agents of Change" in chapter 9, "Our Critiques" in chapter 10, and "Reasoning to Best Explanation and Teleology" in chapter 11.)

So, can co-option explain the genesis of biochemical systems? Insight from work in biomimetics and bioinspiration may help settle the matter.

Biomimetics and Bioinspiration

One of the most exciting areas in engineering today centers around the use of biological and biochemical designs to drive technology advances. This area of study is called biomimetics and bioinspiration. And toward this end, engineers

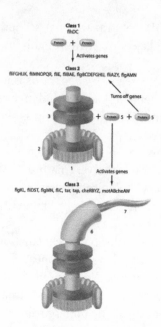

Figure 20.2: Illustration of the Assembly Process for the Bacterial Flagellum

have turned to the design and the biochemical assembly process of the bacterial flagellum to inspire their own designs.

An international team of physicists and engineers designed artificial bacterial flagella that are the same size and shape as those found in bacteria.[10] These artificial flagella are microrobots with a magnetic head region and a flagellar-like tail. The researchers can control the movement of the microrobots by varying the three-dimensional intensity of a magnetic field surrounding the solution harboring the mini-machines.

Additionally, researchers from the University of Hertfordshire have mathematically modeled the assembly of the bacterial flagellum with the intent of using these insights to improve industrial operations, particularly ones that rely on autonomous decision-making.[11]

This work highlights the fact that the production of the bacterial flagellum resembles a well-orchestrated manufacturing process. This assembly pathway displays an exquisite molecular logic that results in efficient and orderly production. Each step in the process seems preplanned with subsequent steps in mind. To illustrate: the information required to produce the 40+ proteins that make up the bacterial flagellum resides within the bacteria's DNA. In bacteria, genes specifying proteins involved in the same cellular process often lie next to one another along the DNA molecule. Biochemists use the term "operon" to describe these groupings. The flagellar genes are organized into over 14 different operons that, in turn, cluster into three operon classes: Class I, Class II, and Class III.

Typically, the flagellar operons are "turned off" until the bacterial cell "senses" that the time has arrived to produce flagella. When this happens, the Class I operons "turn on" and direct the production of two proteins. The two Class I proteins, in turn, activate Class II operon genes. The Class II operons turn on, one at a time, according to the spatial positioning of the proteins within the flagellum. Proteins forming the innermost structures of the flagellum (such as the rotor and stator) are produced first, followed by the proteins forming the drive shaft and bushings. Once these four structures have been assembled into what's called the basal body, the Class III operons turn on and the Class II operons shut down. The genes of the Class III operons produce the proteins that form the universal joint and whip-like flagellum.

This well-orchestrated process of gene expression ensures that the proper proteins are present at the proper time during the assembly of the flagellum. The cell avoids wasting precious resources and making mistakes by producing proteins only when they are needed. For example, if the cell makes the protein for the whip-like flagellum before the basal body comes together, it would result in that protein assembling inside the cell. This out-of-sequence scenario would make it impossible for the flagellum to be assembled once the basal body forms.

Production begins with the assembly of the flagellum's basal body component, consisting of the rotor and stator. The rod-like drive shaft, bushings, universal joint, and flagellar whip assemble sequentially from the basal body outward. To affect the assembly, proteins are brought to the basal body and then transported through its central channel to form the drive shaft. The bushings are assembled in a similar manner. But in addition to passing through the basal body's central channel, the bushing proteins also pass through the hollow interior of the drive shaft, and so on and so forth until the entire flagellum is put together.

The export apparatus, a protein complex positioned below the basal body, controls the transport process.

No one who has observed the efficiency and orderliness of a manufacturing process would conclude that it just happened by itself. Likewise, the assembly of the bacterial flagellum shows all the telltale signs of planning and careful design.

Work in biomimetics and bioinspiration raise questions about the role co-option would have played in generating new biochemical systems after life originated. (It also provides a response to the blind Watchmaker challenge discussed in chapter 22.) Recall that evolutionary biologists view biological systems as the outworking of random, historically contingent processes that co-opt preexisting designs to cobble together new systems. Once these designs are in place, evolutionary mechanisms can optimize them, but these systems remain kludges.

Most evolutionary biologists are quick to emphasize that evolutionary processes and pathways seldom yield perfect designs. Instead, most biological designs are flawed in some way. To be certain, most biologists would concede that natural selection has produced biological designs that are *well adapted*, but they would maintain that biological systems are *not* well designed. Why? Because evolutionary processes do not produce biological systems from scratch but by hijacking preexisting systems. Once co-opted, these become modified through evolutionary mechanisms to generate a new functional biological system or machine. Natural selection optimizes the new product to become *well-adapted* systems or machines. Nevertheless, they are not *well-designed* systems. Biologist Ken Miller points out that evolution "does not produce perfection." He adds:

> The fact that every intermediate stage in the development of an organ must confer a selective advantage means that the simplest and most elegant design for an organ cannot always be produced by evolution. In fact, the hallmark of evolution is the modification of pre-existing structures. An evolved organism, in short, should show the tell-tale signs of this modification.[12]

If biological systems are, in effect, kludged together, why would engineers and technologists turn to them for inspiration? As a case in point, if the bacterial flagellum is the product of co-option, why would it inspire new technologies? If produced by evolutionary processes—even if these processes operated over the course of millions of years—biological systems should make unreliable muses. Does it make sense for engineers to rely on biological systems—historically contingent and exapted in their origin—to solve problems and inspire new technologies, much less build an entire subdiscipline around mimicking biological designs?

The random, historically contingent processes foundational to evolutionary biology make it unlikely that co-option produced biological and biochemical systems. Using biological designs to guide engineering efforts seems to be fundamentally incompatible with an evolutionary explanation for life's origin and history. On the other hand, biomimetics and bio-inspiration naturally flow out of a creation model approach to biology. Using biological systems to inspire engineering makes better sense if the designs in nature arise from an intelligent mind. All the more so given that these systems are also irreducibly complex.

If biological systems are, in effect, kludged together, why would engineers and technologists turn to them for inspiration?

Discussion Questions

1. Name five minimum biochemical requirements required for cell-like entities to be true life-forms. Does their simultaneous emergence say anything about evolution?

2. How has the bacterial flagellum's irreducible complexity been explained by evolutionary biologists and by intelligent design theorists?

3. How does the discipline of biomimetics and bioinspiration contribute to the complexity debate?

Chapter 21

Has Evolution Refuted the Watchmaker Argument?

by Fazale Rana

The mascot for my high school in Poca, West Virginia, was the "Poca Dot"—true story. The rallying cry for our sports teams went, "We are the Dots! We are the Dots! We are the mighty Poca Dots!" So, the cheer didn't inspire much fear in our opponents, but it was heartfelt.

If there is a rallying cry for advocates of the evolutionary paradigm, it would be the words made famous by the Russian geneticist Theodosius Dobzhansky. He wrote, "Nothing in biology makes sense except in the light of evolution."[1] It's not as rhythmic as the Poca Dot chant, but Dobzhansky's heartfelt declaration reflects the importance of the evolutionary framework as the organizing principle in biology.

Today, life scientists interpret every aspect of biology from an evolutionary vantage point. It goes without saying, this framework was first erected when Charles Darwin proposed his theory of evolution in *On the Origin of Species*. According to this idea, species evolve from preexisting species when natural selection operates iteratively on random, heritable variation that exists within a population.

Darwin did more than simply explain the origin of species. He argued that, over the course of vast time periods, this mechanism could also explain the origin of life's major groups and account for the diversity and biogeographical distribution of life throughout Earth's history. In effect, Darwin revolutionized biology. He brought mechanism into the forefront. Instead of biology being organized around a teleological (design) or morphological (typology) framework, it was now organized around mechanism. Darwin even went so far as to argue that the mechanistic processes of evolution could account for biological innovation and explain the exquisite adaptations organisms have for their environment and the appearance of design, both characteristic of biological systems.

Darwin's revolution supplanted the view of biology forged by thinkers who preceded him, such as William Paley and Sir Richard Owen, both who interpreted the designs in biology as a manifestation of the One Cause. Many life scientists found Darwin's ideas appealing because they provided biology with a mechanistic undergirding, just like geology, physics, and chemistry. The ideas of Paley and Owen were abandoned—and along with them the idea that biological systems reflect the handiwork of a Creator.

The Underdetermination Thesis

To be clear, it is not merely the appeal to mechanism that has led to the widespread acceptance of the evolutionary paradigm. Many life scientists would argue that this paradigm has explanatory power. And it does. The evolutionary framework accounts for many of the features of biological systems, and it also explains the patterns observed in the living realm and the fossil record.

But so does a creation model shaped by the ideas of Paley and Owen. This ambiguity highlights one of the frustrating aspects of science. Often, two competing theories can explain the same set of data. This problem is called the underdetermination thesis[2] (see chapter 3). According to this idea, theories are underdetermined by data. In other words, the methodology of science never leads to one unique theory. Because of this shortcoming, other nonscientific factors influence the acceptance or rejection of a scientific theory. And, since Darwin's time, nonscientific factors—such as the preference of materialism over intelligent design—have favored the evolutionary paradigm and led to the rejection of the teleological framework that was in place in biology until the mid-1800s.

So, has the evolutionary paradigm refuted the design argument?

> **So, has the evolutionary paradigm refuted the design argument?**

In my opinion, the answer is no. Thanks to scientific advances, I think that Paley's design argument and Owen's teleological views are stronger today than ever before and offer a valid alternative to an evolutionary interpretation of biology.

To defend this bold claim, I am going to focus on biochemical systems for one reason: biochemical systems are the fundamental, most basic systems of life. If these systems were designed, then interpreting biology from a creation model gains legitimacy. I'll start with Paley's argument for biological design.

The Watchmaker Argument

In his 1802 work, *Natural Theology, or Evidences of the Existence and Attributes of the Deity Collected from the Appearances of Nature*, Anglican natural theologian William Paley posited the Watchmaker argument. Paley set the stage for his famous analogy by asking his readers to imagine finding a stone and a watch on a heath, and then asking how each came to be there. The stone might be dismissed as having been there forever, but the watch is another story.

> When we come to inspect the watch, we perceive (what we could not discover in the stone) that its several parts are framed and put together for a purpose. . . . If the different parts had been differently shaped from what they are . . . or placed after any other manner, or in any other order, than that in which they are placed, either no motion at all would have been carried on in the machine, or none which would have answered the use that is now served by it. . . . This mechanism being observed . . . the inference we think is inevitable, that the watch must have had a maker . . . who comprehended its construction, and designed its use.[3]

For Paley, the characteristics of a watch and the complex interaction of its precision parts for timekeeping purposes implied the work of a mind. By analogy, Paley concluded that just as a watch requires a Watchmaker, so, too, life requires a Creator, since biological systems display a wide range of features characterized by the precise interplay of complex parts for specific purposes.

According to the Watchmaker analogy, both watches and biology display design. Watches are the product of a Watchmaker. Therefore, biological systems must be the product of a Creator.

Biochemistry and the Watchmaker Argument

Advances in biochemistry over the last few decades have brought new energy to the Watchmaker argument, allowing us to reformulate the argument focusing on biochemical systems instead of biological ones. As a biochemist, I marvel at hallmark features of the cell's chemical systems that are identical to features that we would recognize as evidence for human design.

As human beings, whenever we design, create, and invent systems, objects, and devices, we leave behind telltale signatures in our creations that reflect the work of a mind. Following the reasoning of William Paley, if certain features reflect the work of a human mind, and we see those very features in the cell, then is it not reasonable to conclude that a mind engineered that cell and, hence, life itself?

I am not afforded the space here to detail the characteristics shared by human designs and biochemical systems, but I have done so in my book *The Cell's Design*. Instead, I will illustrate the strength of the revitalized Watchmaker argument by focusing on two protein complexes that operate as molecular-scale machines: (1) the F_1-F_0 ATPase protein complex and (2) the biochemical Turing machines that manipulate DNA. These molecular complexes are two of many that display machine-like properties. As you will see, the similarity between machines designed by humans and these two protein complexes is startling, even eerie.

F_1-F_0 ATPase

This well-studied protein complex plays a key role in the cell's primary energy-harvesting pathway. F_1-F_0 ATPase is a molecular-scale rotary motor. This complex is embedded in the inner membrane of mitochondria and the plasma membrane of bacteria (see chapter 18). The F_1 portion of the complex is mushroom-shaped and extends above the membrane's surface. The button of the mushroom literally corresponds to an engine turbine. It interacts with the part of the complex that looks like a mushroom stalk, which functions as a rotor.

F_1-F_0 ATPase makes use of a proton gradient across the membrane to drive the production of ATP (adenosine triphosphate), a compound used as a cellular energy source. Because protons are positively charged, the region outside the membrane is positively charged and the interior region is negatively charged. The charge differential created by the proton gradient is analogous to a battery, and the inner membrane is like a capacitor.

The flow of positively charged hydrogen ions through the F_0 component, embedded in the cell membrane, drives the rotation of the rotor. A rod-shaped protein structure that also extends above the membrane surface serves as a stator. This protein rod holds the turbine stationary as the rotor moves.

The electrical current that flows through the channels of the F_0 complex is transformed into mechanical energy, which then drives the rotor's movement. Specifically, the protons are shuttled through channels in the F_0 motor, triggering conformational changes that drive the rotation of the rotor by one full turn before they exit the channel. A cam that extends at a right angle from the rotor's surface causes displacements of the turbine. These back-and-forth motions are used to produce ATP.

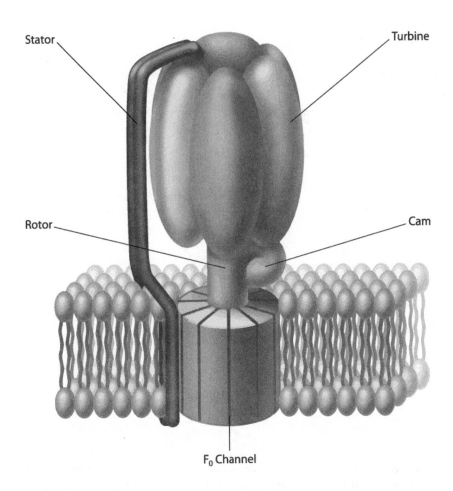

Figure 21.1: F_1-F_0 ATPase

Biochemical Turing Machines

Computer scientists and molecular biologists have come to recognize that the biomolecular machinery that manipulates DNA during replication, transcription, and repair literally functions like a computer system at its most basic level of operation. British mathematician Alan Turing, considered to be the father of theoretical computer science, came up with a theoretical construct for computer systems dubbed Turing machines. These are not actual machines but abstract entities that existed in Turing's mind.

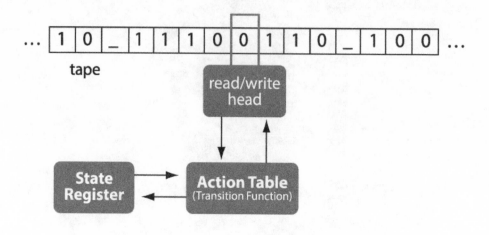

Figure 21.2: Illustration of a Turing Machine

Turing machines consist of three simple components: (1) the input, (2) the finite control, and (3) the output. The input is a string of data that flows into the finite control. The finite control operates on a data string in a prescribed manner, altering it and generating an output stream of data. The finite control can only perform limited operations on the data string. Turing's genius was to recognize that the output of one such machine could become the input to another. In this way, an ensemble of Turing machines can be combined in many ways to perform numerous distinct complex operations.

This is precisely the way that the cell's machinery manipulates the information within DNA. Information housed in DNA is digital information. Whenever a complex biochemical process (e.g., DNA replication) takes place, proteins act as the finite control, taking the digital information in DNA as input, altering it in a prescribed manner, and producing output strands of digital DNA information. While each protein can only perform a limited transformation of the DNA information, by working in combination with other proteins, complex biochemical operations ensue. In other words, when the cell's machinery replicates, transcribes, or repairs DNA, it is essentially carrying out a computer operation.

I think it is obvious how these two biochemical machines (and many others like it) bring new vitality to the Watchmaker argument. If I come across a rotary motor on a heath, I will, upon inspecting its machinery, conclude that it was designed by an intelligent mind. Since biomolecules operate with the same levels of ingenuity and share the same features, does it not make sense to attribute them to the work of God?

Challenges to the Watchmaker Argument

Scholars have leveled objections against Paley's analogy almost since its inception. Today's criticisms of the reinvigorated Watchmaker argument have been shaped by Darwin and the eighteenth-century Scottish skeptic David Hume.

As already noted, Darwin claimed that evolutionary mechanisms could account for the appearance of design in biology. Biological—and, in our case, biochemical designs—are the work of a *blind* Watchmaker, if you will. I will address the blind Watchmaker challenge in greater detail in the next chapter. Here, I will focus attention on challenges inspired by Hume.

In his 1779 work *Dialogues Concerning Natural Religion*, Hume leveled several criticisms against design arguments. The foremost centered around the nature of analogical reasoning. Hume argued that the conclusions resulting from analogical reasoning are only sound when the things compared are highly similar to each other. Less similarity means a weaker conclusion. Thus, Hume dismissed the reasoning that supports analogies like Paley's. Along these lines, critics insist that organisms and watches are nothing alike. They are too dissimilar for a good analogy. What is true for a watch is not necessarily true for an organism. Therefore, it doesn't follow that organisms require a divine Watchmaker just because a watch requires a human one.

Following in Hume's footsteps, philosopher Massimo Pigliucci insists that the analogy between biomolecular machines and human designs is purely *metaphorical* and does not reflect a true analogical relationship. He maintains that any similarity between them is merely *illustrative*, used by life scientists to communicate complex concepts using familiar language. Accordingly, in his assessment, analogies between biomolecular machines and human-made machines do not help the case for a Creator.[4]

A Response Informed by Advances in Nanotechnology

Work in nanotechnology provides a rejoinder to the challenges leveled by Hume and Pigliucci and strengthens Paley's analogy. One of the big challenges for nanotechnology centers around generating and controlling movement in nanodevices. To address this problem, some nanotechnologists have been exploring the prospects of isolating biomolecular machines from the cell and incorporating these protein complexes into nanodevices with the explicit purpose of taking advantage of their machine-like properties. These researchers have demonstrated, in principle, that these transplanted biomachines can overcome current hurdles to powering nanodevice movements. Nanotechnologists view and utilize these biomolecular systems *as actual machines*.

Cornell University scientists carried out a landmark study that produced a hybrid nanomechanical device powered by F_1-F_0 ATPase.[5] The Cornell researchers attached nickel nanopropellers to the F_1-F_0 ATPase rotor. Upon the addition of ATP, the nanopropellers rotated at a velocity of 0.74 to 8.3 revolutions per second. The F_1-F_0 ATPase-powered nanodevice operated at nearly 80 percent efficiency. (For comparison, an automobile engine runs at 20 percent efficiency.)

Biomolecular machines are not metaphorical machines; instead, they really *are* machines in a literal, functionally equivalent sense. The same goes for the biochemical Turing machines that operate on DNA. The similarity between DNA replication, transcription, and DNA repair and the fundamental operation of computer systems has inspired a brand-new area of nanotechnology called DNA computing, the brainchild of computer scientist Leonard Adleman.[6]

DNA computers are made up of DNA and the proteins that manipulate this biomolecule inside the cell. These computers are housed in tiny test tubes, yet they are more powerful than the best supercomputer system available to us. Their power stems largely from the capacity of DNA computers to perform a vast number of parallel computations simultaneously. Adleman describes the relationship between computers and biology:

> The most important thing about DNA computing is that it shows that DNA molecules can do what we normally think only computers can do. This implies that computer science and biology are closely related. That every living thing can be thought to be computing something, and that, sometimes, we can understand living things better by looking at them as computers.[7]

In other words, biochemical Turing machines *are* veritable Turing machines.

Despite the derision of naturalists, the Watchmaker argument has yet to be nullified. In fact, the opposite appears to be the case. Advances in biochemistry have breathed new life into this argument. Moreover, advances in nanotechnology effectively dismantle the critique that Hume, Pigliucci, and others have leveled against the analogical reasoning of Paley's argument. And, as we will see in the next chapter, advances in synthetic biology undermine the blind Watchmaker challenge leveled by Darwin and others.

Using the Watchmaker argument to successfully demonstrate the validity of creationism paves the way to reinstate the teleological framework for biology laid out by Sir Richard Owen and others.

Archetype or Ancestors?

Many biologists today consider homologies—the shared anatomical, physiological, biochemical, and genetic features possessed by organisms that naturally group together—as the most compelling evidence for biological evolution.

Yet, prior to Darwin, biologists interpreted shared features quite differently. Biologist Sir Richard Owen's work demonstrates that it is possible to understand features like homology independent of the evolutionary paradigm. Sixteen years before Darwin published *On the Origin of Species*, Owen delivered a discourse at the meeting of the Royal Institution of Great Britain entitled "On the Nature of Limbs." In this presentation (and elsewhere), Owen proposed interpreting homologies as archetypical designs. Using the concept of the vertebrate archetype, Owen provided a theoretical framework to interpret anatomical and physiological similarities shared among organisms. Owen saw these mutual features as manifestations of a common blueprint.

Prior to Darwin, biologists interpreted shared features quite differently.

Even though the human hand, the bat's wing, the horse's hoof, and a whale's flipper all perform distinct functions, Owen recognized that these structures all had the same basic design (or form). Therefore, he argued, a Creator designed these appendages using the same archetype. Interestingly, Owen (and other like-minded biologists) even explained vestigial structures, like the pelvis and hind limb bones found in whales and snakes, as structures necessary to the architectural design of the organism.

Owen believed the archetype represented teleology of a higher order. In his presentation Owen stated:

> The satisfaction felt by the rightly constituted mind must ever be great in recognizing the fitness of parts for their appropriate function; but when this fitness is gained as in the great-toe of the foot of man and the ostrich, by a structure which at the same time betokens harmonious concord with a common type, the prescient operations of the One Cause of all organization becomes strikingly manifested to our limited intelligence.[8]

Owen's conception of function and form were strongly theistic. According to Owen, the archetype points to a "deep and pregnant principle . . . some archetypal exemplar on which it has pleased the Creator to frame certain of his living creatures."[9]

When Darwin proposed his theory of biological evolution, he made use of the vertebrate archetype in support of his theory. He argued that homologous structures were physically instantiated in the common ancestor that gave rise to land vertebrates. In doing so, Darwin replaced the archetype with the common ancestor. As a result, homology began serving as evidence for common descent. *But,* because theories are underdetermined by data, evolutionists cannot claim that their theory alone explains homologies. A creation model also accommodates the data.

Extending Owen's Archetypal Designs

The world of biochemistry and genetics was unknown to Owen and Darwin, but Owen's idea of the archetype applies to a molecular level, as well as the morphological level.

For example, all life on Earth makes use of the same biochemical systems. Every living system harbors DNA. And this DNA is replicated, transcribed, and repaired by the same mechanisms. Every life-form utilizes proteins built from the same 20 amino acids. These proteins are made by the same process. The genetic code is the same for every organism.

Many life scientists regard the universal nature of biochemical systems—a form of homology—as evidence that life descended from a last universal common ancestor. But, taking Owens's lead, I would argue that these shared, fundamental features reflect archetypical designs, not common descent. Likewise, genetic similarities observed among organisms that are grouped together or distributed widely (i.e., evolutionary convergences) could be understood as reflecting common design. However, many life scientists would disagree because of the shared "junk DNA" sequences in genomes. Frequently, the identical junk DNA segments reside in corresponding locations in these genomes. For many biologists, this clearly indicates that these organisms shared a common ancestor. Accordingly, the junk DNA segment arose prior to the time that the organisms diverged from their shared evolutionary ancestor. I respond to the junk DNA challenge in chapter 23.

The argument from design seems an empirical equivalent to that of evolution. For some this recognition elicits cheers, for others, boos.

Discussion Questions

1. How does the underdetermination thesis inform the evolution vs. teleology argument?

2. Evaluate the statement that "organisms and watches are nothing alike." What bearing does it have on the Watchmaker analogy?

3. Are biomolecular machines real machines? Why or why not, and what do they suggest about analogical reasoning?

4. Name several examples of homologies and how Owen argued for "teleology of a higher order."

5. Do shared fundamental biological features better reflect common descent or common design?

Chapter 22

Is the Watchmaker Really Blind?

by Fazale Rana

Evolutionary biologist Ernst Mayr once called *On the Origin of Species* "one long argument."[1] I would describe it as one long rebuttal. When Darwin wrote his masterpiece, he had William Paley's *Natural Theology* in full view. Arguably, one of Darwin's objectives was to replace Paley's notion of the divine Watchmaker (see chapter 21) with natural selection as a way to account for adaptation and the appearance of design.

In the chapter in *On the Origins of Species* devoted to difficulties with his theory, Darwin addresses "organs of extreme perfection." He acknowledges that it was hard to envision how natural selection could produce organs as sophisticated and elaborate as the camera eye found in vertebrates. Darwin chose to focus on the vertebrate eye because Paley highlighted it as the quintessential example of design in *Natural Theology*. For Paley, if the only example of a biological contrivance available to us was the vertebrate eye, then its sophisticated design alone justifies the necessity of an intelligent Designer to explain its origin.

Yet, Darwin was convinced that natural selection could even create a biological system as seemingly perfect as the vertebrate eye:

> To suppose that the eye, with all its inimitable contrivances for adjusting the focus to different distances, for admitting different amounts of light, and for the correction of spherical and chromatic aberration . . . could have been formed by natural selection, seems, I freely confess, absurd in the highest possible degree. If numerous gradations from a perfect and complex eye to one very imperfect and simple, each grade

being useful to its possessor, can be shown to exist . . . if further, the eye does vary ever so slightly, and the variations be inherited, which is certainly the case; and if any variation or modification in the organ be ever useful to an animal under changing conditions of life, then the difficulty of believing that a perfect and complex eye could be formed by natural selection, though insuperable by our imagination, can hardly be considered real.[2]

Many in the scientific community believe this explanation for the vertebrate eye sealed the deal for Darwin's theory of evolution and rang the death knell for design arguments. Evolutionary biologist Richard Dawkins puts it this way in his book *The Blind Watchmaker*:

[Paley] had a proper reverence for the complexity of the living world, and he saw that it demands a very special kind of explanation. The only thing he got wrong was the explanation itself. . . . Natural selection, the blind, unconscious, automatic process which we now know is the explanation for the existence and apparently purposeful form of all life, has no purpose in mind. It has no mind and no mind's eye. It does not plan for the future. It has no vision, no foresight, no sight at all. If it can be said to play the role of watchmaker in nature, it is the blind watchmaker.[3]

Can evolutionary mechanisms fully account for the designs that we see in biology and biochemistry? Is the Watchmaker really blind?

But is this really the case? Can evolutionary mechanisms fully account for the designs that we see in biology and biochemistry? Is the Watchmaker really blind?

I'm not so sure. I'm not convinced that the Watchmaker is blind. I'm not convinced that evolutionary mechanisms alone can account for the design of biological and biochemical systems, and part of the reason for my skepticism finds its basis in synthetic biology.

Synthetic Biology

Synthetic biology is a relatively new interdisciplinary research program at the intersection of biology and engineering. Its chief goal is the production of artificial biological systems with the hopes that these laboratory creations will have use in biomedicine, agriculture, and industry. Some scientists working in synthetic biology also hope that their attempts to create nonnatural biological systems and life-forms will help them develop a fundamental understanding of life's processes.

Other researchers see synthetic biology as a powerful tool to help them elucidate key transitions in life's history. Their objective is to use synthetic biology to help them understand how life could have originated and evolved, but they've achieved the opposite of what they intended. Instead of developing insights into key evolutionary transitions, synthetic biologists have demonstrated the central role intelligent agency *must* play in any scientific explanation for the origin, design, and history of life. They have shown that the Watchmaker must be fully sighted and insightful.

I will illustrate this point by examining four recent studies designed by synthetic biologists to understand the origin of life, new metabolic pathways, eukaryotic cells, and the human genome.

Creating Self-Replicating Protocells

In attempts to understand the origin of life, researchers strive to create protocells—chemical super-systems with the properties of life. For example, in 2015, a team of Japanese researchers created protocells with the capacity to self-replicate continuously for multiple generations. Specifically, these scientists formed vesicles that they could stimulate to grow and divide. They coupled the replication of DNA in the vesicles' internal compartment to the growth and division process. They even devised a way to replenish the daughter vesicles with nutrients after cell division took place so that these newly formed entities could, in turn, grow and divide. These researchers concluded that their work "demonstrates how collaborative dynamics emerged from nonliving matter under certain circumstances."[4]

I interpret the results of this study very differently. In my view, their work *undermines* the evolutionary paradigm. It provides empirical evidence that an intelligent agent must play a crucial role in the transformation of nonliving material into cell-like entities.

To achieve their results, the researchers had to devise a sophisticated strategy that required extremely knowledgeable and skilled scientists to execute the experiment under highly controlled conditions in the laboratory. For example, the researchers selected the right types of phospholipids—the molecules that play a key role in forming cell membranes—to form stable vesicles. They also designed and manufactured two synthetic, nonbiological lipids with specialized properties.

These lipids helped in coupling DNA replication to vesicle growth and division. One of these lipids, a catalyst dubbed C, was added to the two phospholipid species used to form the initial vesicle population. The researchers had to adjust the initial phospholipid and C compositions to form stable vesicles that would then be capable of growing, dividing, and becoming tied to DNA replication.

Next, the scientists encapsulated nucleotides (dNTPs)—the building blocks of DNA— single-stranded DNA, carefully designed DNA primers, and a special type of DNA polymerase (an enzyme that replicates DNA) into the vesicles' interior compartment. This encapsulation process required the researchers to implement an exacting laboratory protocol that involved drying the lipids so that they formed a film and then rehydrating the film (with a solution containing the dNTPs, single-stranded DNA, DNA primers, and DNA polymerase), followed by incubation under a precise set of conditions.

Once the materials for replication were encapsulated, the researchers carefully heated the vesicles to trigger DNA replication. The interior walls of the vesicles automatically absorbed newly formed DNA molecules. This binding took place because the lipid catalyst (C) was designed to possess a positive charge, triggering its interaction with negatively charged DNA.

After cooling down the system, the researchers added another synthetic lipid (V) to the vesicles. The C reacted with the V, converting V into a derivative material that caused the vesicles to grow and become destabilized. The destabilization caused the vesicles to fissure into two daughter vesicles.

In the next step, the researchers replenished the newly formed daughter vesicles with dNTPs so that the next round of DNA replication could take place. They accomplished this feat by encapsulating the dNTPs in vesicles dubbed conveyor vesicles. The lipid composition of these vesicles had to be carefully adjusted so that they possessed a negative charge on their surface. The negative charge made it possible for the conveyor vesicles to fuse with the daughter vesicles, which were designed to possess a positively charged surface. The fusion events were triggered by a dramatic change in solution pH, orchestrated by the researchers. The researchers also had to adjust the amount of the C in the conveyor vesicles so that when they fused with the daughter vesicles the newly formed DNA would bind to the membrane wall of the daughter vesicles, allowing the cycle of growth and division to repeat.

Even though the Japanese scientists see their research efforts as providing support for a chemical evolutionary origin of life, their own description of the work betrays their convictions (emphasis added):

> To achieve this goal, we *selected* well-defined suitable lipids and macromolecules, including newly *designed* ones, and *constructed* a giant vesicle (GV)-based model protocell that links self-replication of information molecules (RNA/DNA) with the self-reproduction of a compartment (GV).[5]

These scientists can't avoid using design language because the self-replicating protocells they produced were intelligently designed and fabricated.

Creating Novel Metabolic Pathways

Each year, tons of noscapine is harvested from thousands of tons of raw poppy plants. The drug (and its chemically modified derivatives) has a variety of uses, including as a cough suppressant and, as biomedical researchers recently learned, as a potential anti-cancer drug. However, biochemical engineers question whether the agricultural supply line will be able to meet the extra demand if noscapine finds use as an anti-cancer agent. Chemists have developed synthetic routes to make noscapine, but this method is too complex and costly for large-scale production.

In 2018, researchers from Stanford University proposed a possible solution to the noscapine supply problem. They have genetically engineered brewer's yeast to produce large quantities of noscapine.[6] To do so, the Stanford scientists had to construct a biosynthetic pathway that would convert simple carbon- and nitrogen-containing compounds into noscapine. They then added genes to the yeast's genome that would produce the enzymes needed to carry out this transformation. Specifically, they added 25 genes from plants, bacteria, and mammals to this microbe's genome. The team also had to modify six of the yeast's own genes.

Biosynthetic pathways that yield complex molecules such as noscapine can be rather elaborate. Enzymes form these pathways. These enzymes bind molecules and convert them into new materials by facilitating chemical reactions. The first enzyme in the pathway modifies the starting molecule. After its transformation, the modified molecule is shuttled to the second enzyme. This process continues until the original molecule is converted step-by-step into the final product.

Designing a biosynthetic route from scratch would be nearly impossible. Fortunately, the team from Stanford took advantage of previous work that had characterized the metabolic reactions that produce noscapine in opium poppies. They identified a cluster of 10 genes that encode enzymes that work collaboratively to convert the compound scoulerine to noscapine.

The Stanford researchers used these 10 poppy genes as the basis for the noscapine biosynthetic route they designed. They expanded the pathway by using genes that encode for the enzymes that convert glucose into reticuline, which is converted into scoulerine by the berberine bridge enzyme. Dopamine, one of the intermediary compounds in the pathway, created a complication for the research team. Life scientists don't have a good understanding of how poppies make dopamine, so the Stanford team used the genes that encode the enzymes to make dopamine from rats. They discovered that when they added all these genes into the yeast these modified microbes produced low levels of noscapine. At this point, the research team carried out a series of steps to optimize noscapine production:

- Genetically altering some of the enzymes in the noscapine biosynthetic pathway to improve their efficiency
- Manipulating other metabolic pathways (by altering the expression of the genes that encode enzymes in these metabolic routes) to divert the maximum amounts of metabolic intermediates into the newly constructed noscapine pathway
- Varying the media used to grow the yeast

These steps led to an 18,000-fold improvement in noscapine production. With this accomplishment, the scientific community is one step closer to a commercially viable source of noscapine. In short, these researchers demonstrated that intelligent agency is required to originate new metabolic capabilities in an organism. This work also illustrates the level of ingenuity required to optimize a metabolic pathway once it is in place.

Creating Endosymbionts

I discussed the endosymbiosis hypothesis in chapter 18, summarizing some key evidence in support of this idea, but I left out one important piece of evidence: endosymbionts are widespread throughout the biological realm.

Numerous examples exist of bacterial endosymbionts that reside inside the cells of eukaryotic organisms. For example, between 10 to 15 percent of insect species serve as hosts for intracellular microbes. Some of these endosymbionts provide benefits for the host cell, others are parasites. Often, the endosymbionts are obligate intracellular parasites with reduced genomes. These microbes can jettison genes because they can exploit host cell biochemistry.

Evolutionary biologists argue that if these types of endosymbiotic relationships exist today, then it supports the idea that endosymbiosis led to the formation of mitochondria. However, it is worth pointing out that the formation of endosymbiotic relationships is just the first presumed step in the process of symbiogenesis—and perhaps the easiest. The endosymbiont hypothesis still faces many serious questions (see chapter 18).

To help resolve some of these questions, in 2018, scientists from Scripps Research tried to replicate the earliest stages of mitochondrial evolution by engineering *E. coli* and brewer's yeast (*Saccharomyces cerevisiae*) to form an endosymbiotic relationship.[7]

This work was a scientific tour de force. First, the research team disabled a gene involved in making thiamine to generate a strain of *E. coli* that could no longer produce this compound. Without this metabolic capacity, this strain becomes dependent on an exogenous source of thiamine to survive. *E. coli* can grow if an external supply of thiamine is available because its genome encodes for a transporter protein that can pump this metabolite into the cell from the exterior environment. For modified *E. coli* incorporated into yeast cells, the thiamine in the yeast cytoplasm serves as the exogenous source and renders *E. coli* dependent on the yeast cell's metabolic processes.

Next, the research team transferred the gene that encodes ADP/ATP translocase into the *E. coli* strain. This gene was harbored on a plasmid (a small circular piece of DNA). Normally, the gene is found in the genome of an endosymbiotic bacterium that infects amoeba. This protein pumps ATP from the interior of the bacterial cell to the exterior environment.

The team then exposed yeast cells deficient in ATP production to polyethylene glycol, which creates a passageway for *E. coli* to make their way into the yeast cells. In doing so, *E. coli* become established as endosymbionts within the yeast cells' interior. The *E. coli* provided ATP to the yeast cell and the yeast cell provided thiamine to the bacterial cells.

However, researchers discovered that the *E. coli* did not persist inside the cell's interior. They reasoned that the lysosomal degradation pathway destroyed the bacterial cells. To prevent this destruction, the research team had to introduce three additional genes into the E. coli from three separate endosymbiotic bacteria. Each of these genes encodes proteins that interfere with the lysosomal destruction pathway. Finally, to establish a mutual relationship between the modified E. coli and the yeast cell, the researchers used a yeast strain with defective mitochondria that hampered ATP production. This defect made the yeast cells dependent on the engineered E. coli as a source of ATP, with the bacterial cells transporting ATP from their cellular interior to their exterior environment (the yeast cytoplasm).

The researchers observed that the yeast cells with E. coli endosymbionts appeared to be stable for 40 rounds of cell doublings.

Establishing mutualistic interactions between the two organisms required a significant amount of ingenuity—genius that is reflected in the experimental strategy and design of their study. In other words, the endosymbiotic relationship between these two organisms was intelligently designed. Moreover, all this work recapitulated *only* the presumed *first* step in the process of symbiogenesis.

Creating Fused Chromosomes

For many people, the genetic comparisons between humans and chimpanzees convince them that human evolution is true. Presumably, the shared genetic features in the human and chimpanzee genomes reflect the species' shared evolutionary ancestry (see chapter 14).

One high-profile example of these similarities is the structural features human chromosome 2 shares with two chimpanzee chromosomes labeled chromosome 2A and chromosome 2B. When the two chimpanzee chromosomes are placed end to end, they look remarkably like human chromosome 2. Evolutionary biologists interpret this genetic similarity as evidence that human chromosome 2 arose when ancestral chromosomes 2A and 2B underwent an end-on-end fusion. They claim that this fusion took place in the human evolutionary lineage at some point *after* it separated from the lineage that led to chimpanzees and bonobos. Therefore, the similarity in these chromosomes provides strong evidence that humans and chimpanzees share an evolutionary ancestry.

Natural fusion of human chromosome 2 shouldn't be taken as a foregone conclusion. I would argue that God intervened to create human chromosome 2—because combining chromosomes 2A and 2B to form it would have required a succession of highly unlikely events.

The events required for end-on-end fusion of two chromosomes at the telomeres would almost always result in chromosomal instability before the actual fusion took place. Even if the fusion *did* result in a stable product, it would alter the number of chromosomes and lead to one of three possible scenarios: (1) nonviable offspring, (2) viable offspring that suffer from a diseased state, or (3) viable but likely infertile offspring. Each of these scenarios would prevent the fused chromosome from entering and becoming entrenched in the human gene pool. On the slim chance that a stable fused chromosome could be passed on, the event would have had to create such a large evolutionary advantage that it would rapidly sweep through the population. With such hurdles facing evolutionary explanations, human chromosome 2 makes more sense as the work of the divine Creator.

> **With such hurdles facing evolutionary explanations, human chromosome 2 makes more sense as the work of the divine Creator.**

In 2018, work by two separate teams of synthetic biologists (one from the United States and the other from China) also raised questions about this evolutionary scenario. Both research teams devised similar gene-editing techniques that they used to fuse chromosomes in brewer's yeast.[8] Their work demonstrates the central role intelligent agency must play in end-on-end chromosome fusion.

Both research groups conducted similar experiments using gene editing to reduce the number of chromosomes in brewer's yeast, through a succession of fusion events. The Chinese team took the yeast's chromosome count from 16 to 1; the US team took it from 16 to 2. The teams worked in stages, fusing pairs of chromosomes, one set at a time. The first fusion attempt reduced the number from 16 to 8. In the next round, they fused pairs of the newly created chromosomes to reduce the number from 8 to 4, and so on.

To both teams' surprise, the yeast seemed to tolerate this radical genome editing quite well—although their growth rate slowed and the yeast failed to thrive under certain laboratory conditions. Gene expression was altered in the modified yeast genomes, but only for a few genes. Most of the 5,800 genes in the brewer's yeast genome were expressed normally, compared to the wild-type strain.

I would argue that this work with brewer's yeast provides empirical

Figure 22: Comparison of Human Chromosome 2 and Chimpanzee Chromosomes 2A and 2B

evidence that human chromosome 2 must have been shaped by an intelligent agent. This research also reinforces my concerns about the capacity of evolutionary mechanisms to generate human chromosome 2 via the fusion of two ancestral chromosomes.

Both research teams had to carefully design the gene-editing system they used so that it would delete two distinct regions in the chromosomes. This process affected end-on-end chromosome fusions in a way that would allow the yeast cells to survive. Specifically, they had to delete regions of the chromosomes near the telomeres (see figure 22), including the highly repetitive telomere-associated sequences. While they carried out this deletion, they had to carefully avoid deleting gene-harboring sequences near the telomeres. They also had to simultaneously delete one of the two centromeres (see figure 22) to ensure that the fused chromosome would properly replicate and segregate during cell division. Finally, the teams had to make sure that when the two chromosomes fused, the remaining centromere was positioned near the center of the resulting chromosome.

Both experiments also required careful construction of the sequence of donor DNA that accompanied the CRISPR gene-editing package so that the chromosomes with the deleted telomeres could be directed to fuse end on end. Without the donor DNA, the fusion would have been haphazard.

Successful outcomes depended on the researchers possessing detailed understanding of chromosome structure and biology and a strategy to use this knowledge to design precise gene-editing protocols. Such planning would ensure that chromosome fusion occurred without the loss of important genetic information and without disrupting key processes. The researchers' painstaking efforts are a far cry from random or haphazard events that evolutionary biologists think led to human chromosome 2. In fact, it is hard to envision how random evolutionary processes could ever achieve what these teams accomplished.

On top of this, both research teams made a discovery that further complicates the evolutionary explanation for human chromosome 2. Namely, the yeast cells could not replicate unless the fused chromosomes had one of its two centromeres deleted during the laboratory-directed fusion. Omitting this step disrupted cell division. Centromeres serve as the point of attachment for the mitotic apparatus. If a chromosome possesses two centromeres, then mistakes occur in the chromosome segregation step during cell division.

It is interesting, then, that human chromosome 2 has two centromeres, but one of them has been inactivated. If human chromosome 2 resulted from the fusion of two ancestral chromosomes, then the initial fusion product would have possessed two activate centromeres. It would have taken millennia to deactivate one of the centromeres as mutations accrued slowly in this region of the chromosome. Yet, the yeast studies indicate that centromere loss must take place *simultaneously* with end-on-end fusion. Evolutionary mechanisms, by their nature, cannot follow this sequence. The fusion of yeast chromosomes in the lab makes it hard to think that unguided evolutionary processes could ever successfully fuse two chromosomes, including human chromosome 2, end on end. Creation makes more sense.

Synthetic Biology and the Case for a Creator

These four sample studies represent science at its very best. In each case, researchers demonstrated that intelligent agency played a critical role in originating protocells, engineering new metabolic capabilities, establishing endosymbiotic relationships, and producing end-on-end chromosomal fusions.

All these scientists relied on hundreds of years of scientific knowledge to begin their work. Then, each team developed an elaborate experimental strategy to effect these transformations. It took highly educated and skilled life scientists to go in the lab to carry out the experimental strategy, under highly controlled conditions and utilizing highly sophisticated equipment.

The level of ingenuity displayed by the research teams in all four cases is something to behold. It is for this reason I maintain that these studies (along with other work in synthetic biology) provide empirical evidence that the origin, history, and design of life requires a Watchmaker that is neither absent nor blind.

Discussion Questions

1. How has the design of the vertebrate eye been interpreted historically and currently?

2. What key element is involved in the four studies relating to the origin of life, chromosome 2, eukaryotic cells, and new metabolic pathways?

3. Do breakthroughs in synthetic biology seem to support evolution or creation? If the latter, what does this evidence suggest about the trend of scientific advance?

Chapter 23

Is Junk DNA Evidence for Evolution?

by Fazale Rana

My wife enjoys looking for antiques (and, to my horror, buying them). For Amy, antiques are priceless treasures. To me, these relics are just old junk. For years, biochemists thought the same of a vast proportion of the genome.

Many life scientists consider the existence of so-called junk DNA in the genomes of organisms as one of the most potent pieces of evidence for biological evolution. According to this view, junk DNA results when undirected processes and random events transform once-functional DNA into a useless string of nucleotides—a molecular artifact. Junk sequences of DNA remain part of an organism's genome solely because of the proximity of these sequences to functional regions. In this way, junk DNA persists from generation to generation.

Identical (or nearly identical) segments of junk DNA often appear in a wide range of related organisms and reside in corresponding locations in these genomes. For many life scientists, this clearly indicates that these organisms shared a common ancestor. Accordingly, their shared evolutionary ancestors harbored junk DNA segments that were passed on to divergent lineages.

Junk DNA has become an icon of evolution. Scientists and skeptics alike maintain that because junk DNA is vestigial, it provides incontrovertible proof of evolution. They rightly ask where shared junk DNA fits in a creation model.

Molecular biologists and geneticists have discovered many categories of junk DNA. It is beyond the scope of this chapter to describe all the different types, let alone the biochemical mechanisms scientists believe were responsible for generating them. So, I will focus on pseudogenes, one of the most important classes of junk DNA.

Pseudogenes and the Case for Biological Evolution

Traditionally, evolutionary biologists have regarded pseudogenes as dead, useless remains of once-functional genes. Nevertheless, pseudogenes possess telltale signatures that allow molecular biologists to recognize them as genes. There exists three distinct classes of pseudogenes.

Unitary Pseudogenes

The relatively rare unitary pseudogenes occur as single copies in genomes. Presumably, the loss of the gene that degenerated into a unitary pseudogene does not compromise the organism's fitness if its lifestyle doesn't depend on that gene.

Evolutionary biologists have discovered several identical unitary pseudogenes shared among humans and other primates. The classic example is the one that supposedly encoded the enzyme L-gulono-gamma-lactone oxidase (GLO) in primates. In other mammals (except guinea pigs), GLO plays a role in ascorbic acid (vitamin C) biosynthesis. However, primates do not have a functional GLO enzyme—rather they possess a GLO pseudogene. According to the evolutionary paradigm, mutations corrupted this gene and render vitamin C biosynthesis impossible for primates. This does not hamper their fitness, however, because they receive the vitamin through dietary sources.

Duplicated Pseudogenes

Molecular biologists suggest that duplicated pseudogenes arose when genes underwent duplication in the genome. Afterwards, the copies experienced severe mutations that rendered them unrecognizable as a functional gene by the cell's machinery. Loss of the duplicated gene's function has little, if any, effect on an organism's fitness, since an intact functional copy still exists.

Processed Pseudogenes

The process that generates processed pseudogenes (as conceived by molecular biologists) is complex. Biologists believe that these types of pseudogenes originated from the RNA transcribed from these genes. RNA messages undergo several alterations before making their way to the ribosome. This includes removing segments in the RNA that correspond to noncoding regions (introns) of the gene, splicing together the segments that correspond to coding regions (exons), and modifying and making additions to the ends of the RNA molecule.

Processed pseudogenes are thought to arise when reverse transcriptase generates DNA from the processed messenger RNA. Once produced, this newly formed DNA—now called a processed pseudogene—is inserted back into the genome. The pseudogene resembles the gene from which it originated. However, the gene also contains telltale signs of having been processed. Presumably this type of pseudogene is nonfunctional because it lacks the regions that surround functional genes, regions used by the cell's machinery to initiate the production of the RNA transcript.

The Assumptions Shaping the Case for Common Descent

Humans and primates share all three types of pseudogenes. These shared DNA sequences occur in the same locations of their genomes and often possess nearly the same types of mutations. Evolutionary biologists assume this indicates shared ancestry among humans and other primates. Their case—based on shared pseudogenes (and other types of junk DNA sequences)—appears compelling, but it is critical to remember that it is shaped by a prior commitment to the evolutionary framework. Moreover, it hinges on the belief that junk DNA isn't functional, even though, for the most part, this belief has not been established experimentally.

Over the last few decades, molecular biologists and geneticists have discovered numerous examples in which noncoding DNA belonging to virtually every class of junk DNA plays a functional role—based on experimental data. In her book *Junk DNA*, Nessa Carey describes some of the studies that establish the functional importance of junk DNA sequences.[1] These discoveries undermine what appears to be an open-and-shut case for biological evolution, while at the same time offering newfound support for a creation model interpretation of shared genomic features. If the shared junk DNA sequences display function, then one could interpret them as reflecting common design, not common descent.

> **If the shared junk DNA sequences display function, then one could interpret them as reflecting common design, not common descent.**

Pseudogenes Are Functional

It is incorrect to claim that processed pseudogenes are nonfunctional.[2] As noted in my books *Who Was Adam?* and *The Cell's Design*, scientists have determined that a number of processed pseudogenes generate messenger RNA (mRNA) transcripts that are translated into functional proteins or play a role regulating gene expression. (See *Who Was Adam?* for a detailed list references to the scientific literature in support of these two points.)

Equally exciting is the recent recognition that duplicated pseudogenes also help regulate gene expression via a "decoy mechanism." Perhaps the most unexpected discovery is that unitary pseudogenes also have function.

In fact, researchers have proposed the competitive endogenous RNA (ceRNA) hypothesis to provide an elegant and coherent explanation for the functional utility of duplicated and unitary pseudogenes, along with other types of junk DNA sequences (such as those that encode long noncoding RNAs).[3] It explains why pseudogenes must share structural similarity to corresponding intact genes. To fully appreciate the ceRNA hypothesis, some background information is in order.

Regulation of Gene Expression

Gene expression refers to the process employed by the cell's machinery to read the information harbored in DNA and to use it to make proteins. Some genes are expressed throughout the cell cycle (a cycle of cellular growth, rest, and division). Biochemists call these "housekeeping" genes because they specify the production of proteins required for the life-essential biochemical activities that operate continually inside the cell. Other genes are expressed only at certain points in the cell cycle when the proteins they specify are needed. When not required, these genes are turned off. However, gene expression involves more than simply turning genes on and off. It also entails regulating the amount of proteins produced. By way of analogy, gene expression is both the on-off switch *and* volume control for each gene in the organism's genome.

Biochemists and molecular biologists believed that the primary mechanism for regulating gene expression involved controlling the frequency and amount of mRNA produced during transcription. In other words, mRNA is produced continually for housekeeping genes, but for genes that specify situational proteins, it is produced as needed. More mRNA is produced for highly expressed genes and less for genes expressed at low levels.

Researchers long thought that mRNA was translated into proteins as soon as it was produced. Recent discoveries indicate this is not the case. Instead, an elaborate mechanism exists that degrades certain mRNA transcripts before they can be used to direct protein production. By permitting or preventing mRNA translation, this mechanism dictates the amount of proteins produced.

Thus, selective degradation of mRNA plays a role in gene expression and functions in a manner complementary to the transcriptional control of gene expression. Selective degradation of mRNA is also mediated by microRNAs. In the early 2000s, biochemists recognized that microRNAs bind to mRNA (in the 3' untranslated region of the transcript) to reduce protein production through multiple mechanisms. There are several distinct microRNA species in the cell that bind to specific sites in the 3' untranslated region of mRNA transcripts.

Duplicated Pseudogenes Are Molecular Decoys

Selective binding by microRNAs explains the role that duplicated pseudogenes play in regulating gene expression. The sequence similarity between the duplicated pseudogene and the corresponding intact gene means that the same microRNAs will bind to both mRNA transcripts. Though apparently never translated into proteins, most duplicated pseudogenes are transcribed into mRNA. It would be an extremely inefficient use of a cell's resource if these transcripts are nonfunctional junk. This is where the ceRNA hypothesis sheds some light.

All transcribed unitary and duplicated pseudogenes serve as molecular decoys by binding microRNAs and, thus, permitting the translation of intact genes to regulate the proper amount of proteins needed in the cell. This important new insight means that shared pseudogenes in the genomes of humans and the great apes do not demand an evolutionary interpretation. From a creation standpoint, one could maintain that the unitary and duplicated pseudogenes shared among the genomes of humans and the great apes reflect common design.

If space permitted, I could describe similar advances that demonstrate the functional importance of other types of junk DNA sequences. All these advances demonstrate that one of the key assumptions in support of common descent is simply invalid.

Can the Evolutionary Framework Account for Functional Junk DNA?

So, what do evolutionary biologists say about these discoveries? Proponents of the evolutionary paradigm offer this rejoinder: *Some* pseudogenes are functional, but the majority lack function; therefore, the majority is still junk. They maintain that, through a process called neofunctionalization, evolutionary mechanisms occasionally generate functional pseudogenes after the genes initially arise through mutational events.

This explanation seems reasonable on the surface, but I don't find it compelling for two reasons:

1. The pervasiveness of function for unitary and duplicated pseudogenes implied by the ceRNA hypothesis
2. Instances of junk DNA convergence, in which it appears as if junk DNA evolved identical function on separate occasions in unrelated organisms

If the ceRNA hypothesis is valid, then it implies that pseudogene function is widespread. It is one thing to say that pseudogenes *occasionally* acquired functions via undirected natural processes. It is another thing entirely to say that this happened over and over, until virtually every pseudogene in the genome possesses function. It is all too common for evolutionary biologists to extrapolate from one or a few observations to general assertions regarding questions of origins when it suits their paradigm. Yet when it comes to junk DNA the growing number of observations seems to have little impact on evolutionary biologists who continue to insist that vast portions of the human genome are useless. It seems to me that this is paradigm-driven storytelling at its worst.

Regarding the convergence of functional junk DNA, one of the most remarkable examples was uncovered by a collaboration of California and New York researchers in 2018.[4] In this instance, the convergence involved a class of junk DNA known as SINE (short interspersed nuclear elements) DNA. SINE DNA sequences range in size from 100 to 300 base pairs. In primates, the most common SINEs are the *Alu* sequences. There are about 1.1 million *Alu* copies in the human genome (roughly 12 percent of the genome). All SINE sequences contain DNA segments used to produce RNAs. Because of this feature, molecular biologists also categorize SINE DNAs as retroposons. Molecular biologists believe that SINE sequences can multiply in number within an organism's genome through the activity of reverse transcriptase (an enzyme). Presumably, once SINE DNAs are transcribed, reverse transcriptase converts SINE RNAs back into DNA. The reconverted DNA sequences then randomly integrate back into the genome. It's through these duplication and reintegration mechanisms that SINE sequences proliferate and move around, or retrotranspose, throughout the genome. To say it another way, molecular biologists believe that over time transcription of SINE DNAs and reverse transcription of SINE RNAs increases the copy number of SINE sequences and randomly disperses them throughout an organism's genome.

As with other types of junk DNA, molecular biologists have discovered numerous instances in which nearly identical SINE segments occur at corresponding locations in the genomes of humans, chimpanzees, and other primates. Due to the random nature of SINE DNA activities, evolutionary biologists think it unlikely that SINE sequences would appear independently in the same locations in primate genomes. And given their supposed nonfunctional nature, shared SINE DNAs in humans and chimpanzees *seemingly* reflect common evolutionary ancestry. Evolutionary biologists have even used SINE *Alu* sequences to construct primate evolutionary trees.

Yet, molecular biologists have learned in recent years that SINE DNAs, as has been the case for pseudogenes, play a vital role in gene regulation through a variety of distinct mechanisms.

Evolutionary biologists think it unlikely that SINE sequences would appear independently in the same locations in primate genomes.

Staufen-mediated mRNA Decay

One way SINE sequences regulate gene expression is through a pathway called Staufen-mediated mRNA decay (SMD). SMD is critical to an organism's development and plays a key role in cellular differentiation. SMD is characterized by a complex mechanism centered around the destruction of mRNA. When this degradation takes place, it down-regulates gene expression. The SMD pathway involves binding of a protein called Staufen-1 to a double-stranded RNA complex, which forms as the result of the association of noncoding RNA and mRNA. The interactions are confined to one end of an mRNA molecule (dubbed the 3′ untranslated region). The *Alu* sequences in the 3′ untranslated regions of mRNA and *Alu* sequences in the long noncoding RNA molecules mediate the double-stranded RNA structures. This binding event triggers a cascade of additional events that leads to the breakdown of mRNA.

Did SMD Evolve Twice?

SINE-mediated SMD appears to have evolved independently—two separate times—in humans and mice. Though rodents don't possess *Alu* sequences, they do possess several other SINE elements, labeled B1, B2, B4, and ID. Remarkably, these B/ID sequences occur in regions of the mouse genome corresponding to regions of the human genome that harbor *Alu* sequences. When the B/ID sequences are associated with the 3′ untranslated regions of genes, they down-regulate mRNAs produced from these genes, suggesting that these genes are under the influence of the SMD-mediated pathway—an unexpected result.

But this finding is not nearly as astonishing as something else the same research team discovered. By comparing about 1,200 human-mouse gene pairs in myoblasts, the researchers discovered 24 genes in this cell type that were identical in the human and mouse genomes. These identical genes performed the same physiological role, possessed SINE elements (*Alu* and B/ID, respectively), and were regulated by the SMD mechanism, which in turn was mediated by a Staufen-1 homologue. Evolutionary biologists believe that *Alu* and B/ID SINE sequences emerged independently in the rodent and human lineages. If so, this means that the evolutionary processes must have independently produced the identical outcome 24 separate times for each of the 24 identical genes. As the researchers point out, chance alone cannot explain their findings. But can evolutionary mechanisms? Keep in mind, evolutionary mechanisms are historically contingent and should *not* yield identical outcomes (see chapter 19). This impossible scenario causes me to question neofunctionalization as an explanation for functional SINE DNA and the other classes of junk DNA in general. So, which is the better explanation for functional junk DNA sequences: neofunctionalization or the work of God? In my view, viewing genomes as the Creator's handiwork makes much better sense of the data.

Discussion Questions

1. What is the basic argument for junk DNA as a product of evolution? Does it seem compelling at first glance?

2. Do shared pseudogenes in humans and great apes require an evolutionary interpretation? Explain.

3. Which explanation for functional junk DNA sequences seems more persuasive: neofunctionalization or intelligent design?

Chapter 24

Why Are We Progressive Creationists?

by Anjeanette Roberts

Each author on this book came to progressive (or old-earth) creationism in a different way. I was once a proponent of theistic evolution (TE); my colleague and coauthor Dr. Rana was, too. Over time, we changed our positions due to closer examination of the evidence and critical scrutiny of the evolutionary claims explaining the data (see Introduction and chapter 5).

Dr. Dykes never thought much about any of these positions until she became serious about studying science. She stumbled on the progressive creation model about that time and has held that position since. Mark Perez was once a proponent of young-earth creationism (YEC).

All this to say, we are each committed to following the truth wherever it leads. Sometimes people find it disturbing when I tell them I was once a TE proponent. I think it disturbs some even more when I say someday I may be one again—if that's where the evidence leads.

Throughout the preceding chapters, we've addressed multiple aspects of evolution and highlighted why we each reject current evolutionary models—because we think current scientific data does not necessitate adoption of *proposed* macroevolutionary explanations. Proposed *not* evidenced. We find the data fits a progressive creation model best. Our position of skepticism is not immutable. It is a viable and prudent position to hold while scientific data continues to accumulate. We each find the progressive creation model superior to any evolutionary model, as it provides greater integration and less theological tension in relating God's revelation in Scripture and God's revelation in nature, while remaining committed to scientific rigor, yet rejecting any framework confined to naturalism (see chapter 5).

Current scientific data does not necessitate adoption of *proposed* macroevolutionary explanations.

Isn't Creationism Bad for Science?

Many critics of creationism complain that its proponents dismiss scientific mysteries. A progressive creation model doesn't do this. Its proponents don't shut down inquiries with, "God did it, so we can't know any more about it."

The problem is that many critics lump most creation models together as some form of young-earth creationism (YEC), where God miraculously formed the world and every living thing in it within the course of six 24-hour periods (144 hours) approximately 6,000–10,000 years ago. They then attack the veracity of those claims and conclude that *all* forms of creationism and appeals to God's action are superfluous, irrelevant, and bad for scientific progress.

Sometimes the criticism is warranted. If Christians or others use "God did it" to say that we don't need any other level of understanding and must reject scientific research into various areas as unnecessary, then the critics raise a valid point. But the critics are being intellectually lazy (or intentionally subversive) if, having defeated one YEC claim and model of creationism, they are unwilling to consider and engage more robust creation models.

In truth, our progressive creationist position is much more frustrating to some critics of creationism than an easily dismissed YEC view or a synchronistic evolutionary creationism position. We think the complexity and fine-tuning of biological mechanisms, systems, and organisms are so overwhelming that we must remain in a posture of saying we don't yet fully understand these things. We must continue to do the laborious experiments to identify mechanisms and functions, under varying developmental and environmental conditions, before affirming foregone conclusions of common descent. It is hubris to rush to easy conclusions that deny greater complexity and offer only partial insight into the functions of such complex systems and subsystems.

Keep on Studying and Keep on Testing

Unlike cosmological systems, biological systems can be manipulated and studied directly. We need not rely on mathematical modeling and speculation to form our central theories. We have the power to validate theories through biological studies. For this reason, we reject similar positions that say, "Evolution or natural selection did it." This is just a naturalistic placeholder that glosses over the need to identify real mechanisms, causal relationships, and plausible pathways that could demonstrate the veracity of a robust evolutionary model.

A scientific model is not sufficient if it merely explains every possible finding. It must also be able to discriminate and adequately predict future findings with some degree of rigor in its predictions. We think the progressive creation model fares best here as it makes actual predictions. For example, most organism's genomes will be shown to be highly functional when examined under greater diversity of developmental and environmental conditions. In other words, the idea of junk DNA will eventually be buried in the garbage dumps of history. Additionally, the information-bearing capacity of cellular biomolecules (proteins, sugars, lipids, etc.) will continue to reveal greater complexity and design.

We think that many things that are overlooked today will be found to be of relevant biological significance, including DNA copy number variants in different cell types and organisms, small intracellular concentrations of regulatory RNAs or other peptides, variations in glycosylation and other epigenetic phenomena, etc. We believe the significance and functional relevance of taxa-specific orphan genes will be a breakthrough in differentiating one organism from another. And we believe that experimental, not computational, biology will be the key to understanding biologically relevant differences, as well as system-level information and regulatory networks. These are all positive predictions of new findings, not mere predictions of a continued absence of evidence. The future experimental research scope entailed in a progressive creation model is limitless.

Evolutionary Theory Can Impede Discovery

In contrast, an evolutionary paradigm often leads to premature and poor conclusions (e.g., orphan genes are of little interest; the huge amounts of intracellular transcription is mostly insignificant noise; copy number variants within DNA repetitive sequences are insignificant; the compounding complexity of biological systems is merely circumstantial accrual of mindless, neutral evolutionary, ratchet-like processes). Such conclusions truncate discovery and are shortsighted.

De-emphasizing the significance of complexity either because it is difficult to parse or simply for the sake of maintaining a paradigm squelches scientific

De-emphasizing the significance of complexity either because it is difficult to parse or simply for the sake of maintaining a paradigm squelches scientific advancement.

advancement. Such a tack only serves to propagate a vacuous naturalistic, neo-Darwinian narrative. To a certain extent this judgment mirrors the critiques that extended evolutionary theory (EES) proponents raise against the dogma of biologists who limit considerations to gradualistic, evolutionary processes driven by random mutations and natural selection. (See "Harsh Criticism" and following sections starting on page 111 and "Reasoning to Best Explanation and Teleology" on page 140.) We believe a progressive creation model brings critical new perspectives to research in a way that can expand scientific inquiry and lead to greater discovery (similar to evolutionary developmental biology or EES research programs).

May the Best Model Prevail

Arguably, we are left with two competing, empirically equivalent models: progressive creation and evolution. We must continue collecting data and evaluating evidence to discriminate between the two. In the interim, we continue to reason and engage in respectful discourse as to which model best fits the data and which requires growing layers of complexity to account for unexpected findings.

As astrophysicist Sir Fred Hoyle put it, one should "be suspicious of a theory if more and more hypotheses are needed to support it as new facts become available, or as new considerations are brought to bear."[1] This may not always be true, but it is certainly a wise and reasonable posture to adopt, especially if a simpler model accounts for the data as well or better. In evaluating these empirical equivalents, two positions seem possible:[2]

1. Evolution or evolutionary creationism: Proponents would say evolutionary processes get the benefit of the doubt until the point where they become scientifically indefensible. (It's difficult to imagine when

that might happen or when one might concede this point—perhaps at
the point of abiogenesis.)

2. Progressive (or old-earth) creationism: Proponents would say evolutionary processes do not get the benefit of the doubt and God's creation
by fiat is a reasonable assumption until evolutionary mechanisms have
been demonstrated for various transitions and claims.

We embrace the second option. It is consistent with our understanding
of the data and with a cautious approach to addressing apparently conflicting
scientific theories. When faced with abandoning traditional biblical interpretations, we err on the side of caution (as per Theodore Cabal and Peter J. Rasor's
theological conservative principle) and amend interpretations over time only
when clear evidence demonstrates the tradition wrong.[3]

But what if we're wrong? What if the grand evolutionary paradigm really
is the factual and truthful account of life's history, complexity, and diversity?

Discussion Questions

1. Evaluate the statement that creation proponents "dismiss scientific
mysteries."

2. What does the author mean by saying that "a scientific model is not
sufficient if it merely explains every possible finding"?

3. Of the two empirically equivalent models—evolution and progressive
creation—which seems a better evidentiary fit and why?

Chapter 25

What If Big-E Evolution
Is True?

by Anjeanette Roberts

M y coauthors and I are evidentialists. We believe the scientific data supports a progressive creation model as well as, or better than, an evolutionary account—but what if we're wrong?

What if plausible evidential mechanisms and processes, backed by empirical data, fill in the significant gaps, clarify the muddy middle layer of mechanism, and cross all significant remaining hurdles? Does this leave Christians two choices: deny God's revelation in nature (or at least the possibility of any real integration of God's revelation in nature and the Bible) or flounder in an existential faith crisis? Well, those may be two options, but not by any means the only or best options if evolution with a big-E is true.

Since the time of evolution's earliest Darwinian versions, Christians committed to biblical authority and inerrancy have argued for God's creation through natural mechanisms. The conservative Reformed principal of Princeton Theological Seminary Benjamin Breckinridge Warfield (1851–1921) serves as a prominent example. Warfield was a staunch defender of the verbal plenary inspiration of Scripture and deeply committed to biblical inerrancy. Mark Noll articulates Warfield's position in *Jesus Christ and the Life of the Mind*: "Besides his openness toward evolution . . . Warfield was also the ablest modern defender of the theologically conservative belief in the inerrancy of the Bible."[1] Noll continues:

> While he defended biblical inerrancy, Warfield was also a cautious, discriminating, but entirely candid proponent of the possibility that evolution might offer the best way to understand the natural history of earth and of humankind. On this

score his views place him with more recent thinkers who maintain ancient trust in the Bible while also affirming the modern scientific enterprise and mainstream scientific conclusions. Warfield did not simply assert these two views randomly, but he sustained them learnedly, as coordinate arguments.[2]

As Warfield did in his day, there are many faithful Christians today who confess Christ as Lord, hold the Bible as the authoritative Word of God, and believe in real miraculous events (e.g., Jesus's resurrection and the virgin birth) *while* also holding that God used the initial conditions he established at the creation along with evolutionary processes to accomplish his purposes for life's biological history on Earth. We call many of these scientists, with whom we disagree, friends. Many folks at Peaceful Science, BioLogos, the Discovery Institute, and the Faraday Institute for Science and Religion interpret the scientific evidence differently than we do at Reasons to Believe. Nevertheless, we embrace them as brothers and sisters in Christ.

After all, it is not one's view of origins that determines a person's Christian status.

After all, it is not one's view of origins that determines a person's Christian status. Scripture tells us it's not enough even to know the truth about God's existence, for even the demons know this truth and tremble (James 2:19). It matters whether we have a life transformed by and reconciled with God or not. It's about what we do with Jesus. Through God's revelation in nature and the Scriptures, we are invited to "taste and see that the Lord is good" (Psalm 34:8). We are called to recognize God's power, glory, and provision and our insufficiency and need to receive God's provision in Jesus for our reconciliation and restoration. We must be born again of the Spirit. In other words, we must have a real encounter with the risen Lord Jesus. This is the hallmark of being in Christ and the litmus of Christian orthodoxy, as is demonstrating love for one another as Christ did and commanded us to do (John 13:35).

As Noll points out, Warfield did not assert his two views (of God's activity through evolution and the inerrancy of Scripture) randomly, but "learnedly, as coordinate arguments." Warfield's approach continues today as many devoted Christ followers are doing hard, scholarly work together to advance the doctrine of creation in dialogue with scientists, theologians, and biblical scholars.

Included in these conversations are discussions about how an evolutionary paradigm of biological origins and biblical Christianity might be reconciled. At the time this book is published there will have been five meetings, one every summer since 2016, where biblical scholars, pastors, theologians, and scientists have come together to wrestle with the best ways to assess or accomplish this. These conferences are part of a larger effort known as the Creation Project at the Carl F. H. Henry Center for Theological Understanding.[3] Dr. Rana and I have been privileged to participate each year. Much work with scholars in dialogue goes on between the conferences as well. Initiatives such as the Creation Project are and will be critical for the Christian community as theological challenges, such as those raised in chapter 5, are continually engaged.

One significant work, facilitated by these and additional dialogues, is the emergence of a genealogical model of human origins[4] that aligns with either a sequential or independent rendering of the creation accounts in Genesis 1–2 and that is in line with the range of faithful biblical exegesis. This model, championed by computational biologist and physician S. Joshua Swamidass, comports well with the genealogical emphasis in Genesis and throughout the Scriptures, as well as the *de novo* creation of Adam and Eve. It is arguably a nontraditional interpretation, but it lays a foundation for faithful interpretations that, rightly handled, pose no threat to the central tenets of biblical Christianity. In fact, it provides a way for biblical interpretations of a historical Adam and Eve—understood as universal, genealogical ancestors for all humanity living at the time of Christ and today—to be reconciled with mainstream evolutionary science.

If at some point in the future, the scientific evidence shows that evolutionary mechanisms are the mechanisms of God's creation, then interpretive models such as the one above will fill a needed space in biblical Christian thought. Meanwhile, for those who believe that evolutionary mechanisms have already attained sufficient evidentiary support, the fruits of this model and the laboring together as Christian scholars is already vitally important.

At this point, it is critical to realize and remind ourselves that Christianity is not a monolithic faith. It has existed in diverse forms across centuries and cultures. Orthodox, Catholic, and Protestant manifestations of Christ followers attest to this wide diversity. The apostle Paul shows us that even in early Christianity there were significant differences regarding nonessential details (e.g., Romans 14 and Ephesians 4:1–6). But he also emphasized that some details *are* essential and differences in those could impede the gospel and lead to something other than Christianity.

As we keep Christ at the center and follow the evidence where it leads, we can remain confident that we have nothing to fear from the truth.

Paul abandoned unnecessary traditions for the sake of becoming as close to his audience as he could to bring the central message of salvation to as many as possible (1 Corinthians 9:19–23). Christ died for our sins that we might be made new and reconciled to God (1 Corinthians 15:3–4 and 2 Corinthians 5:14–21). Certainly, this is the one nonnegotiable, the Cornerstone: who do you say that Christ is? Have you acknowledged the truth of his claim as Lord of all by surrendering your life to his lordship?

As we keep Christ at the center and follow the evidence where it leads, we can remain confident that we have nothing to fear from the truth. All truth is God's truth and his revelation rightly understood and interpreted will be consistent and beautiful and lead to his glory and praise. If evolution is the mechanism of God's creation, then the grounds for his glory and praise are not diminished. A 2017 song by Hillsong UNITED demonstrates this beautifully:

> God of Creation . . .
> You don't speak in vain
> No syllable empty or void.
> For once You have spoken
> All nature and science
> Follow the sound of Your voice.
> And as You speak
> A hundred billion creatures catch Your breath
> Evolving in pursuit of what You said.
> If it all reveals Your nature so will I.[5]

In the End

We are not progressive creationists because we think theistic evolution/evolutionary creation is a nonviable theological position or because it pushes God to the background. We are progressive creationists because we think the scientific data fits best with this position. Considering evolution's continual failure to account for major transitions and human uniqueness, we find no convincing reasons why it should be adopted over a progressive creation understanding of God's intimate and continual interaction with his creation in providential and revelatory ways.

Many suggest that in assuming our position we err regarding modern science in ways like the err of the church in the times of Galileo. We disagree. We stand firm on grounds that Galileo would hold as well. His statements suggest reexamination of the meaning of Scripture when faced with "natural phenomenon which is placed before our eyes by sensory experience or proved by necessary demonstrations." This is exactly what we wait and call for—*necessary demonstrations.*

> I think that in disputes about natural phenomena one must begin not with the authority of scriptural passages, but with sensory experiences and necessary demonstration. For the Holy Scripture and nature derive equally from the Godhead . . . God reveals Himself to us no less excellently in the effects of nature than in the sacred words of Scripture . . . and so it seems that a natural phenomenon which is placed before our eyes by sensory experience or proved by necessary demonstrations should not be called into question, let alone condemned, on account of scriptural passages whose words appear to have a different meaning.

> However, by this I do not wish to imply that one should not have the highest regard for passages of Holy Scripture; indeed, after becoming certain of some physical conclusions, we should use these as very appropriate aids to the correct interpretation of Scripture and to the investigation of the truths they must contain, for they are most true and agree with demonstrated truths. . . . I do not think one has to believe that the same God who has given us senses, language, and intellect would want to set aside the use of these and give us by other means the information we can acquire with them, so that we would deny our senses and reason even in the case of those physical conclusions which are placed before our eyes and intellect by our sensory experiences or by necessary demonstrations.[6]

Warfield's "commitment to harmonizing a sophisticated conservative theology and the most securely verified conclusions of modern science"[7] arguably suggests that he would have stood with us, too. His approach reflects the approach that Reasons to Believe takes to integrating God's revelation in nature and Scripture.

As Christ followers and scholars who care deeply about pursuing truth in science and rightly handling the Word of truth, we acknowledge that we must have intellectual humility and a love for others, especially in areas of strong disagreement. It is important as we study and wrestle together to ask ourselves if we are doing kingdom work and following Christ faithfully in respect to loving others and pursuing truth. In regard to our study and scholarship, the perspective of Dominican Albert Robertson, OP, is helpful:

> Study helps us to love God more deeply, and it does this by purifying our understanding of God. Sometimes as students this means that we have to give up on favourite analogies or metaphors for our understanding of God for ones which more accurately correspond to revelation, and this should draw us into a closer relationship to God, for knowledge and love share a common source and ultimate end in God.[8]

Scripture, too, calls us to maintain unity in love. It is the way we treat one another that will show the world that Jesus is who he claimed to be. As we continue to ask questions and search for answers, perhaps this is the most important thing to keep in mind—this, and God's promise of blessing on peacemakers, who will be called the children of God.

Discussion Questions

1. What was theologian B. B. Warfield's position on the Bible and science? What can we learn from his example?

2. Evaluate the statement that "all truth is God's truth." Is this your position? Explain.

3. What does intellectual humility look like for anybody, regardless of education or experience?

Notes

Outing Our Bias

1. Progressive creation is used throughout this book, as the emphasis here is in reference to how God created all things—through a series of creation-by-fiat events as well as through secondary causal events throughout a progression of time. Old-earth creationism (terminology more clearly designating an appropriate emphasis relating to cosmology) and progressive creation are fully synonymous in the RTB model, as is day-age creationism. Any reference to progressive creation as synonymous with God creating progressively only through evolutionary mechanisms is a misappropriation of the term.

2. Belgic Confession; Carisa A. Ash, *A Critical Examination of the Doctrine of Revelation in Evangelical Theology* (Eugene, OR: Wipf and Stock, 2015); Mark A. Noll, *Jesus Christ and the Life of the Mind* (Grand Rapids, MI: Eerdmans Publishing Company, 2011), 107.

3. There is some disagreement among Hebrew scholars whether the use of *bara* in Ezekiel 21:19 (NASB) stems from the same root as the occurrences in Genesis. In each instance the verb means to create or make something that does not already exist. However, since in the Ezekiel 21:19 passage the subject is son of man (Ezekiel), and not God, many think the underlying words are not the same. I thank E. W. Carlson for pointing out this possible exception to me.

Chapter 1 – Does Evolution Explain Life on Earth?

1. Mark Twain, *Life on the Mississippi* (Boston: James R. Osgood, 1883; Project Gutenberg, 2004), chap. 17, gutenberg.org/ebooks/245.

2. For more on speciation, see the bonus material online available at reasons.org/evolutionbonus.

3. Charles Darwin, Notebook B, 1837, DAR 121: 36, Charles Darwin Papers, Cambridge University Library; and Charles Darwin, "[Branching Tree Diagram of Primate Descent]," 1868, DAR 80: B91r, Charles Darwin Papers, Cambridge University Library; Both available at amnh.org/research/darwin-manuscripts/catalogue-darwin-manuscripts/cambridge-university-library.

4. John L. Pollock, "Defeasible Reasoning," *Cognitive Science* 11, no. 4 (October 1987): 481–518, doi:10.1207/s15516709cog1104_4.

5. Charles Blinderman and David Joyce, "Darwin's Bulldog" and "Agnosticism," *The Huxley Files*, 1998, https://mathcs.clarku.edu/huxley/.

Chapter 2 – Is Religious Belief the Only Reason to Question Evolution?

1. David Berlinski, *The Deniable Darwin and Other Essays*, ed. David Klinghoffer (Seattle: Discovery Institute Press, 2018), 107.

2. Thomas H. Huxley, *Essays Upon Some Controverted Questions* (New York: D. Appleton and Company, 1892; Project Gutenberg, 2010), chap. 9, gutenberg.org/ebooks/34698. For further reading, see Charles Blinderman and David Joyce, "Darwin's Bulldog" and "Agnosticism," *The Huxley Files*, 1998, mathcs.clarku.edu/huxley.

3. Niles Eldredge and Stephen Jay Gould, "Punctuated Equilibria: An Alternative to Phyletic Gradualism," in *Models in Paleobiology*, ed. Thomas J. M. Schopf (San Francisco: Freeman, Cooper and Company, 1972), 82–115.

4. Kyle Stanford, "Underdetermination of Scientific Theory," ed. Edward N. Zalta, in *The Stanford Encyclopedia of Philosophy* (Winter 2017 Edition), plato.stanford.edu/archives/win2017/entries/scientific-underdetermination.

5. John Stuart Mill, *A System of Logic, Ratiocinative and Inductive: Being a Connected View of the Principles of Evidence, and the Methods of Scientific Investigation*, 8th ed. (New York: Harper & Brothers, 1904), 356, books.google.com/books?id=Tx2FIr1sD50C.

6. Stanford, "Underdetermination."

7. John L. Pollock, "OSCAR: An Architecture for Generally Intelligent Agents," paper presented at the First Conference on Artificial General Intelligence, March 2008.

8. Gerald Rau, *Mapping the Origins Debate: Six Models of the Beginning of Everything* (Westmont, IL: InterVarsity, 2012), 25.

9. Eugene V. Koonin, "The Origin at 150: Is a New Evolutionary Synthesis in Sight?," *Trends in Genetics* 25, no. 11 (November 1, 2009): 473–75, doi:10.1016/j.tig.2009.09.007.

10. Eugene V. Koonin, "Darwinian Evolution in the Light of Genomics," *Nucleic Acids Research* 37, no. 4 (March 1, 2009): 1011–34, doi:10.1093/nar/gkp089.

11. Motoo Kimura, "Evolutionary Rate at the Molecular Level," *Nature* 217, no. 5129 (February 17, 1968): 624–26, https://doi.org/10.1038/217624a0.

12. Koonin, "Origin at 150."

13. Koonin, "Origin at 150."

Chapter 3 – What's Philosophy Got to Do with Evolution?

1. "'Love of knowledge' is what philosophia literally means. Systematic pursuit of intellectual questions and logical argumentation were the signs of this love, a passion exemplified by no one more than Socrates." Nigel Spivey and Michael Squire, *Panorama of the Classical World* (Los Angeles: Getty Publications, 2011), 230.

2. Albert Einstein, "Physics and Reality," *Journal of the Franklin Institute*, vol. 221, no. 3 (March 1936): 351, doi:10.1016/S0016-0032(36)91047-5.

3. Sir Fred Hoyle and Chandra Wickramasinghe, *Evolution from Space* (New York: Touchstone, 1981), 135.

4. Howard Hughes Medical Institute. See "Programs," Howard Hughes Medical Institute, accessed August 26, 2019, hhmi.org/programs.

Chapter 4 – How Can We Keep Our Thinking Free from Fallacy?

1. There is another form of the vestigial structure claim we will not deal with here. That claim takes the form, "Since species A has a structure similar to another similar but apparently nonfunctioning structure in species B; and species A apparently came before species B; the nonfunctioning structure of B is a vestige of the functioning structure of A, its predecessor." This claim does not suffer the *argument from ignorance* fallacy. However, it may suffer others, e.g., *defective analogy* and *coincidental correlation* (also known as *post hoc*). Expositing the homologous vestigial structures argument and its logical problems is beyond the scope of this chapter.

2. Loren G. Martin, "What Is the Function of the Human Appendix? Did It Once Have a Purpose That Has Since Been Lost?," *Scientific American*, October 21, 1999, scientificamerican.com/article/what-is-the-function-of-the-human-appendix-did-it-once-have-a-purpose-that-has-since-been-

lost.

3. Wojciech Makalowski, "What Is Junk DNA, and What Is It Worth?," *Scientific American*, February 12, 2007, scientificamerican.com/article/what-is-junk-dna-and-what.

4. "What Is the Encyclopedia of DNA Elements (ENCODE) Project?," National Institutes of Health, U.S. National Library of Medicine, published August 20, 2019, ghr.nlm.nih.gov/primer/genomicresearch/encode.

5. The form of evolutionary psychology discussed in this chapter would best be called "popular evolutionary psychology," and is presented here because its claims appear more often than any other in popular discussions of evolutionary psychology.

6. A likelihood is "noncircular" when it is not presumed to be likely merely because the theory requires it. In this case, an evolutionist might argue that all solvable problems are likely to result in physical explanations because evolution theory accepts only physical explanations. However, because the question at issue is whether there are cases where a nonphysical explanation is reasonable, one cannot prove the answer by presuming it. To do so is circular reasoning, the fallacy of begging the question.

7. The representative young-earth position asserted by Answers in Genesis, arguably the most prominent young-earth creationist organization, asserts that Earth is between 6,000 and 12,000 years old. See item 10 in "Young Earth Creationist View Summarized and Defended," Answers in Genesis, accessed August 26, 2019, answersingenesis.org/creationism/young-earth/young-earth-creationist-view-summarized-and-defended. The most prominent progressive creation organization, Reasons to Believe, holds that Earth is about 4.6 billion years old, in line with the prevailing scientific position on the age of the earth. See "Scientific Evidence for an Old Earth," reasons.org/explore/publications/rtb-101/scientific-evidence-old-earth.

8. John Rennie, "15 Answers to Creationist Nonsense," *Scientific American* 287, no. 1 (July 2002): 78–85, doi:10.1038/scientificamerican0702-78.

9. I offer this example not engaging the question of whether Rennie is properly stating Dembski's case. My purpose is solely to show the fallacy appearing in Rennie's critique.

10. Those interested in delving deeper into fallacies, see Kenneth Samples, "How to ERASE Logical Fallacies," *Reflections* (blog), February 14, 2017, reasons.org/explore/blogs/reflections/read/reflections/2017/02/14/how-to-erase-logical-fallacies.

Chapter 5 – Is Evolution Really a Problem for the Christian Faith?

1. Richard Dawkins, *The Blind Watchmaker: Why the Evidence of Evolution Reveals a Universe without Design* (New York: W. W. Norton, 1996), 6.

2. Asa Gray, *Darwiniana: Essays and Reviews Pertaining to Darwinism* (New York: D. Appleton and Company, 1876; Project Gutenberg, 2004), gutenberg.org/ebooks/5273.

3. Charles Darwin to Asa Gray, "Letter no. 2814," May 22, 1860, Darwin Correspondence Project, darwinproject.ac.uk/DCP-LETT-2814.

4. Charles Darwin to J. D. Hooker, "Letter no. 1924," July 13, 1856, Darwin Correspondence Project, darwinproject.ac.uk/DCP-LETT-1924.

5. Henry Gee, *The Accidental Species: Misunderstandings of Human Evolution* (Chicago: University of Chicago Press, 2013), 12.

6. Stephen Jay Gould, *Wonderful Life: The Burgess Shale and the Nature of History* (New York: W. W. Norton, 1989), 291.

7. Darrel Falk, "Biological Evolution: What Is It? Does It Explain Life's History?," in *Old-Earth or Evolutionary Creation?: Discussing Origins with Reasons to Believe and BioLogos*, ed. Kenneth Keathley, J. B. Stump, and Joe Aguirre (Downers Grove, IL: InterVarsity, 2018), 125.

8. For example, see Kenneth Samples, "What Is the Range of Viable Positions Concerning Adam and Eve?," in *Old-Earth or Evolutionary Creation?*, 55–60.

9. Anjeanette Roberts, "An Evangelical Scientist Rescues Methodological Naturalism," *Canadian-American Theological Review* 6, no. 2, (2017).

10. Nicolaas A. Rupke, *Richard Owen: Biology without Darwin*, rev. ed. (Chicago: University of Chicago Press, 2009).

Chapter 6 – What Is Chemical Evolution?

1. Sara Imari Walker and Paul C. W. Davies, "The Algorithmic Origin of Life," *Journal of the Royal Society Interface* 10, no. 79 (February 6, 2013), doi:10.1098/rsif.2012.0869.

2. Paul C. W. Davies, *The Fifth Miracle: The Search for the Origin and Meaning of Life* (New York: Simon and Schuster, 1999), 81–82.

3. Noam Lahav, *Biogenesis: Theories of Life's Origin* (New York: Oxford University Press, 1999), 138–39.

4. David P. Horning and Gerald F. Joyce, "Amplification of RNA by an RNA Polymerase Ribozyme," *Proceedings of the National Academy of Sciences, USA* 113, no. 35 (August 30, 2016), doi:10.1073/pnas.1610103113.

5. Leslie E. Orgel, "The Implausibility of Metabolic Cycles on the Prebiotic

Earth," *PLoS Biology* 6, no. 1 (January 22, 2008): e18, doi:10.1371/journal. pbio.0060018.

6. Orgel, "Implausibility."

Chapter 7 – Is Microevolution a Fact?

1. Kenneth N. Kreuzer, "DNA Damage Responses in Prokaryotes: Regulating Gene Expression, Modulating Growth Patterns, and Manipulating Replication Forks," *Cold Spring Harbor Perspectives in Biology* 5, no. 11 (November 2013): a012674, doi:10.1101/cshperspect.a012674.

2. Bregje Wertheim, Leo W. Beukeboom, and Louis van de Zande, "Polyploidy in Animals: Effects of Gene Expression on Sex Determination, Evolution and Ecology," *Cytogenetic and Genome Research* 140, no. 2–4 (July 2013): 256–69, doi:10.1159/000351998.

3. John Baptiste Lamark postulated in his 1801 theory of evolution that off-spring could inherit parental traits acquired and developed by specific interactions with their immediate environments. See "Early Concepts of Evolution: Jean Baptiste Lamarck," Understanding Evolution (website), accessed August 23, 2019, evolution.berkeley.edu/evolibrary/article/history_09.

4. It's important to note in regard to complex diploid, multicellular, sexual organisms that mutations in somatic cells are not directly passed on to off-spring. Although some epigenetic changes may be passed on to offspring, unless these epigenetic changes occur in the egg of the maternal parent (or the sperm of the paternal parent) or in utero, they would not be "inherited." Arguably changes occurring in utero or infancy may not be detected and would indicate non-inheritance. These changes would rather result from continual, shared environmental influences resulting in individually reproducible, repeated, concordant epigenetic changes in the parents and the offspring.

5. Bruce S. Grant, "Fine Tuning the Peppered Moth Paradigm," *Evolution* 53, no. 3 (June 1999): 980–84, https://doi.org/10.1111/j.1558-5646.1999.tb05394.x.

Chapter 8 – Do Microbes Evolve?

1. Benoît Lacroix et al., "Will You Let Me Use Your Nucleus? How Agrobacterium Gets Its T-DNA Expressed in the Host Plant Cell," *Canadian Journal of Physiology and Pharmacology* 84, no. 3–4 (March 2006): 333–45, doi:10.1139/y05-108.

2. Marilyn C. Roberts, "Update on Acquired Tetracycline Resistance Genes," *FEMS Microbiology Letters* 245, no. 2 (April 2005): 195–203, doi:10.1016/j. femsle.2005.02.034; and "Marilyn C. Roberts, Ph.D.," faculty webpage, University of Washington, accessed August 23, 2019, faculty.washington. edu/marilynr.

3. Kevin J. Forsberg et al., "The Tetracycline Destructases: A Novel Family of Tetracycline-Inactivating Enzymes," *Chemistry and Biology* 22, no. 7 (July 2015): 888–97, doi:10.1016/j.chembiol.2015.05.017; Roberts, "Update;" and B. S. Speer, N. B. Shoemaker, and A. A. Salyers, "Bacterial Resistance to Tetracycline: Mechanisms, Transfer, and Clinical Significance," *Clinical Microbiology Reviews* 5, no. 4 (October 1, 1992): 387–99, doi:10.1128/ CMR.5.4.387.

4. See "Overview of the *E. coli* Long-Term Evolution Experiment," Experimental Evolution (website), Michigan State University, accessed August 23, 2019, myxo.css.msu.edu/ecoli/overview.html.

5. Zachary D. Blount, Christina Z. Borland, and Richard E. Lenski, "Historical Contingency and the Evolution of a Key Innovation in an Experimental Population of Escherichia coli," *Proceedings of the National Academy of Sciences, USA* 105, no. 23 (June 2008): 7899–906, doi:10.1073/ pnas.0803151105.

Chapter 9 – Does Natural Selection Drive Evolution?

1. Jane B. Reece et al., *Campbell Biology*, 10th ed. (Boston: Pearson, 2013), Concept 22.2, xxxviii, 462, 465, 478.

2. Reece et al., 13.

3. Theodosius Dobzhansky, "Nothing in Biology Makes Sense except in the Light of Evolution," *The American Biology Teacher* 35, no. 3 (March 1973): 125–29, doi:10.2307/4444260.

4. Reece et al., *Campbell Biology*, 473.

5. Reece et al., 15.

6. Reece et al., 264.

7. Reece et al., 21.

8. Reece et al., 473.

9. Nicholas G. Crawford et al., "Loci Associated with Skin Pigmentation Identified in African Populations," *Science* 358, no. 6365 (November 17, 2017): eaan8433, doi:10.1126/science.aan8433. See also Philip Perry, "The Genes for White Skin Didn't Develop in Europe, UPenn Study Finds," *Big Think*, October 19, 2017, bigthink.com/philip-perry/the-genes-for-white-skin-

didnt-develop-in-europe-upenn-study-finds, L. M. Cook et al., "Selective Bird Predation on the Peppered Moth: The Last Experiment of Michael Majerus," *Biology Letters* 8, no. 4 (February 8, 2012): 609–12, doi:10.1098/rsbl.2011.1136.

10. Hugo de Vries, *Species and Varieties: Their Origin by Mutation*, ed. Daniel Trembly MacDougal (Chicago: The Open Court Publishing Company, 1904), 825–26.

11. Constructive neutral evolution (CNE) theory involves fixation of interdependence between different components of a complex system through partial mutational impairment of each of them. Eugene V. Koonin, "Splendor and Misery of Adaptation, or the Importance of Neutral Null for Understanding Evolution," *BMC Biology* 14, no. 1 (December 23, 2016): article 114, doi:10.1186/s12915-016-0338-2. CNE describes processes that conceptually account for evolution of complex machines in the absence of positive selection. In a CNE scenario an autonomously functioning cellular component acquires mutations that make it dependent for function on another, preexisting component or process. If there "are multiple ways in which such dependence may arise, then dependence inevitably will arise and reversal to independence is unlikely. Thus, CNE is a unidirectional evolutionary ratchet leading to complexity, if complexity is equated with the number of components or steps necessary to carry out a cellular process." Julius Lukeš et al., "How a Neutral Evolutionary Ratchet Can Build Cellular Complexity," *IUBMB Life* 63, no. 7 (July 2011): 528–37, doi:10.1002/iub.489. See also Michael W. Gray et al., "Irremediable Complexity?," *Science* 330, no. 6006 (November 12, 2010): 920–21, doi:10.1126/science.1198594.

12. Michael Egnor, "A Darwinian Pilgrimage," *Evolution News and Science Today*, August 10, 2018, evolutionnews.org/2018/08/a-darwinian-pilgrimage.

13. Reece et al., *Campbell Biology*, 491, 493.

14. Gerd B. Müller, "The Extended Evolutionary Synthesis," (lecture, Royal Society, London, Scientific Meeting: New Trends in Evolutionary Biology: Biological, Philosophical and Social Science Perspectives, London, UK, November 7, 2016), https://royalsociety.org/science-events-and-lectures/2016/11/evolutionary-biology/.

15. In Julius Lukeš et al., "Neutral Evolutionary Ratchet," the authors describe CNE as "a similar ratchet process, combining mutation, drift, epistasis, and negative selection." They explain that molecular biologists often ignore the intricacies of the cell's molecular machinery and instead offer selectionist

or panadaptationist explanations. "The one exception to this neglect," they claim, "is the 'neutral subfunctionalization' model for the retention of gene duplicates." The authors continue, "Subfunctionalization is a special case of CNE. And, Lynch's perspective on population size expands the explanatory potential of CNE, because the presuppressive interactions that become fixed via CNE need not be assumed to be completely neutral." Yet, as the authors explain, "CNE is not simply the neutral theory of evolution nor is it simply a necessary consequence of small population sizes." Rather, it posits that the "inevitable gratuitous preexistence of potentially suppressive molecular interactions" will diffuse cellular functions as they become dependent on the interactions of an increasing number of components.

16. Sir Fred Hoyle and Chandra Wickramasinghe, *Evolution from Space* (New York: Touchstone, 1981), 6.
17. Eugene V. Koonin, "Towards a Postmodern Synthesis of Evolutionary Biology," *Cell Cycle* 8, no. 6 (March 15, 2009): 799–800.
18. Perry Marshall, *Evolution 2.0: Breaking the Deadlock Between Darwin and Design* (Dallas: BenBella Books, 2015).
19. Raymond Noble and Denis Noble, "Was the Watchmaker Blind? Or Was She One-Eyed?," *Biology (Basel)* 6, no. 4 (December 20, 2017): 47, doi:10.3390/biology6040047.

Chapter 10 – Does Evolution Have a Novelty Problem?

1. Gerd B. Müller and Stuart A. Newman, "The Innovation Triad: An EvoDevo Agenda," *Journal of Experimental Zoology Part B: Molecular and Developmental Evolution* 304, no. 6 (November 15, 2005): 487–503, doi:10.1002/jez.b.21081.
2. Zachary D. Blount et al., "Genomic Analysis of a Key Innovation in an Experimental *Escherichia coli* Population," *Nature* 489 (September 19, 2012): 513–18.
3. Zachary D. Blount, Christina Z. Borland, and Richard E. Lenski, "Historical Contingency and the Evolution of a Key Innovation in an Experimental Population of *Escherichia coli*," *Proceedings of the National Academy Sciences, USA* 105, no. 23 (June 10, 2008): 7899–906, doi:10.1073/pnas.0803151105.
4. Blount, Borland, and Lenski, "Historical Contingency."
5. Klaas Martinus Pos, Peter Dimroth, and Michael Bott, "The *Escherichia coli* Citrate Carrier CitT: A Member of a Novel Eubacterial Transporter Family Related to the 2-Oxoglutarate/Malate Translocator from Spinach Chloroplasts," *Journal of Bacteriology* 180, no. 16 (August 15, 1998): 4160–

65, jb.asm.org/content/180/16/4160.

6. Gerd B. Müller, "The Extended Evolutionary Synthesis," (lecture, Royal Society, London, Scientific Meeting: New Trends in Evolutionary Biology: Biological, Philosophical and Social Science Perspectives, London, UK, November 7, 2016), https://royalsociety.org/science-events-and-lectures/2016/11/evolutionary-biology/.

7. Michael Denton, *Evolution: Still a Theory in Crisis* (Seattle: Discovery Institute Press, 2016), 43–101; James A. Shapiro, "Biological Action in Read-Write Genome Evolution" (lecture, Royal Society, London, Scientific Meeting: New Trends in Evolutionary Biology: Biological, Philosophical and Social Science Perspectives, London, UK, November 7, 2016), https://royalsociety.org/science-events-and-lectures/2016/11/evolutionary-biology/; Eva Jablonka, "The Role of Epigenetic Inheritance in Evolution" (lecture, Royal Society, London, Scientific Meeting: New Trends in Evolutionary Biology: Biological, Philosophical and Social Science Perspectives, London, UK, November 7, 2016), https://royalsociety.org/science-events-and-lectures/2016/11/evolutionary-biology/; Eugene V. Koonin, "Darwinian Evolution in the Light of Genomics," *Nucleic Acids Research* 37, no. 4 (March 1, 2009): 1011–34, doi:10.1093/nar/gkp089.

8. Gerd B. Müller, "EvoDevo Shapes the Extended Synthesis," *Biological Theory* 9, no. 2 (June 1, 2014): 119–21, doi:10.1007/s13752-014-0179-6.

9. Müller, "Extended Evolutionary Synthesis," lecture.

10. Murat Acar, Attila Becskei, and Alexander van Oudenaarden, "Enhancement of Cellular Memory by Reducing Stochastic Transitions," *Nature* 435, no. 7039 (May 12, 2005): 228–32, doi:10.1038/nature03524.

11. Müller, "Extended Evolutionary Synthesis," lecture; and Gerd B. Müller, "Experimental Strategies in Evolutionary Embryology," *American Zoologist* 31, no. 4 (August 1, 1991): 605–15, jstor.org/stable/3883560.

12. Gerd B. Müller and Günter P. Wagner, "Novelty in Evolution: Restructuring the Concept," *Annual Review of Ecology and Systematics* 22 (November 1991): 229–56, doi.org/10.1146/annurev.es.22.110191.001305.

13. Müller, "Experimental Strategies."

14. Denton, *Evolution*, chap. 5.

15. Müller, "Extended Evolutionary Synthesis," lecture.

16. Perry Marshall, *Evolution 2.0: Breaking the Deadlock Between Darwin and Design* (Dallas: BenBella Books, 2015), 144.

17. James A. Shapiro, "Biological Action," lecture; Eugene V. Koonin, "Towards a Postmodern Synthesis of Evolutionary Biology," *Cell Cycle* 8, no. 6 (March

15, 2009): 799–800; and Marshall, *Evolution 2.0.*

18. James A. Shapiro, "What Natural Genetic Engineering Does and Does Not Mean" *HuffPost*, February 28, 2013, updated Apr 30, 2013, huffpost.com/entry/what-natural-genetic-engi_b_2783419; and J. A. Shapiro, "Natural Genetic Engineering in Evolution," *Genetica* 86, no. 1–3 (January 1992): 99–111, doi:10.1007/BF00133714.

19. Wesley C. Warren et al., "The Genome of a Songbird," *Nature* 464, no. 7289 (April 1, 2010): 757–62, doi:10.1038/nature08819. Accessory Table 5 available only in the PMC version online: ncbi.nlm.nih.gov/pmc/articles/PMC3187626.

20. James A. Shapiro, "No Genome Is an Island: Toward a 21st Century Agenda for Evolution," *Annals of the New York Academy of Sciences* 1447, no. 1 (July 2019): 21–52, doi:10.1111/nyas.14044.

21. James A. Shapiro, "Bacteria Are Small but Not Stupid: Cognition, Natural Genetic Engineering and Socio-Bacteriology," *Studies in History and Philosophy of Biological and Biomedical Sciences* 38, no. 4 (December 2007): 807–19, doi:10.1016/j.shpsc.2007.09.010; and Shapiro, "Biological Action," lecture Q&A.

22. Abstract to Douglas Futuyma, "The Evolutionary Synthesis Today: Extend or Amend?," (lecture, Royal Society, London, Scientific Meeting: New Trends in Evolutionary Biology: Biological, Philosophical and Social Science Perspectives, London, UK, November 7, 2016), https://royalsociety.org/science-events-and-lectures/2016/11/evolutionary-biology/.

23. Roy A. Jensen, "Orthologs and Paralogs—We Need to Get It Right," *Genome Biology* 2 (August 3, 2001): interactions1002.1.

24. Shapiro, "Bacteria Are Small;" and James A. Shapiro, "Biological Action in Read-Write Genome Evolution," *Interface Focus* 7, no. 5 (October 6, 2017): 20160115, doi:10.1098/rsfs.2016.0115.

25. Kerstin Howe et al., "The Zebrafish Reference Genome Sequence and Its Relationship to the Human Genome," *Nature* 496, no. 7446 (April 25, 2013): 498–503, doi:10.1038/nature12111; Diana Ekman and Arne Elofsson, "Identifying and Quantifying Orphan Protein Sequences in Fungi," *Journal of Molecular Biology* 396, no. 2 (February 19, 2010): 396–405, doi.org/10.1016/j.jmb.2009.11.053; John K. Colbourne et al., "The Ecoresponsive Genome of Daphnia Pulex," *Science* 331, no. 6017 (Feb 4, 2011): 555–61, doi:10.1126/science.1197761; Amanda K. Gibson et al., "Why So Many Unknown Genes? Partitioning Orphans from a Representative Transcriptome of the Lone Star Tick Amblyomma Americanum," *BMC*

Genomics 14 (February 27, 2013): 135, doi:10.1186/1471-2164-14-135; Chih-Horng Kuo and Jessica C. Kissinger, "Consistent and Contrasting Properties of Lineage-Specific Genes in the Apicomplexan Parasites Plasmodium and Theileria," *BMC Evolutionary Biology* 8 (April 11, 2008): 108, doi:10.1186/1471-2148-8-108; Chu-Yu Ye et al., "Evolutionary Analyses of Non-Family Genes in Plants," *Plant Journal* 73, no. 5 (March 2013): 788–97, doi:10.1111/tpj.12073; Zebulun W. Arendsee, Ling Li, and Eve Syrkin Wurtele, "Coming of Age: Orphan Genes in Plants," *Trends in Plant Science* 19, no. 11 (November 1, 2014): 698–708, doi:10.1016/j.tplants.2014.07.003; Gareth A. Wilson et al., "Large-Scale Comparative Genomic Ranking of Taxonomically Restricted Genes (TRGs) in Bacterial and Archaeal Genomes," *PLoS ONE* 2, no. 3 (March 28, 2007): e324, doi:10.1371/journal.pone.0000324; Lothar Wissler et al., "Mechanisms and Dynamics of Orphan Gene Emergence in Insect Genomes," *Genome Biology and Evolution* 5, no. 2 (January 24, 2013): 439–55, doi.org/10.1093/gbe/evt009; Nicola Palmieri, Carolin Kosiol, and Christian Schlötterer, "The Life Cycle of *Drosophila* Orphan Genes," *eLife* 3 (February 19, 2014): e01311, doi:10.7554/eLife.01311.

26. Daniel Fischer and David Eisenberg, "Finding Families for Genomic ORFans," *Bioinformatics* 15, no. 9 (September 1, 1999): 759–62, doi:10.1093/bioinformatics/15.9.759.

27. G. A. Wilson et al., "Orphans as Taxonomically Restricted and Ecologically Important Genes," *Microbiology* 151, no. 8 (August 2005): 2499–501, doi:10.1099/mic.0.28146-0.

28. Elizabeth S. A. Sollars et al., "Genome Sequence and Genetic Diversity of European Ash Trees," *Nature* 541, no. 7636 (January 12, 2017): 212–16, doi:10.1038/nature20786.

29. Richard J. A. Buggs, "The Evolutionary Mystery of Orphan Genes," *Nature Ecology and Evolution Community*, December 28, 2016, natureecoevocommunity.nature.com/users/24561-richard-buggs/posts/14227-the-unsolved-evolutionary-conundrum-of-orphan-genes.

30. Michael S. Werner et al., "Young Genes Have Distinct Gene Structure, Epigenetic Profiles, and Transcriptional Regulation," *Genome Research* 28, no. 11 (November 2018): 1675–87, doi:10.1101/gr.234872.118; Buggs, "Evolutionary Mystery"; Paul A. Nelson and Richard J. A. Buggs, "Next Generation Apomorphy: The Ubiquity of Taxonomically Restricted Genes," in *Next Generation Systematics*, ed. Peter D. Olson, Joseph Hughes, and James A. Cotton (Cambridge: Cambridge University Press, 2016), 237–63.

31. José Luis Villanueva-Cañas et al., "New Genes and Functional Innovation in Mammals," *Genome Biology and Evolution* 9, no. 7 (July 21, 2017): 1886–1900, doi:10.1093/gbe/evx136.

32. Ekman and Elofsson, "Identifying and Quantifying Orphan Protein Sequences."

33. Buggs, "Evolutionary Mystery;" Nelson and Buggs, "Next Generation Apomorphy."

34. Jose Ruiz-Orera et al., "Origins of *de novo* Genes in Human and Chimpanzee," *PLoS Genetics* 11, no. 12 (December 31, 2015): e1005721, doi:10.1371/journal.pgen.1005721.

35. Villanueva-Cañas et al., "New Genes."

36. Jonathan F. Schmitz and Erich Bornberg-Bauer, "Fact or Fiction: Updates on How Protein-Coding Genes Might Emerge *de novo* from Previously Non-coding DNA [version 1; peer review: 3 approved]," *F1000Research* 6 (January 19, 2017): 57, doi:10.12688/f1000research.10079.1.

37. Schmitz and Bornberg-Bauer, "Fact or Fiction."

38. Buggs, "Evolutionary Mystery."

39. Macarena Toll-Riera et al., "Origin of Primate Orphan Genes: A Comparative Genomics Approach," *Molecular Biology and Evolution* 26, no. 3 (March 2009): 603–12, doi:10.1093/molbev/msn281; Schmitz and Bornberg-Bauer, "Fact or Fiction."

40. Jane B. Reece et al., *Campbell Biology*, 10th ed. (Boston: Pearson, 2013), 30.

41. Futuyma, "The Evolutionary Synthesis Today."

42. Shapiro, "Does and Does Not Mean." Shapiro made a similar comment during the Q&A following his 2016 Royal Society lecture: Shapiro, "Biological Action," lecture.

Chapter 11 – What to Do with Teleology in Evolution?

1. Theodosius Dobzhansky, "Nothing in Biology Makes Sense Except in the Light of Evolution," *The American Biology Teacher* 35, no. 3 (March 1973): 125–29, doi:10.2307/4444260.

2. Perry Marshall, *Evolution 2.0: Breaking the Deadlock between Darwin and Design* (Dallas: BenBella Books, 2015), 222–23.

3. Francis Crick, *What Mad Pursuit: A Personal View of Scientific Discovery* (New York: Basic Books, Harper Collins Publishers, 1988), 138.

4. Marshall, *Evolution 2.0*, 151.

5. James Lovelock explains, "The Gaia theory posits that *the Earth is a self-regulating complex system* involving the biosphere, the atmosphere, the

hydrospheres and the pedosphere, tightly coupled as an evolving system. The theory sustains that *this system as a whole, called Gaia, seeks a physical and chemical environment optimal for contemporary life;*" and "The originality of the Gaia theory relies on the assessment that *such homeostatic balance is actively pursued with the goal of keeping the optimal conditions for life,* even when terrestrial or external events menace them" (emphasis added). James Lovelock, *The Vanishing Face of Gaia* (New York: Basic Books, 2009), 255, 179.

6. Julius Lukeš et al., "How a Neutral Evolutionary Ratchet Can Build Cellular Complexity," *IUBMB Life* 63, no. 7 (July 2011): 528–37, doi:10.1002/iub.489.

7. Crick, *What Mad Pursuit,* 138.

8. Richard C. Lewontin, "Billions and Billions of Demons," review of *The Demon-Haunted World: Science as a Candle in the Dark,* by Carl Sagan, *New York Review of Books* (January 9, 1997): 31, nybooks.com/articles/1997/01/09/billions-and-billions-of-demons.

9. Anjeanette Roberts, "Viruses Are People Too," *Theorems and Theology* (blog), Reasons to Believe, July 26, 2018, reasons.org/explore/blogs/theorems-theology/read/theorems-theology/2018/07/26/viruses-are-people-too.

Chapter 12 – Can Evolutionary Processes Generate New Information?

1. Bernd-Olaf Küppers, *Information and the Origin of Life* (Cambridge, MA: MIT Press, 1990).

2. Georgi Muskhelishvili and Andrew Travers, "Integration of Syntactic and Semantic Properties of the DNA Code Reveals Chromosomes as Thermodynamic Machines Converting Energy into Information," *Cellular and Molecular Life Sciences* 70, no. 23 (December 2013): 4555–67, doi:10.1007/s00018-013-1394-1.

3. Walter L. Bradley and Charles B. Thaxton, "Information and the Origin of Life," in *The Creation Hypothesis: Scientific Evidence for an Intelligent Designer,* ed. J. P. Moreland (Downers Grove, IL: InterVarsity, 1994), 190.

4. Hubert P. Yockey, *Information Theory and Molecular Biology* (Cambridge: Cambridge University Press, 1992), 246–57.

5. Inna S. Povolotskaya and Fyodor A. Kondrashov, "Sequence Space and the Ongoing Expansion of the Protein Universe," *Nature* 465, no. 7300 (June 17, 2010): 922–26, doi:10.1038/nature09105.

6. For example, see Cyrus Chothia et al., "Protein Folds in the All-β and All-α

Classes," *Annual Review of Biophysics and Biomolecular Structures* 26 (June 1997): 597–627, doi:10.1146/annurev.biophys.26.1.597.

7. Sara Imari Walker and Paul C. W. Davies, "The Algorithmic Origins of Life," *Journal of the Royal Society Interface* 10, no. 79 (February 6, 2013), doi:10.1098/rsif.2012.0869.

Chapter 13 –Does Evolution Explain the Fossil Record?

1. *Les Lettres de Blaise Pascal: Accompagnés de Lettres de ses Correspondants Publiées,* 6th ed., ed. Maurice Beaufreton (Paris: G. Crès, 1922), 25–26, available at bibliotheq.net/blaise-pascal/lettres/page-3.html. Translated in Saul Fisher, *Pierre Gassendi's Philosophy and Science: Atomism for Empiricists,* vol. 131 of Brill's Studies in Intellectual History (Leiden: Brill, 2005), 126n7.

2. Niles Eldredge and Stephen Jay Gould, "Punctuated Equilibria: An Alternative Phyletic Gradualism," in *Models in Paleobiology,* ed. Thomas J. M. Schopf (San Francisco: Freeman Cooper, 1972), 82–115. Reprinted in Niles Eldredge, *Time Frames: The Evolution of Punctuated Equilibria* (Princeton: Princeton University Press, 1985), 193–223, available at: somosbacteriasy-virus.com/phyletic.pdf.

3. Colin Barras, "These Half-Billion-Year-Old Creatures Were Animals—but unlike Any Known Today," *Science,* August 8, 2018, doi:10.1126/science.aav0347.

4. Ulf Linnemann et al., "New High-Resolution Age Data from the Ediacaran–Cambrian Boundary Indicate Rapid, Ecologically Driven Onset of the Cambrian Explosion," *Terra Nova* 31, no. 1 (February 2019): 49–58, doi:10.1111/ter.12368.

5. S. A. Bowring et al., "Calibrating Rates of Early Cambrian Evolution," *Science* 261, no. 5126 (September 3, 1993): 1293–98, doi:10.1126/science.11539488; Douglas H. Erwin and James W. Valentine, *The Cambrian Explosion: The Construction of Animal Biodiversity* (Greenwood Village, CO: Roberts and Company, 2013).

6. Douglas E. Soltis et al., "Origin and Early Evolution of Angiosperms," *Annals of the New York Academy of Sciences* 1133, no. 1 (June 2008): 3–25, doi:10.1196/annals.1438.005.

7. J. David Archibald, "Timing and Biogeography of the Eutherian Radiation: Fossils and Molecules Compared," *Molecular Phylogenetics and Evolution* 28, no. 2 (August 2003): 350–59, doi:10.1016/S1055-7903(03)00034-4; Richard O. Prum et al., "A Comprehensive Phylogeny of Birds (Aves) Using

Targeted Next-Generation DNA Sequencing," *Nature* 526, no. 7574 (October 22, 2015): 569–73, doi:10.1038/nature15697.

8. Philipp Gunz et al., "Brain Development after Birth Differs between Neanderthals and Modern Humans," *Current Biology* 20, no. 21 (November 9, 2010): PR921–22, doi:10.1016/j.cub.2010.10.018.

9. Richard E. Green et al., "A Draft Sequence of the Neanderthal Genome," *Science* 328, no. 5979 (May 7, 2010): 710–22, doi:10.1126/science.1188021; Matthias Meyer et al., "A High-Coverage Genome Sequence from an Archaic Denisovan Individual," *Science* 338, no. 6104 (October 12, 2012): 222–26, doi:10.1126/science.1224344; Cedric Boeckx and Antonio Benítez-Burraco, "The Shape of the Human Language-Ready Brain," *Frontiers in Psychology* 5 (April 4, 2014): 282, doi:10.3389/fpsyg.2014.00282.

10. Johan J. Bolhuis et al., "How Could Language Have Evolved?," *PLoS Biology* 12, no. 8 (August 2014): e1001934, doi:10.1371/journal.pbio.1001934; Chris Knight, "Puzzles and Mysteries in the Origins of Language," *Language and Communication* 50 (September 2016): 12–21, doi:10.1016/j.langcom.2016.09.002.

11. Grzegorz Niedźwiedzki et al., "Tetrapod Trackways from the Early Middle Devonian Period of Poland," *Nature* 463, no. 7277 (January 7, 2010): 43–48, doi:10.1038/nature08623.

12. For example, see Karen Carr, "Evolutionary Relationships among Major Groups of Cetaceans," illustration, Karen Carr Studio, karencarr.com/portfolio-images/Marine-animals-and-fish/Modern/The-Teaching-Company/Evolutionary-relationships-among-major-groups-of-cetaceans/525.

13. Philip D. Gingerich et al., "New Protocetid Whale from the Middle Eocene of Pakistan: Birth on Land, Precocial Development, and Sexual Dimorphism," *PLoS ONE* 4, no. 2 (February 4, 2009): e4366, doi:10.1371/journal.pone.0004366.

14. Mónica R. Buono et al., "Eocene Basilosaurid Whales from the La Meseta Formation, Marambio (Seymour) Island, Antarctica," *Ameghiniana* 53, no. 3 (June 2016): 296–315, doi:10.5710/AMGH.02.02.2016.2922.

15. Alain Houle, "The Origin of Platyrrhines: An Evaluation of the Antarctic Scenario and the Floating Island Model," *American Journal of Physical Anthropology* 109, no. 4 (August 1999): 541–59, doi:10.1002/(SICI)1096-8644(199908)109:4<541::AID-AJPA9>3.0.CO;2-N.

16. Michael F. Whiting et al., "Loss and Recovery of Wings in Stick Insects" *Nature* 421, no. 6920 (January 16, 2003): 264–67, doi:10.1038/nature01313.

17. John J. Wiens, "Re-evolution of Lost Mandibular Teeth in Frogs after More

than 200 Million Years, and Re-evaluating Dollo's Law," *Evolution* 65, no. 5 (May 2011): 1283–96, doi:10.1111/j.1558-5646.2011.01221.x.

18. J. Jaime Zúñiga-Vega et al., "Repeated Evolution of Viviparity in Phryno-somatid Lizards Constrained Interspecific Diversity in Some Life-History Traits," *Biology Letters* 12, no. 11 (November 30, 2016): 20160653.

19. Fazale R. Rana, "Molecular Convergence: Repeated Evolution or Repeated Designs?," in *The Nature of Nature: Examining the Role of Naturalism in Science*, ed. Bruce L. Gordon and William A. Dembski (Wilmington, DE: ISI Books, 2011); Joe Parker et al., "Genome-Wide Signatures of Convergent Evolution in Echolocating Mammals," *Nature* 502, no. 10 (October 10, 2013): 228–31, doi:10.1038/nature12511; John D. Pettigrew et al., "Convergence of Specialised Behaviour, Eye Movements and Visual Optics in the Sandlance (Teleostei) and the Chameleon (Reptilia)," *Current Biology* 9, no. 8 (April 22, 1999): 421–24, doi:10.1016/S0960-9822(99)80189-4.

20. Caroline B. Albertin et al., "The Octopus Genome and the Evolution of Cephalopod Neural and Morphological Novelties," *Nature* 524, no. 7564 (August 13, 2015): 220–24, doi:10.1038/nature14668; Alison Abbott, "Octopus Genome Holds Clues to Uncanny Intelligence," *Nature News*, August 12, 2015, doi:10.1038/nature.2015.18177.

21. Elisabeth S. Vrba, "Turnover-Pulses, the Red Queen, and Related Topics," *American Journal of Science* 293, no. A (January 1, 1993): 418–52, doi:10.2475/ajs.293.A.418.

22. Eugene V. Koonin, "The Biological Big Bang Model for the Major Transitions in Evolution," *Biology Direct* 2 (August 20, 2007): 21, doi:10.1186/1745-6150-2-21.

23. Fazale R. Rana, "Biology's Big Bangs," *Today's New Reason to Believe* (blog), December 13, 2007, reasons.org/explore/blogs/todays-new-reason-to-believe/read/tnrtb/2007/12/13/biology-s-big-bangs.

24. Kevin N. Laland et al., "The Extended Evolutionary Synthesis: Its Structure, Assumptions and Predictions," *Proceedings of the Royal Society B* 282 (August 22, 2015): 20151019, doi:10.1098/rspb.2015.1019.

Chapter 14 – What about the Genetic Similarity between Humans and Chimps?

1. Sharon Begley, "Psst, the Human Genome Was Never Fully Sequenced. Some Scientists Say It Should Be," *Stat News*, June 20, 2017, statnews.com/2017/06/20/human-genome-not-fully-sequenced.

2. Anjeanette Roberts, "Exploring the Human Genome: Can We Make

Predictions from Infancy?," *Today's New Reason to Believe* (blog), September 14, 2015, reasons.org/explore/blogs/todays-new-reason-to-believe/read/tnrtb/2015/09/15/exploring-the-human-genome-can-we-make-predictions-from-infancy; Anjeanette Roberts, "Genomic Leftovers: Identifying Novel Microsatellites, Overrepresented Motifs and Functional Elements in the Human Genome," July 23, 2016, in *Scientifica*, produced by Reasons to Believe, podcast, ep. 23, 1:44–28:08, podbean.com/media/share/pb-9z22y-60f68b.

3. Peter A. Audano et al., "Characterizing the Major Structural Variant Alleles of the Human Genome," *Cell* 176, no. 3 (January 24, 2019): 663–75.e19, doi:10.1016/j.cell.2018.12.019; Mark J. Chaisson, Richard K. Wilson, and Evan E. Eichler, "Genetic Variation and the *De Novo* Assembly of Human Genomes," *Nature Review Genetics* 16, no. 11 (October 7, 2015): 627–40, doi:10.1038/nrg3933; Megan Aldrup-MacDonald and Beth Sullivan, "The Past, Present, and Future of Human Centromere Genomics," *Genes* 5, no. 1 (January 23, 2014): 33, doi:10.3390/genes5010033.

4. Rebecca C. Iskow et al., "Exploring the Role of Copy Number Variants in Human Adaptation," *Trends in Genetics* 28, no. 6 (June 1, 2012): 245–57, doi:10.1016/j.tig.2012.03.002.

5. Iskow et al., "Exploring."

6. Michael J. McConnell et al., "Mosaic Copy Number Variation in Human Neurons," *Science* 342, no. 6158 (November 1, 2013): 632–37, doi:10.1126/science.1243472.

7. Iskow et al., "Exploring."

8. Feng-Chi Chen et al., "Human-Specific Insertions and Deletions Inferred from Mammalian Genome Sequences," *Genome Research* 17 (2007): 16–22, doi:10.1101/gr.5429606.

9. Yong E. Zhang and Manyuan Long, "New Genes Contribute to Genetic and Phenotypic Novelties in Human Evolution," *Current Opinion in Genetics and Development* 29 (December 2014): 90–96, doi:10.1016/j.gde.2014.08.013.

10. Henrik Kaessmann, "Origins, Evolution and Phenotypic Impact of New Genes," *Genome Research* 20, no. 10 (2010): 1313–26, doi:10.1101/gr.101386.109.

11. Elizabeth H. B. Hellen and Andrew D. Kern, "The Role of DNA Insertions in Phenotypic Differentiation between Humans and Other Primates," *Genome Biology Evolution* 7, no. 4 (April 2015): 1168–78, doi:10.1093/gbe/evv012.

12. Ulfur Aranson, Xiufeng Xu, and Anette Gullberg, "Comparison between the Complete Mitochondrial DNA Sequences of *Homo* and the Common Chimpanzee Based on Nonchimeric Sequences," *Journal of Molecular Evolution* 42, no. 2 (February 1996): 145–52, doi:10.1007/BF02198840.

13. I. E. Scheffler, *Mitochondria* (New York: Wiley, 1999), 273–25.

14. Paz Polak and Eytan Domany, "Alu Elements Contain Many Binding Sites for Transcription Factors and May Play a Role in Regulation of Developmental Processes," *BMC Genomics* 7 (June 1, 2006): 133–47, doi:10.1186/1471-2164-7-133.

15. Peter A. Larsen et al., "Warning SINEs: *Alu* Elements, Evolution of the Human Brain, and the Spectrum of Neurological Disease," *Chromosome Research* 26, no. 1–2 (March 2018): 93–111, doi:10.1007/s10577-018-9573-4.

16. Katja Nowick et al., "Differences in Human and Chimpanzee Gene Expression Patterns Define an Evolving Network of Transcription Factors in Brain," *Proceedings of the National Academy of Sciences, USA* 106, no. 52 (December 29, 2009): 22358–63, doi:10.1073/pnas.0911376106.

17. Nuno L. Barbosa-Morais et al., "The Evolutionary Landscape of Alternative Splicing in Vertebrate Species," *Science* 338, no. 6114 (December 21, 2012): 1587–93, fig. 1, doi:10.1126/science.1230612.

18. Hyo Jung De Smet et al., "The Cerebellum: Its Role in Language and Related Cognitive and Affective Functions," *Brain and Language* 127, no. 3 (December 2013): 334–42, doi:10.1016/j.bandl.2012.11.001.

19. Jia Zeng et al., "Divergent Whole-Genome Methylation Maps of Human and Chimpanzee Brains Reveal Epigenetic Basis Human Regulatory Evolution," *American Journal of Human Genetics* 91, no. 3 (September 7, 2012): 455–65, doi:10.1016/j.ajhg.2012.07.024.

20. Hennady P. Shulha et al., "Human-Specific Histone Methylation Signatures at Transcription Start Sites in Prefrontal Neurons," *PLoS Biology* 10, no. 11 (November 20, 2012): e1001427, doi:10.1371/journal.pbio.1001427.

21. Leela R. L. Davies and Ajit Varki, "Why Is *N*-Glycolylneuraminic Acid Rare in the Vertebrate Brain?," *Topics in Current Chemistry* 366 (2015): 31–54, doi:10.1007/128_2013_419.

22. "Chromosome Diagram," Genetics Home Reference (website), published October 1, 2019, ghr.nlm.nih.gov/chromosome/2#idiogram.

23. Karen H. Miga, "Chromosome-Specific Centromere Sequences Provide an Estimate of the Ancestral Chromosome 2 Fusion Event in Hominin Genomes," *Journal of Heredity* 108, no. 1 (January 1, 2017): 45–52, doi:10.1093/jhered/esw039.

24. J. S. Tushir and S. Akbarian, "Chromatin-Bound RNA and the Neurobiology of Psychiatric Disease," *Neuroscience* 264 (April 4, 2014): 131–41, doi:10.1016/j.neuroscience.2013.06.051.

25. Roy J. Britten, "Divergence between Samples of Chimpanzee and Human DNA Sequences Is 5%," Counting Indels," *Proceedings of the National Academy of Sciences, USA* 99, no. 21 (2002): 13633–35, doi:10.1073/pnas.172510699.

26. S. Neubauer et al., "The Evolution of Modern Human Brain Shape," *Science Advances* 4, no. 1 (January 24, 2018): eaao5961, doi:10.1126/sciadv.aao5961.

27. C. Boeckx et al., "The Shape of the Human Language-Ready Brain," *Frontiers in Psychology* 5 (2014): e282.

28. Andrew G. Clarke et al., "Inferring Nonneutral Evolution from Human-Chimp-Mouse Orthologous Gene Trios," *Science* 302, no. 5652 (December 12, 2003): 1960–63, doi:10.1126/science.1088821; Elizabeth Pennisi, "Genome Comparisons Hold Clues to Human Evolution," *Science* 302, no. 5652 (December 12, 2003): 1876–77, doi:10.1126/science.302.5652.1876a; Ajit Varki and Taska K. Altheide, "Comparing the Human and Chimpanzee Genomes: Searching for Needles in a Haystack," *Genome Research* 15 (2005): 1746–58, doi:10.1101/gr.3737405.

29. The role of epigenetic mechanisms and their effects on the brain is dealt with in a special edition of the *Philosophical Transactions of the Royal Society of London, B* 369 (September 26, 2014), ncbi.nlm.nih.gov/pmc/issues/241903.

Chapter 15 – Are the Hominin Fossils Evidence for Human Evolution?

1. John Hawks, "New Hominin Shakes the Family Tree—Again," *Sapiens*, April 10, 2019, sapiens.org/evolution/homo-luzonensis-discovery.

2. Matthew G. Baron et al., "A New Hypothesis of Dinosaur Relationships and Early Dinosaur Evolution," *Nature* 543 (March 23, 2017): 501–6, doi:10.1038/nature21700.

3. Max C. Langer et al., "Untangling the Dinosaur Family Tree," *Nature* 551 (November 2, 2017): E1–E3, doi:10.1038/nature24011; Baron, "A New Hypothesis"; Baron, "Baron *et al.* reply," *Nature* 551 (November 2, 2017): E4–E5, doi:10.1038/nature24012.

4. Thomas H. Huxley, *Evidence as to Man's Place in Nature* (London: Williams and Norgate, 1863).

5. Francis Clark Howell, *Early Man* (New York: Time-Life Books, 1970).

6. R. E. F. Leakey, "New Hominid Fossils from the Koobi Fora Formation in Northern Kenya," *Nature* 261 (June 17, 1976): 574–76, doi:10.1038/26157a0.

7. John Hawks, "What Is the 'Braided Stream' Analogy for Human Evolution?," *John Hawks Weblog*, November 26, 2015, johnhawks.net/weblog/topics/news/finlayson-braided-stream-2013.html.

8. John Hawks, "Three Big Insights into Our African Ancestry," *Medium*, January 3, 2019, medium.com/@johnhawks/three-big-insights-into-our-african-origins-3fa01eb5f03?sk=1d44a1e2a218a60314361ceec4af3e38.

9. Bernard Wood and Eve K. Boyle, "Hominin Taxic Diversity: Fact or Fantasy?," *American Journal of Physical Anthropology* 159, no. S61 (January 2016): S37–S78, doi:10.1002/ajpa.22902.

10. Dates cited from Wood and Boyle, "Hominin Taxic Diversity," table 1, see "Conservative FAD" and "Conservative LAD."

11. Michel Brunet et al., "A New Hominid from the Upper Miocene of Chad, Central Africa," *Nature* 418 (July 11, 2002): 145–51, doi:10.1038/nature00879.

12. Brigitte Senut et al., "First Hominid from the Miocene (Lukeino Formation, Kenya)," *Comptes Rendus de l'Académie des Sciences, Series IIA, Earth and Planetary Science* 332, no. 2 (January 30, 2001): 137–44, doi:10.1016/S1251-8050(01)01529-4.

13. Yohannes Heile-Selassie, "Late Miocene Hominids from the Middle Awash, Ethiopia," *Nature* 412 (July 12, 2001): 178–81, doi:10.1038/35084063.

14. C. Owen Lovejoy et al., "Careful Climbing in the Miocene: The Forelimbs of *Ardipithecus ramidus* and Humans Are Primitive," *Science* 326 (October 2, 2009): 70–70e8, doi:10.1126/science.1175827.

15. Thomas Cody Prang, "The African Ape-like Foot of *Ardipithecus ramidus* and Its Implications for the Origin of Bipedalism," *eLife* (April 30, 2019): 8:e44433, doi.org/10.7554/eLife.44433.

16. Aylwyn Scally et al., "Insights into Hominid Evolution from the Gorilla Genome Sequence," *Nature* 438 (March 7, 2012): 169–75, doi.org/10.1038/nature10842; Kay Prüfer et al., "The Bonobo Genome Compared with the Chimpanzee and Human Genomes," *Nature* 486 (June 28, 2012): 527–31, doi.org/10.1038/nature11128; Rhesus Macaque Genome Sequencing and Analysis Consortium et al, "Evolutionary and Biomedical Insights from the Rhesus Macaque Genome," *Science* 316 (April 13, 2007): 222–34, doi:10.1126/science.1139247.

17. Richard D. Wilkinson et al., "Dating Primate Divergences through an Integrated Analysis of Palaeontological and Molecular Data," *Systematic*

Biology 60, no. 1 (January 2011): 16–31, doi.org/10.1093/sysbio/syq054.

18. Kevin E. Langergraber, "Generation Times in Wild Chimpanzees and Gorillas Suggest Earlier Divergence Times in Great Ape and Human Evolution," *Proceedings of the National Academy of Sciences, USA* 109, no. 39 (September 25, 2012): 15716–21, doi.org/10.1073/pnas.1211740109.

19. John Hawks et al., "Recent Acceleration of Human Adaptive Evolution," *Proceedings of the National Academy of Sciences, USA* 104, no. 52 (December 26, 2007): 20753–58, doi.org/10.1073/pnas.0707650104.

20. Wood and Boyle, "Hominin Taxic Diversity."

21. Henry M. McHenry and Katherine Coffing, "*Australopithecus* to *Homo*: Transformations in Body and Mind," *Annual Review of Anthropology* 29 (October 2000): 125–46, doi.org/10.1146/annurev.anthro.29.1.125.

22. Robyn Pickering, "*Australopithecus sediba* at 1.977 Ma and Implications for the Origins of the Genus *Homo*," *Science* 333, no. 6048 (September 9, 2011): 1421–23, doi:1126/science.1203697.

23. Unless otherwise indicated, all mean brain volume calculations are taken from: William H. Kimbel and Brian Villmoare, "From *Australopithecus* to *Homo*: The Transition that Wasn't," *Philosophical Transactions of the Royal Society B* 371, no. 1698 (July 5, 2016): 20150248, doi.org/10.1098/rstb.2015.0248.

24. Brian Villmoare et al., "Early *Homo* at 2.9 Ma from Ledi-Geraru, Afar, Ethiopia," *Science* 347, no. 6228 (March 4, 2015): aaa1343, doi:10.1126/science.aaa1343.

25. Wood and Boyle, "Hominin Taxic Diversity."

26. Simon Neubauer, Jean-Jacques Hublin, and Philipp Gunz, "The Evolution of Modern Human Brain Shape," *Science Advances* 4, no. 1 (January 24, 2018): eaao5961, doi:10.1126/sciadv.aao5961.

27. Fred Spoor, Bernard Wood, and Frans Zonneveld, "Implications of Early Hominid Labyrinthine Morphology for Evolution of Human Bipedal Locomotion," *Nature* 369 (June 23, 1994): 645–48, doi:10.1038/369645ao.

28. Figures taken from table 1 of Henry M. McHenry and Katherine Coffing, "*Australopithecus* to *Homo*: Transformations in Body and Mind," *Annual Review of Anthropology* 29 (October 2000): 127, doi.org/10.1146/annurev.anthro.29.1.125.

29. Mark Collard and Bernard Wood, "Defining the Genus *Homo*," *Handbook of Paleoanthropology*, ed. Winfried Henke and Ian Tattersall (December 24, 2014): 2108–44, doi.org/10.1007/978-3-642-39979-4_51.

30. Brian G. Richmond, "Origin of Human Bipedalism: The Knuckle-

walking Hypothesis Revisited," *Yearbook of Physical Anthropology* 44, no. S33 (January 2, 2002): 70–105, doi.org/10.1002/ajpa.10019; Kwang Hyun Ko, "Origins of Bipedalism," *Brazilian Archives of Biology and Technology* 58, no. 6 (November–December 2015): 929–34, doi.org/10.1590/S1516-89132015060399.

31. L. S. B. Leakey, P. V. Tobias, and J. R. Napier, "A New Species of the Genus *Homo* from the Olduvai Gorge," *Nature* 202 (April 4, 1964): 7–9, doi:10.1038/202007a0..

32. Andrew Du et al., "Pattern and Process in Hominin Brain Size Evolution Are Scale-Dependent," *Proceedings of the Royal Society B* 285 (February 21, 2018): 20172738, doi.org/10.1098/rspb.2017.2738.

33. Du et al., "Pattern and Process," supplementary table S1, available at datadryad.org/resource/doi:10.5061/dryad.c30g9?show=full.

34. John Hawks, "Human Brain Evolution Looks Gradual. If You Ignore Enough Data . . .," *John Hawks Weblog*, February 21, 2018, johnhawks.net/weblog/reviews/brain/brain-size-gradual-naledi-left-out-2018.html.

35. Lee R. Berger et al., "*Homo naledi*, a New Species of the Genus *Homo* from the Dinaledi Chamber, South Africa," *eLife* 4 (September 10, 2015): e09560, doi:10.7554/eLife.09560; Debbie Argue et al., "The Affinities of *Homo floresiensis* Based on Phylogenetic Analyses of Cranial, Dental and Postcranial characters," *Journal of Human Evolution* 107 (June 2017): 107–33, doi.org/10.1016/j.jhevol.2017.02.006; Florent Détroit et al., "A New Species of *Homo* from the Late Pleistocene of the Philippines," *Nature* 568 (April 10, 2019): 181–86, doi:10.1038/s41586-019-1067-9.

36. Paul HGM Dirks, "The Age of *Homo naledi* and Associated Sediments in the Rising Star Cave, South Africa," *eLife* 6 (May 9, 2017): e24231, doi:10.7554/eLife.24231.

37. Thomas Sutikna et al., "Revised Stratigraphy and Chronology for *Homo floresiensis* at Liang Bua in Indonesia," *Nature* 532 (March 30, 2016): 366–69, doi:10.1038/nature17179.

38. Adam Brumm et al., "Age and Context of the Oldest Known Fossils from Flores," *Nature* 534 (June 8, 2016): 249–53, doi:10.1038/nature17663.

39. Détroit et al., "A New Species."

40. T. Ignicco et al., "Earliest Known Hominin Activity in the Philippines by 709 Thousand Years Ago," *Nature* 557 (May 2, 2018): 233–37, doi:10.1038/s41586-018-0072-8.

41. M. Gascoyne et al., "Sea-Level Lowering during the Illinoian Glaciation: Evidence from a Bahama 'Blue Hole,'" *Science* 205, no. 4408 (August 24,

1979): 806–8, doi:10.1126/science.205.4408.806; Lawrence R. Heaney, "Zoogeographic Evidence for Middle and Late Pleistocene Landbridges to the Philippine Islands," *Modern Quaternary Research in Southeast Asia* 9 (January 1985): 127–43.

42. Debbie Argue et al., "The Affinities of *Homo floresiensis*."

43. G. Philip Rightmire, "Middle and Later Pleistocene Hominins in Africa and Southwest Asia," *Proceedings of the National Academy of Sciences, USA* 106, no. 38 (September 22, 2009): 16046–50, doi.org/10.1073/pnas.0903930106.

44. Bridget Alex, "Neanderthal Brains: Bigger, Not Necessarily Better," *The Crux* (blog), *Discover*, September 21, 2018, blogs.discovermagazine.com/crux/2018/09/21/neanderthal-brains-bigger-but-not-necessarily-better/#.XMww044zZPY.

45. Neubauer, Hublin, and Gunz, "Evolution of Modern Human Brain"; Eva María Poza-Rey, Aida Gómez-Robles, and Juan Luis Arsuada, "Brain Size and Organization in the Middle Pleistocene Hominins from Sima de los Huesos. Inferences from Endocranial Variation," *Journal of Human Evolution* 129 (April 2019): 67–90, doi.org/10.1016/j.hevol.2019.01.006.

46. Philipp Gunz et al., "Brain Development after Birth Differs between Neanderthals and Modern Humans," *Current Biology* 20, no. 21 (November 9, 2010): R921–R922, doi:10.1016/j.cub.2010.10.018.

47. Aaron B. Wolf and Joshua M. Akey, "Outstanding Questions in the Study of Archaic Hominin Admixture," *PLoS Genetics* 14, no. 5 (May 31, 2016): e1007349, doi.org/10.1371/journal.pgen.1007349.

48. Richard E. Green et al., "A Draft Sequence of the Neanderthal Genome," *Science* 328, no. 5979 (May 7, 2010): 710–22, doi:10.1126/science.1188021, together with supporting online information.

49. Cedric Boeckx and Antonio Benítex-Burraco, "The Shape of the Human Language-Ready Brain," *Frontiers in Psychology* 5 (April 4, 2014): e282, doi.org/10.3389/fpsyg.2014.00282.

50. Johan J. Bolhuis, Ian Tattersall, Noam Chomsky, Robert C. Berwick, "How Could Language Have Evolved?," *PLoS Biology* 12, no. 8 (August 26, 2014): e1001934, doi.org/10.1371/journal.pbio.1001934.

Chapter 16 – Did Humans and Neanderthals Interbreed?

1. William Davies, "The Time of the Last Neanderthals," *Nature* 512 (August 21, 2014): 260–61, doi:10.1038/512260a.

2. Matthias Meyer et al., "A High-Coverage Genome Sequence from an Archaic Denisovan Individual," *Science* 338, no. 6104 (October 12, 2012):

222–26, doi:10.1126/science.1224344; Kay Prüfer et al., "The Complete Genome Sequence of a Neanderthal from the Altai Mountains," *Nature* 505 (January 2, 2014): 43–49, doi:10.1038/nature12886.

3. Suzanna White, John A. J. Gowlett, and Matt Grove, "The Place of the Neanderthals in Hominin Phylogeny," *Journal of Anthropological Archaeology* 35 (September 2014): 32–50, doi:10.1016/j.jaa.2014.04.004.

4. Ian Tattersall, "Neanderthals, *Homo sapiens*, and the Question of Species in Paleoanthropology," *Journal of Anthropological Sciences* 85 (January 2007): 139–46.

5. Marcia S. Ponce de León and Christoph P. E. Zollikofer, "Neanderthal Cranial Ontogeny and Its Implications for Late Hominid Diversity," *Nature* 412 (August 2, 2001): 534–38, doi:10.1038/35087573; Markus Bastir, Paul O'Higgins, and Antonio Rosas, "Facial Ontogeny in Neanderthals and Modern Humans," *Proceedings of the Royal Society B* 274, no. 1614 (May 7, 2007): 1125–32, doi:10.1098/rspb.2006.0448.

6. Shara E. Bailey, "A Closer Look at Neanderthal Postcanine Dental Morphology: The Mandibular Dentition," *The Anatomical Record* 269 (December 26, 2002): 149–56, doi:10.1002/ar.10116.

7. Tanya M. Smith, "Teeth and Human Life-History Evolution," *Annual Review of Anthropology* 42 (October 2013): 191–208, doi:10.1146/annurev-anthro-092412-155550.

8. Alexandra de Sousa and Eugénia Cunha, "Hominins and the Emergence of the Modern Human Brain," in Michel A. Hofman and Dean Falk, eds., *Evolution of the Primate Brain*, vol. 195, *Progress in Brain Research* (Elsevier B.V.: 2012), 293–322, doi:10.1016/B978-0-444-53860-4.00014-3.

9. Philipp Gunz et al., "Brain Development after Birth Differs between Neanderthals and Modern Humans," *Current Biology* 20, no. 21 (November 9, 2010): PR921–R22, doi:10.1016/j.cub.2010.10.018.

10. Takanori Kochiyama et al., "Reconstructing the Neanderthal Brain Using Computational Anatomy," *Scientific Reports* 8 (April 26, 2018): 6296, doi:10.1038/s41598-018-24331-0.

11. Emiliano Bruner, "Morphological Differences in the Parietal Lobes within the Human Genus: A Neurofunctional Perspective," *Current Anthropology* 51, no. S1 (June 2010): S77–S88, doi:10.1086/650729; Antoine Balzeau, "Variations and Asymmetries in Regional Brain Surface in the Genus *Homo*," *Journal of Human Evolution* 62, no. 6 (June 2012): 696–706, doi:10.1016/j.hevol.2012.03.007.

12. Markus Bastir et al., "Evolution of the Base of the Brain in Highly

Encephalized Human Species," *Nature Communications* 2 (December 13, 2011): 588, doi:10.1038/ncomms1593; Simon Neubauer, Jean-Jacques Hublin, and Philipp Gunz, "The Evolution of Modern Human Brain Shape," *Science Advances* 4, no. 1 (January 24, 2018): eaao5961, doi:10.1126/sciadv.aao5961.

13. Balzeau, "Variations and Asymmetries."
14. Neubauer, Hublin, and Gunz, "Evolution of Modern Human Brain"; Richard E. Green et al., "A Draft Sequence of the Neanderthal Genome," *Science* 328, no. 5979 (May 7, 2010): 710–22, doi:10.1126/science.1188021; Prüfer et al., "Complete Genome Sequence"; Cedric Boeckx and Antonio Benítez-Burraco, "The Shape of the Human Language-Ready Brain," *Frontiers in Psychology* 5 (April 4, 2014): e282, doi:10.3389/fpsyg.2014.00282.
15. Torsten Günther and Carl Nettelblad, "The Presence and Impact of Reference Bias on Population Genomic Studies of Prehistoric Human Populations," *PLoS Genetics* 15, no. 7 (July 26, 2019): e1008302, doi:10.1371/journal.pgen.1008302.
16. Qiaomei Fu et al., "An Early Modern Human from Romania with a Recent Neanderthal Ancestor," *Nature* 524 (August 13, 2015): 216–19, plus supplemental online data, doi:10.1038/nature14558.
17. James P. Noonan, "Neanderthal Genomics and the Evolution of Modern Humans," *Genome Research* 20, no. 5 (May 2010): 547–53, doi:10.1101/gr.076000.108.
18. Benjamin Vernot, "Excavating Neandertal and Denisovan DNA from the Genomes of Melanesian Individuals," *Science* 352, no. 6282 (April 8, 2016): 235–39, doi:10.1126/science.aad9416.
19. Jeffrey D. Wall et al., "Higher Levels of Neanderthal Ancestry in East Asians than in Europeans," *Genetics* 194, no. 1 (May 1, 2013): 199–209, doi:10.1534/genetics.112.148213.
20. Armando G. M. Neves and Maurizio Serva, "Extremely Rare Interbreeding Events Can Explain Neanderthal DNA in Living Humans," *PLoS One* 7, no. 10 (October 24, 2012): e47076, doi:10.1371/journal.pone.0047076.
21. Benjamin Vernot and Joshua M. Akey, "Complex History of Admixture between Modern Humans and Neandertals," *American Journal of Human Genetics* 96, no. 3 (March 5, 2015): 448–53, doi:10.1016/j.ajhg.2015.01.006.
22. Mathias Currat and Laurent Excoffier, "Modern Humans Did Not Admix with Neanderthals during Their Range Expansion into Europe," *PLoS Biology* 2, no.12 (November 30, 2004): doi:10.1371/journal.pbio.0020421.
23. Fernando L. Mendez et al., "The Divergence of Neandertal and Modern

Human Y Chromosomes," *American Journal of Human Genetics* 98, no. 4 (April 7, 2016): 728–34, doi:10.1016/j.ajhg.2016.02.023.

24. Sriram Sankararaman et al., "The Genomic Landscape of Neanderthal Ancestry in Present-Day Humans," *Nature* 507 (March 20, 2014): 354–57, doi:10.1038/nature12961.

25. David Reich, quoted in Ewen Callaway, "Modern Human Genomes Reveal Our Inner Neanderthal," *Nature News*, January 29, 2014, doi:10.1038/nature.2014.14615.

26. Boeckx and Benítez-Burraco, "The Shape of Human Language-Ready Brain."

27. Green et al., "Draft Sequence of Neanderthal Genome."

28. Sankararaman et al., "Genomic Landscape of Neanderthal Ancestry."

29. Sankararaman et al., "Genomic Landscape of Neanderthal Ancestry."

30. Aaron B. Wolf and Joshua M. Akey, "Outstanding Questions in the Study of Archaic Hominin Admixture," *PLoS Genetics* 14, no. 5 (May 31, 2018): e1007349, doi:10.1371/journal.pgen.1007349.

31. Raymundo Báez-Mendoza and Wolfram Schultz, "The Role of the Striatum in Social Behavior," *Frontiers in Neuroscience* 7 (December 10, 2013): 233, doi:10.3389/fnins.2013.00233.

32. Meyer et al., "High-Coverage Genome Sequence."

33. Benjamin Vernot and Joshua M. Akey, "Resurrecting Surviving Neandertal Lineages from Modern Human Genomes," *Science* 343, no. 6174 (February 28, 2014): 1017–21, doi:10.1126/science.1245938.

34. Tomislav Marici et al., "A Recent Evolutionary Change Affects a Regulatory Element in the Human *FOXP2* Gene," *Molecular Biology and Evolution* 30, no. 4 (April 2013): 844–52, doi:10.1093/molbev/mss271.

35. Ajit Varki, "Why Are There No Persisting Hybrids of Humans with Denisovans, Neanderthals, or Anyone Else?," *Proceedings of the National Academy of Sciences, USA* 13, no. 17 (April 26, 2016): E2354, doi:10/1073/pnas.1602270113.

36. Wolf and Akey, "Outstanding Questions in the Study."

37. Wolf and Akey, "Outstanding Questions in the Study."

38. Vernot and Akey, "Resurrecting Surviving Neandertal Lineages."

39. Vernot and Akey, "Resurrecting Surviving Neandertal Lineages."

40. Green et al., "Draft Sequence of Neanderthal Genome"; Meyer et al., "High-Coverage Genome Sequence"; Prüfer et al., "Complete Genome Sequence."

41. Michael Dannemann, Aida M. Andrés, and Janet Kelso, "Introgression of Neanderthal- and Denisovan-like Haplotypes Contributes to Adaptive

Variation in Human Toll-Like Receptors," *American Journal of Human Genetics* 98, no. 1 (January 7, 2016): 22–23, doi:10.1016/j.ajhg.2015.11.015.

42. Prüfer et al., "Complete Genome Sequence"; Sebastian Temme et al., "A Novel Family of Human Leukocyte Antigen Class II Receptors May Have Its Origin in Archaic Human Species," *Journal of Biological Chemistry* 289, no. 2 (January 10, 2014): 639–53, doi:10.1074/jbc.M113.515767.

43. Sankararaman et al., "Genomic Landscape of Neanderthal Ancestry."

44. Ekaterina E. Khrameeva, "Neanderthal Ancestry Drives Evolution of Lipid Catabolism in Contemporary Europeans," *Nature Communications* 5 (April 1, 2014): 3584, doi:10.1038/ncomms4584.

45. Emilia Huerta-Sánchez et al., "Altitude Adaptation in Tibet Caused by Introgression of Denisovan-like DNA," *Nature* 512 (July 2, 2014): 194–97, doi:10.1038/nature13408.

46. Rachel M. Gittelman et al., "Archaic Hominin Admixture Facilitated Adaptation to Out-of-Africa Environments," *Current Biology* 26, no. 24 (December 19, 2016): 3375–82, doi:10.1016/j.cub.2016.10.041.

47. Andrew D. Kern and Matthew W. Hahn, "The Neutral Theory in Light of Natural Selection," *Molecular Biology and Evolution* 35, no. 6 (June 2018): 1366–71, doi:10.1093/molbev/msy092.

48. Josephine T. Daub et al., "Evidence for Polygenic Adaptation to Pathogens in the Human Genome," *Molecular Biology and Evolution* 30, no. 7 (July 2013): 1544–58, doi:10.1093/molbev/mst080.

49. Viviane Callier, "Theorists Debate How 'Neutral' Evolution Really Is," *Quanta Magazine*, November 8, 2018, quantamagazine.org/neutral-theory-of-evolution-challenged-by-evidence-for-dna-selection-20181108/?mc_cid=56140ad1d1&mc_eid=a2bccb49a5.

50. F. Pouyet et al., "Background Selection and Biased Gene Conversion Affect More than 95% of the Human Genome and Bias Demographic Inferences," *eLife* 7 (August 20, 2018): e36317, doi:10.7554/eLife.36317.039.

51. L. B. Barreiro et al., "Natural Selection Has Driven Population Differentiation in Modern Humans," *Nature Genetics* 40, no. 3 (February 3, 2008): 340–45, doi:10.1038/ng.78; Shaohua Fan et al., "Going Global by Adapting Local: A Review of Recent Human Adaptation," *Science* 354, no. 6308 (October 7, 2016): 54–59, doi:10.1126/science.aaf5098.

52. Sandra Beleza et al., 2012. "The Timing of Pigmentation Lightening in Europeans," *Molecular Biology and Evolution* 30, no. 1 (January 2013): 24–35, doi:10.1093/molbev/mss207; Meng Lin et al., "Rapid Evolution of a Skin-Lightening Allele in Southern African KhoeSan," *Proceedings of*

the National Academy of Sciences, USA 115, no. 52 (December 26, 2018): 13324–29, doi:10.1073/pnas.1801948115.

53. Sandra Wilde et al., "Direct Evidence for Positive Selection of Skin, Hair, and Eye Pigmentation in Europeans during the last 5,000 y," *Proceedings of the National Academy of Sciences, USA* 111, 13 (April 1, 2014): 4832–37, doi:10.1073/pnas.1316513111.

54. Pardis C. Sabeti et al., "Genome-Wide Detection and Characterization of Positive Selection in Human Populations," *Nature* 449 (October 18, 2007): 913–18, doi:10.1038/nature06250.

55. Benjamin F. Voight et al., "A Map of Recent Positive Selection in the Human Genome," *PLoS Biology* 4, no. 3 (March 7, 2006): e72, doi:10.1371/journal.pbio.0040072.

56. Melissa Ilardo and Rasmus Nielsen, "Human Adaptation to Extreme Environmental Conditions," *Current Opinion in Genetics & Development* 53 (December 2018): 77–82, doi:10.1016/j.gde.2018.07.003.

57. Luis B. Barreiro and Lluís Quintana-Murci, "From Evolutionary Genetics to Human Immunology: How Selection Shapes Host Defence Genes," *Nature Reviews Genetics* 11 (December 1, 2009): 17–30, doi:10.1038/nrg2698.

58. Franck Prugnolle et al., "Pathogen-Driven Selection and Worldwide HLA Class I Diversity," *Current Biology* 15, no. 11: 1022–27, doi:10.1016/j.cub.2005.04.050.

59. Matteo Fumagalli et al., "Signatures of Environmental Genetic Adaptation Pinpoint Pathogens as the Main Selective Pressure through Human Evolution," *PLoS Genetics* 7, no. 11 (November 3, 2011): e1002355, doi:10.1371/journal.pgen.1002355.

60. David Enard et al., "Viruses Are a Dominant Driver of Protein Adaptation in Mammals," *eLife* 5 (May 17, 2016): e12469, doi:10.7554/eLife.12469.

61. Barreiro and Quintana-Murci, "From Evolutionary Genetics to Human Immunology."

62. Barreiro and Quintana-Murci, "From Evolutionary Genetics to Human Immunology"; Philip W. Hedrik, "Resistance to Malaria in Humans: The Impact of Strong, Recent Selection," *Malaria Journal* 11 (October 22, 2012): 349, 10.1186/1475-2875-11-349.

63. Matteo Fumagalli et al., "Parasites Represent a Major Selective Force for Interleukin Genes and Shape the Genetic Predisposition to Autoimmune Conditions," *Journal of Experimental Medicine* 206, no. 6 (June 8, 2009): 1395–408, doi:10.1084/jem.2008779.

64. Kaspar Delhey, "Gloger's Rule," *Current Biology* 27, no. 14 (July 24, 2017):

R689–R691, doi:10.1016/j.cub.2017.04.031.

65. Nina G. Jablonski and George Chaplin, "Human Skin Pigmentation as an Adaptation to UV Radiation," *Proceedings of the National Academy of Sciences, USA* 107, supplemental 2 (May 11, 2010): 8962–968, doi:10.1073/pnas.0914628107.

66. Yi Peng et al., "Down-Regulation of *EPAS1* Transcription and Genetic Adaptation of Tibetans to High-Altitude Hypoxia," *Molecular Biology and Evolution* 34, no. 4 (April 1, 2017): 818–30, doi:10.1093/molbev/msw280; Ian Mathieson et al., "Genome-Wide Patterns of Selection in 230 Ancient Eurasians," *Nature* 528 (December 24, 2015): 499–503, doi:10.1038/nature16152; Lin et al., "Rapid Evolution of a Skin-Lightening."

67. Michael Dannemann and Fernando Racimo, "Something Old, Something Borrowed: Admixture and Adaptation in Human Evolution," *Current Opinion in Genetics and Development* 53 (December 2018): 1–8, doi.10.1016/j.gde.2018.05.009.

68. Fu et al., "Early Modern Human."

Chapter 17 – Did Neanderthals Create Art?

1. Richard G. Klein with Blake Edgar, *The Dawn of Human Culture* (New York: John Wiley and Sons, 2002).

2. Johna J. Bolhuis et al., "How Could Language Have Evolved?," *PLoS Biology* 12, no. 8 (August 26, 2014):e1001934, doi:10.1371/journal.pbio.1001934.

3. Harold Dibble, quoted in Michael Balter, "Did Neandertals Truly Bury Their Dead?," *Science* 337, no. 6101 (September 21, 2012): 1443–44, doi:10.1126/science.337.6101.1443.

4. Robert H. Gargett et al., "Grave Shortcomings: The Evidence for Neandertal Burial," *Current Anthropology* 30, no. 2 (April 1989): 157–90. The following article includes discussion of geological processes and sites such as La Chapelle-aux-Saints, Krapina, Shanidar, Le Moustier, La Ferrassie, Teshik-Tash, and Regourdou: Robert H. Gargett, "Middle Palaeolithic Burial Is Not a Dead Issue: The View from Qafzeh, Saint-Césaire, Kebara, Amud, and Dederiyeh," *Journal of Human Evolution* 37, no. 1 (July 1999): 27–90, doi:10.1006/jhev.199.0301; Dennis M. Sandgathe et al., "The Roc de Marsal Neandertal Child: A Reassessment of Its Status as a Deliberate Burial," *Journal of Human Evolution* 61, no. 3 (September 2011): 243–53, doi:10.1016/j.jhevol.2011.04.003; Harold L. Dibble et al., "A Critical Look at Evidence from La Chapelle-aux-Saints Supporting an Intentional Neandertal Burial," *Journal of Archaeological Science* 53 (January 2015): 649–57,

doi.10.1016/j.jas.2014.04.019.

5. Ian Tattersall and Jeffrey H. Schwartz, "Evolution of the Genus *Homo*," *Annual Review of Earth and Planetary Sciences* 37 (May 30, 2009): 67–92, doi:10.1146/annurev.earth.031208.100202.

6. Darryl E. Granger et al., "New Cosmogenic Burial Ages for Sterkfontein Member 2 *Australopithecus* and Member 5 Oldowan," *Nature* 522 (June 4, 2015): 85–88, doi:10.1038/nature14268; Jan D. Kramers and Paul H. G. M. Dirks, "The Age of Fossil StW573 ('Little Foot'): An Alternative Interpretation of $^{26}Al/^{10}Be$ Burial Data," *South African Journal of Science* 113, no. 3–4 (March/April 2017): 1–8, doi:10.17159/sajs.2017/20160085.

7. Paul H. G. M. Dirks, "Geological Setting and Age of *Australopithecus sediba* from Southern Africa," *Science* 328, no. 5975 (April 9, 2010): 205–8, doi:10.1126/science.1184950.

8. Gargett et al., "Grave Shortcomings."

9. Gargett et al., "Grave Shortcomings."

10. Ralph S. Solecki, *Shanidar: The First Flower People* (New York: Knopf, 1971), 247.

11. Solecki, *Shanidar*, 247.

12. Ralph S. Solecki, "Shanidar IV, a Neandertal Flower Burial in Northern Iraq," *Science* 190, no. 4217 (November 28, 1975): 880–81, doi:10.1126/science.190.4217.880.

13. Jeffrey D. Sommer, "The Shanidar IV 'Flower Burial': A Re-evaluation of Neanderthal Burial Ritual," *Cambridge Archaeological Journal* 9, no. 1 (April 1999): 127–29, doi:10.1017/S095977430001529.

14. Marta Fiacconi and Chris O. Hunt, "Pollen Taphonomy at Shanidar Cave (Kurdish Iraq): An Initial Evaluation," *Review of Palaeobotany and Palynology* 223 (December 2015): 87–93, doi:10.1016/j.revpalbo.2015.09.003.

15. Paul Pettitt, "The Neanderthal Dead: Exploring Mortuary Variability in Middle Palaeolithic Eurasia," *Before Farming* 2002, no. 1 (January 2002): 1–26, doi:10.3828/bfarm.2002.1.4.

16. Jared M. Diamond, "Were Neanderthals the First Humans to Bury Their Dead?," *Nature* 340, no. 344 (August 3, 1989): doi:10.1038/340344a0.

17. Gargett et al., "Grave Shortcomings."

18. Lewis R. Binford, *Bones: Ancient Men and Modern Myths* (New York: Academic Press, 1987), 196.

19. Clive Finlayson et al., "Birds of a Feather: Neanderthal Exploitation of Raptors and Corvids," *PLoS One* 7, no. 9 (September 17, 2012): e45927, doi10.1371/journal.pone.0045927.

20. Sibylle Wolf et al., "The Use of Ochre and Painting during the Upper Paleo-
    lithic of the Swabian Jura in the Context of the Development of Ochre Use
    in Africa and Europe," *Open Archaeology* 4, no. 1 (May 12, 2018): 185–205,
    doi:10.1515/opar-2018-0012.

21. Josephine C. A. Joordens et al., "*Homo erectus* at Trinil in Java Used Shells
    for Tool Production and Engraving," *Nature* 518 (February 12, 2015): 228–
    31, doi:10.1038/nature13962

22. D. L. Hoffmann et al., "U-Th Dating of Carbonate Crusts Reveals Nean-
    dertal Origin of Iberian Cave Art," *Science* 359, no. 6378 (February 23,
    2018): 912–15 and supplementary materials, doi:10.1126/science.aap7778.

23. Joaquín Rodríguez-Vidal et al., "A Rock Engraving Made by Neanderthals
    in Gibraltar," *Proceedings of the National Academy of Sciences, USA* 111, no.
    37 (September 16, 2014):13301–6, doi:10.1073/pnas.1411529111.

24. Yolanda Fernández-Jalvo Andrews and Peter Andrews, *Atlas of Taphonomic
    Identifications* in *Vertebrate Paleobiology and Paleoanthropology Series*, eds.
    Eric Delson and Eric J. Sargis (New York: Springer, 2016), New York: 49,
    figure A61.

25. Georges Sauvet et al., "Uranium-Thorium Dating Method and Palaeolithic
    Rock Art," *Quaternary International* 432, part B (March 8, 2017): 86–92,
    doi:10.1016/j.quaint.2015.03.053.

26. Ludovic Slimak et al., "Comment on 'U-Th Dating of Carbonate Crusts
    Reveals Neandertal Origin of Iberian Cave Art,'" *Science* 361, no. 6408
    (September 21, 2018): eaau1371, doi:10.1126/science.aau1371.

27. Tom Higham et al., "The Earliest Evidence for Anatomically Modern Hu-
    mans in Northwestern Europe," *Nature* 479 (November 24, 2011): 521–24,
    doi:10.1038/nature10484.

28. William Davies, "The Time of the Last Neanderthals," *Nature* 512 (August
    21, 2014): 260–61, doi:10.1038/512260a.

29. Dirk L. Hoffmann et al., "Symbolic Use of Marine Shells and Mineral Pig-
    ments by Iberian Neandertals 115,000 Years Ago" *Science Advances* 4, no. 2
    (February 22, 2018): eaar5255, doi:10.1126/sciadv.aar5255.

30. Abdeljalil Bousouggar et al., "82,000-year-old Shell Beads from North Afri-
    ca and Implications for the Origins of Modern Human Behavior," *Proceed-
    ings of the National Academy of Sciences, USA* 104, no. 24 (June 12, 2007):
    9964–69, doi:10.1073/pnas.0703877104; Christopher Henshilwood et al.,
    "Middle Stone Age Shell Beads from South Africa," *Science* 304, no. 5669
    (April 16, 2004): 404, doi:10.1126/science.1095905.

31. Andrews and Andrews, *Atlas of Taphonomic Identifications*, 49, figure A61.

32. Diane E. Riska, "Experiments on Nestling Recognition by Brown Noddies (Anous Stolidus)," *The Auk* 101, no. 3 (July 1984): 605–9, doi:10.1093/auk/101.3.605.

33. Henshilwood et al., "Middle Stone Age Shell Beads," figure S1.

34. Anna Maria Kubicka, "A Systematic Review of Animal Predation Creating Pierced Shells: Implications for the Archaeological Record of the Old World," *PeerJ* 5 (January 17, 2017): e2903, doi:10.7717/peerj.2903.

35. Cajus G. Diedrich, "'Neanderthal Bone Flutes': Simply Products of Ice Age Spotted Hyena Scavenging Activities on Cave Bear Cubs in European Cave Bear Dens," *Royal Society Open Science* 2, no. 4 (April 1, 2015): 14022, doi:10.1098/rsos.140022.

36. Tattersall and Schwartz, "Evolution of Genus *Homo*," 83.

37. Cedric Boeckx and Antonio Benítez-Burraco, "The Shape of the Human Language-Ready Brain," *Frontiers in Psychology* 5 (April 4, 2014): e282, doi:10.3389/fpsyg.2014.00282; Simon Neubauer, Jean-Jacques Hublin, and Philipp Gunz, "The Evolution of Modern Human Brain Shape," *Science Advances* 4, no. 1 (January 24, 2018): eaao5961, doi:10.1126/sciadv.aao5961.

38. Benjamin Vernot and Joshua M. Akey, "Resurrecting Surviving Neandertal Lineages from Modern Human Genomes," *Science* 343, no. 6174 (February 28, 2014): 1017–21, doi:10.1126/science.1245938.

39. Sabine Gaudzinski-Windheuser et al., "Evidence for Close-Range Hunting by Last Interglacial Neanderthals," *Nature Ecology & Evolution* 2 (June 25, 2018): 1087–92, doi:10.1038/s41559-018-0596-1.

40. Vitor A. Nóbrega and Shigeru Miyagawa, "The Precedence of Syntax in the Rapid Emergence of Human Language in Evolution as Defined by the Integration Hypothesis," *Frontiers in Psychology* 6, no. 271 (March 18, 2015): 1–8, doi:10.3389/fpsyg.2015.00271; Johan J. Bolhuis et al., "How Could Language Have Evolved?," *PLoS Biology* 12, no. 8 (August 26, 2014): e1001934, doi:10.1371/journal.pbio.1001934; Chris Knight, "Puzzles and Mysteries in the Origins of Language," *Language & Communication* 50 (September 2016): 12–21, doi:10.1016/j.langcom.2016.09.002.

41. Aristotle, *Eticha Nicomachea*, ed. I. Bywater (Oxford: Oxford University Press, 1920).

42. Michael Balter, "Neandertal Champion Defends the Reputation of Our Closest Cousins," *Science* 337, no. 6905 (August 10, 2012): 642–43, doi:10.1126/science.337.6095.642.

43. Jean-Jacques Hublin, quoted in Balter, "Neandertal Champion Defends Reputation."

44. Steven R. James, "Hominid Use of Fire in the Lower and Middle Pleistocene: A Review of the Evidence," *Current Anthropology* 30, no. 1 (February 1989): 1–26, doi:10.1086/203705.
45. Dennis M. Sandgathe et al., "Timing of the Appearance of Habitual Fire Use," *Proceedings of the National Academy of Sciences, USA* 108, no. 29 (July 19, 2011): E298, doi:10.1073/pnas.1106759108.
46. Harold Dibble, quoted in Balter, "Neandertal Champion Defends Reputation."
47. Ian Tattersall, *Masters of the Planet: The Search for Our Human Origins* (New York: St. Martin's Press, 2012), 177.

Chapter 18 – Can Evolutionary Processes Explain the Origin of Complex, Eukaryotic Cells?

1. István Zachar and Eörs Szathmáry, "Breath-giving Cooperation: Critical Review of Origin of Mitochondria Hypotheses," *Biology Direct* 12, no. 1 (August 14, 2017): id19, doi:10.1186/s13062-017-0190-5.
2. Abigail Clements et al., "The Reducible Complexity of a Mitochondrial Molecular Machine," *Proceedings of the National Academy of Sciences, USA* 106, no. 37 (September 15, 2009): 15791–95, doi:10.1073/pnas.0908264106.
3. Franklin M. Harold, *In Search of Cell History: The Evolution of Life's Building Blocks* (Chicago: University of Chicago Press, 2014), 137.
4. Iain G. Johnston and Ben P. Williams, "Evolutionary Inference across Eukaryotes Identifies Specific Pressures Favoring Mitochondrial Gene Retention," *Cell Systems* 2, no. 2 (February 24, 2016): 101–11, doi:10.1016/j.cels.2016.01.013.
5. Anna L. Duncan, Alan J. Robinson, and John E. Walker, "Cardiolipin Binds Selectively but Transiently to Conserved Lysine Residues in the Rotor of Metazoan ATP Synthases," *Proceedings of the National Academy of Sciences, USA* 113, no. 31 (August 2, 2016): 8687–92, doi:10.1073/pnas.1608396113; Giuseppe Paradies et al., "Functional Role of Cardiolipin in Mitochondrial Bioenergetics," *Biochimica et Biophysica Acta—Bioenergetics* 1837, no. 4 (April 2014): 408–17, doi:10.1016/j.bbabio.2013.10.006.
6. Aline Bender, Parvana Hajieva, and Bernd Moosmann, "Adaptive Antioxidant Methionine Accumulation in Respiratory Chain Complexes Explains the Use of a Deviant Genetic Code in Mitochondria," *Proceedings of the National Academy of Sciences, USA* 105, no. 43 (October 28, 2008): 16496–501, doi:10.1073/pnas.0802779105.

Chapter 19 – Can Evolution Repeat Outcomes?

1. Simon Conway Morris, *Life's Solution: Inevitable Humans in a Lonely Universe* (New York: Cambridge University Press, 2003); George McGhee, *Convergent Evolution: Limited Forms Most Beautiful* (Cambridge, MA: MIT Press, 2011).
2. Fazale Rana, *The Cell's Design: How Chemistry Reveal the Creator's Artistry* (Grand Rapids, MI: Baker 2008).
3. Stephen Jay Gould, *Wonderful Life: The Burgess Shale and the Nature of History* (New York: W. W. Norton, 1990).
4. Gabriel Yedid and Graham Bell, "Macroevolution Simulated with Autonomously Replicating Computer Programs," *Nature* 420 (December 19, 2002): 810–12, doi:10.1038/nature01151.
5. Zachary D. Blount, Christina Z. Borland, and Richard E. Lenski, "Historical Contingency and the Evolution of a Key Innovation in an Experimental Population of *Escherichia coli*," *Proceedings of the National Academy Sciences, USA* 105, no. 23 (June 10, 2008): 7899–906, doi:10.1073/pnas.0803151105.
6. J. D. Pettigrew and S. P. Collin, "Terrestrial Optics in an Aquatic Eye: The Sandlance, *Limnichthytes fasciatus* (Creediidae, Teleostei)," *Journal of Comparative Physiology A* 177, no. 4 (October 1995): 397–408, doi:10.1007/BF00187476.
7. Detlef D. Leipe, L. Aravind, and Eugene V. Koonin, "Did DNA Replication Evolve Twice Independently?," *Nucleic Acids Research* 27, no. 17 (September 1, 1999): 3389–401, doi:10.1093/nar/27.17.3389.
8. J. William Schopf, "When Did Life Begin?," in *Life's Origin: The Beginnings of Biological Evolution*, ed. J. William Schopf (Berkeley: University of California Press, 2002), 163.

Chapter 20 – Can Evolutionary Co-option Explain the Irreducible Complexity of Biochemical Systems?

1. For example, see Claire M. Fraser et al., "The Minimal Gene Complement of *Mycoplasma genitalium*," *Science* 270, no. 5235 (October 20, 1995): 397–404, doi:10.1126/science.270.5235.397.
2. Michael Behe, *Darwin's Black Box: The Biochemical Challenge to Evolution*, 10th anniversary ed. (New York: Free Press, 2006), 39.
3. For example, see Kenneth R. Miller, *Finding Darwin's God: A Scientist's Search for Common Ground between God and Evolution* (New York: Cliff Street Books, 1999), 129–64 and Michael Le Page, "Evolution Myths: The Bacterial Flagellum Is Irreducibly Complex," *New Scientist*, April 16, 2008,

newscientist.com/article/dn13663-evolution-myths-the-bacterial-flagel-lum-is-irreducibly-complex/.

4. For example, see Mark J. Pallen and Nicholas J. Matzke, "From *On the Origin of Species* to the Origin of Bacterial Flagella," *Nature Reviews Microbiology* 4 (October 1, 2006): 784–90, doi:10.1038/nrmicro1493.

5. For example see Ariel Blocker, Kaoru Komoriya, and Shin-Ichi Aizawa, "Type III Secretion Systems and Bacterial Flagella: Insights into Their Function from Structural Similarities," *Proceedings of the National Academy of Sciences, USA* 100, no. 6 (March 18, 2003): 3027–30, doi:10.1073/pnas.0535335100.

6. Milton H. Saier, Jr., "Evolution of Bacterial Type III Protein Secretion Systems," *Trends in Microbiology* 12, no. 3 (March 1, 2004): 113–15, doi:10.1016/j.tim.2004.01.003.

7. Sonia L. Bardy, Sandy Y. M. Ng, and Ken F. Jarrell, "Prokaryotic Motility Structures," *Microbiology* 149, no. 2 (February 1, 2003): 295–304, doi:10.1099/mic.0.25948-0.

8. Pallen and Matzke, "From *On the Origin of Species.*"

9. Michael W. Gray et al., "Irremediable Complexity?," *Science* 330, no. 6006 (November 12, 2010): 920–21, doi:10.1126/science.1198594; Judge Starling (@judgestarling), "Rube Goldberg's 131st Birthday: Irremediable Complexity by Constructive Neutral Evolution," Tumblr, posted June 11, 2014, 12:30 AM, judgestarling.tumblr.com/post/88449119459/rube-goldbergs-131st-birthday-irremediable?soc_src=mail&soc_trk=ma.

10. Li Zhang et al., "Artificial Bacterial Flagella: Fabrication and Magnetic Control," *Applied Physics Letters* 94 (February 13, 2009): 064107, doi:10.1063/1.3079655.

11. Mark T. McAuley et al., "Modeling the Flagellar Motor Assembly Process to Help Improve Industrial Operations Systems Design," preprint, accessed August 28, 2019, researchgate.net/publication/241614062_Modelling_the_flagellar_motor_assembly_process_to_help_improve_industrial_operations_systems_design.

12. Kenneth R. Miller, "Life's Grand Design," *Technology Review* 97, no. 2 (February/March 1994): 24–32.

Chapter 21 – Has Evolution Refuted the Watchmaker Argument?

1. Theodosius Dobzhansky, "Nothing in Biology Makes Sense Except in the Light of Evolution," *American Biology Teacher* 35, no. 3 (March 1971): 125–29, doi:10.2307/4444260.

2. Val Dusek, *Philosophy of Technology: An Introduction* (Malden, MA: Blackwell, 2006), 12.

3. William Paley, *Natural Theology*, ed. Matthew D. Eddy and David Knight, Oxford World's Classics (New York: Oxford University Press, 2006): 7–8.

4. Massimo Pigliucci and Maarten Boudry, "Why Machine-Information Metaphors Are Bad for Science and Science Education," *Science and Education* 20, 5–6 (May 2011): 453–71, doi: 10.1007/s11191-010-9267-6.

5. Robert F. Service, "Borrowing from Biology to Power the Petite," *Science* 283, no. 5308 (January 1, 1999), 27–28, doi:10.1126/science.283.5398.27; Ricky K. Soong et al., "Powering an Inorganic Nanodevice with a Biomolecular Motor," *Science* 290, no. 5496 (November 24, 2000), 1555–58, doi:10.1126/science.290.5496.1555.

6. Leonard M. Adleman, "Computing with DNA," *Scientific American*, August 1, 1998, 54–61.

7. Will Clifford, "DNA Computing: Meet Dr. Adleman," *Youngzine*, February 2, 2013, https://youngzine.org/news/technology/dna-computing-meet-dr-adleman.

8. Richard Owen, *On the Nature of Limbs: A Discourse*, ed. Ron Amundson (Chicago: University of Chicago Press, 2007), 38.

9. Nicolaas A. Rupke, *Richard Owen: Biology without Darwin*, rev. ed. (Chicago: University of Chicago Press, 2009), 112.

Chapter 22 – Is the Watchmaker Really Blind?

1. Ernst Mayer, *One Long Argument: Charles Darwin and the Genesis of Evolutionary Thought* (Boston: Harvard University Press, 1991).

2. Charles Darwin, *On the Origin of Species by Means of Natural Selection* (New York: Collier Press, 1909), 190.

3. Richard Dawkins, *The Blind Watchmaker: Why the Evidence for Evolution Reveals a Universe without Design*, reissued ed. (New York: Norton, 1996), 7–8.

4. Kensuke Kurihara et al., "A Recursive Vesicle-Based Model Protocell with a Primitive Model Cell Cycle," *Nature Communications* 6 (September 29, 2015): 8352, doi:10.1038/ncomms9352.

5. Kurihara et al., "Recursive Vesicle-Based Model."

6. Yanran Li et al., "Complete Biosynthesis of Noscapine and Halogenated Alkaloids in Yeast," *Proceedings of the National Academy of Sciences, USA* 115, no. 17 (April 24, 2018): E3922–E3931, doi: 10.1073/pnas.1721469115.

7. Angad P. Mehta et al., "Engineering Yeast Endosymbionts as a Step toward

the Evolution of Mitochondria," *Proceedings of the National Academy of Sciences, USA* 115, no. 46 (November 13, 2018): 11796–801, doi:10.1073/pnas.1813143115.

8. Gianni Liti, "Yeast Chromosome Numbers Minimized Using Genome Editing," *Nature* 560 (August 1, 2018): 317–18, doi:10.1038/d41586-018-05309-4.

Chapter 23 – Is Junk DNA Evidence for Evolution?

1. Nessa Carey, *Junk DNA: A Journey through the Dark Matter of the Genome* (New York: Columbia University Press, 2015).

2. Hiroaki Sakai et al., "Processed Pseudogenes and Their Functional Resurrection in the Human and Mouse Genomes," *Engineering in Life Sciences* (July 15, 2008): doi:10.1002/9780470015902.a0021000.

3. Ana C. Marques, Jennifer Tan, and Chris P. Ponting, "Wrangling for microRNAs Provokes Much Crosstalk," *Genome Biology* 12, no. 11 (November 21, 2011): 132, doi:10.1186/gb-2011-12-11-132; Leonardo Salmena et al., "A *ceRNA* Hypothesis: The Rosetta Stone of a Hidden RNA Language?," *Cell* 146, no. 3 (August 5, 2011): 353–58, doi:10.1016/j.cell.2011.07.014.

4. Brownyn A. Lucas et al., "Evidence for Convergent Evolution of SINE-Directed Staufen-Mediated mRNA Decay," *Proceedings of the National Academy of Sciences, USA* 115, no. 5 (January 30, 2018): 968–73, doi:10.1073/pnas.1715531115.

Chapter 24 – Why Are We Progressive Creationists?

1. Sir Fred Hoyle and Chandra Wickramasinghe, *Evolution from Space* (New York: Touchstone, 1981), 135.

2. Insight provided in an online conversation between Anjeanette Roberts and physical chemist Jordan Mantha in April 2019, at Peaceful Science, https://peacefulscience.org/.

3. Theodore J. Cabal and Peter J. Rasor II, *Controversy of the Ages: Why Christians Should Not Divide Over the Age of the Earth* (Wooster, OH: Weaver, 2017), 40.

Chapter 25 – What If Big-E Evolution Is True?

1. Mark A. Noll, *Jesus Christ and the Life of the Mind* (Grand Rapids, MI: Eerdmans, 2011), 111.

2. Noll, *Jesus Christ and the Life of the Mind*, 111–12.

3. "Creation Project FAQ," Carl F. H. Henry Center for Theological Understanding, henrycenter.tiu.edu/evangelical-theology-and-the-doctrine-of-creation/creation-project-faq/.

4. S. Joshua Swamidass, *The Genealogical Adam and Eve: The Surprising Science of Universal Ancestry* (Downers Grove, IL: IVP Academic, 2019).

5. "So Will I (100 Billion X)," track 4 on Hillsong UNITED, *Wonder*, Capitol Christian Music Group, 2017.

6. Galileo Galilei, "Galileo's Letter to the Grand Duchess Christina (1615)" in *The Essential Galileo*, ed. and trans. Maurice A. Finocchiaro (New York: Hackett Publishing, 2008), 116–17.

7. Noll, *Jesus Christ and the Life of the Mind*, 112.

8. Br. Albert Robertson, OP, "Dominican Life: Study," *Godzdogz: The Blog of the Dominican Student Brothers at Blackfriars, Oxford*, May 27, 2019, godzdogz.op.org/godzdogz/dominican-life-study.

Index

About the Authors

Anjeanette "AJ" Roberts completed her BS in chemistry at the University of Tulsa and her PhD in molecular and cell biology at the University of Pennsylvania. She conducted postdoctoral research at Yale University and served as a staff scientist at the National Institutes of Health, where she earned a Merit Award for her contributions to research in infectious diseases. She joined the University of Virginia's microbiology faculty and directed graduate studies in microbiology, immunology, and infectious diseases. She has coauthored over 40 articles published in peer-reviewed scientific journals and lectured at institutions around the world.

AJ coauthored her first book, *Building Bridges: Presentations on RTB's Testable Creation Model*, with RTB scholars Fazale Rana and Jeff Zweerink. Today, she uses her passion for truth to engage in science-faith topics such as evolution and design, integrating science and Christianity, and a theological perspective on viruses. AJ lives in Southern California.

Fazale "Fuz" Rana is vice president of research and apologetics at RTB. He completed his BS in chemistry at West Virginia State College, where he was a presidential scholar and elected to two honor societies. He earned a PhD in biochemistry at Ohio University where he was a two-time winner of the Donald Clippinger Research Award. His postdoctoral work was conducted at the Universities of Virginia and Georgia. Fuz worked for seven years as a senior scientist in product development for Procter & Gamble before joining RTB.

Fuz has published articles in peer-reviewed scientific journals, delivered presentations at international scientific meetings, and addressed church and university audiences in the US and abroad. Fuz also coauthored a chapter on antimicrobial peptides for *Biological and Synthetic Membranes* and has contributed numerous feature articles to Christian magazines. He appears frequently on radio, television, and podcasts. Some of his books include *Origins of Life*, *Who Was Adam?*, and *Creating Life in the Lab*. Fuz and his wife, Amy, live in Southern California.

Sue Dykes became interested in questions surrounding human origins while taking Reasons Institute courses through RTB. This experience inspired her to begin graduate studies in paleoanthropology. She earned a PhD in paleoanthropology at the University of the Witwatersrand, where she conducted groundbreaking research on the classification of hominid teeth. Originally from the UK, Sue moved to South Africa with her husband and children, where she lived near some of the most important sites in her field and interacted regularly with leaders in human origins research. Sue served as a long-time instructor for Reasons Institute and became a dear friend and mentor to many of her students. She also served as the chairperson of a hospital/clinic outreach charity and was a sworn translator in French.

In August 2019, Sue unexpectedly passed away while on her way to the US to begin work as a staff scholar at Reasons to Believe. She is survived by her husband and two adult children. Her scholasticism, insight, and friendship made a lasting impact that continues to advance the kingdom of God.

 **Mark Perez** earned a BA in philosophy and an MA in analytic philosophy of science from California State University, Los Angeles, as well as an MPA with an emphasis on organizational development from American Military University. Mark has taught critical thinking and problem solving in the government and private sectors, focusing on decision-making through rational analysis. Mark has worked as a volunteer apologist with Reasons to Believe since the 1990s and as an instructor for Reasons Institute.

About Reasons to Believe

Uniquely positioned within the science-faith discussion since 1986, Reasons to Believe (RTB) communicates that science and the Christian faith are, and always will be, allies, not enemies. Distinguished for integrating science and faith with respect and integrity, RTB welcomes dialogue with both Christians and non-Christians. Addressing topics such as the origin of the universe, the origin of life, and the history and destiny of humanity, RTB's website offers a vast array of helpful resources. Through books, blogs, videos, and speaking events, RTB scholars present powerful reasons from science to trust in the reliability of the Bible and the message it conveys about creation and redemption.

For more information, visit reasons.org.

For inquiries, contact us via:
818 S. Oak Park Rd.
Covina, CA 91724
(855) REASONS | (855) 732-7667
ministrycare@reasons.org